Handbook of
GRAPHIC
PRESENTATION

By

CALVIN F. SCHMID

DIRECTOR, OFFICE OF POPULATION RESEARCH,
AND PROFESSOR OF SOCIOLOGY, UNIVERSITY OF WASHINGTON
EXECUTIVE SECRETARY, WASHINGTON STATE CENSUS BOARD

THE RONALD PRESS COMPANY ⸱ NEW YORK

HA31
S345

3

Library of Congress Catalog Card Number: 54–7652

PRINTED IN THE UNITED STATES OF AMERICA

Preface

This book has been written as a working manual for all who are concerned with the clear presentation and interpretation of statistical data in graphic form. Large sums of money are often spent by businesses and institutions on the gathering of statistics, but far too frequently much of this effort is wasted because sufficient attention is not paid to the details of their analysis and presentation. Statistical data must continually be included in reports to business executives, stockholders, and clients; in research papers addressed to professional colleagues; and in advertising matter, publicity releases, magazine articles, and other presentations designed for the general public. This book shows how charts and graphs can translate such data into attractive, succinct, and readily understood diagrammatic forms. Neither columns and rows of statistics in tabular arrangement, nor the seemingly endless listings of figures in textual form, can possess the clarity, appeal, or meaningfulness of a well-designed chart. By emphasizing important and salient relationships, graphs and charts may also be of immense service in the location and definition of problems and in the discovery of hidden facts.

The book is the outgrowth of many years of experience in directing research projects and teaching graphic presentation to college students. Its aim is to provide all the information likely to be needed by those who construct statistical charts, those who supervise their construction, and those who judge the effectiveness of their presentation. While no attempt has been made to go into the minutiae of every case, the essential theory and practice of graphic techniques is presented in sufficient detail to enable the reader to design appropriate charts and to execute for himself all the basic graphic forms. A separate chapter is devoted to each of the most important types of charts. It describes their advantages and disadvantages in presenting data of various kinds, points out distortions likely to result from their incorrect use, and

iii

discusses any special difficulties which may arise in their construction. The book is profusely illustrated with graphs and charts presenting data taken from many different fields and designed for many audiences. It is hoped that the reader will find in them helpful suggestions for the solution of his own problems.

For those who are concerned with the details of design and construction there is a step-by-step description of the exact procedure for laying out a chart. A chapter on drafting techniques gives specific information on instruments and equipment, materials, lettering, and special methods peculiar to the delineation of graphs and charts. A discussion of the theory of projection gives help in solving the difficult problems involved in the layout of three-dimensional charts. Finally, there is a chapter on methods of reproduction of charts and graphs from the original drawing.

The author is happy to acknowledge his indebtedness to many persons and organizations: first, to the authors of books and other published sources on the subject of graphic presentation for valuable ideas and suggestions; second, to many publishers, governmental agencies, and industrial and commercial concerns for permission to reproduce a large proportion of the illustrative material in this book; third, to Vivian Lomax, Don C. Gibbons, Gloria M. Austin, Warren Kalbach, and Lloyd Kirry for their help in preparing many of the charts, and particularly to Mildred O. Giblin, Mary T. Jacobson, and Earle H. MacCannell for their careful and constructive editorial and statistical assistance.

CALVIN F. SCHMID

Seattle, Washington
    March 1, 1954

Contents

HANDBOOK OF
GRAPHIC PRESENTATION

CHAPTER 1

Basic Principles and Techniques of Chart Design

Charts and graphs represent an extremely useful and flexible medium for explaining, interpreting, and analyzing numerical facts largely by means of points, lines, areas, and other geometric forms and symbols. They make possible the presentation of quantitative data in a simple, clear, and effective manner and facilitate comparison of values, trends, and relationships. Moreover, charts and graphs possess certain qualities and values lacking in textual and tabular forms of presentation. These values may be summarized as follows:

1. In comparison with other types of presentation, well-designed charts are more effective in creating interest and in appealing to the attention of the reader.
2. Visual relationships, as portrayed by charts and graphs, are more clearly grasped and more easily remembered.
3. The use of charts and graphs saves time, since the essential meaning of large masses of statistical data can be visualized at a glance.
4. Charts and graphs can provide a comprehensive picture of a problem that makes possible a more complete and better balanced understanding than could be derived from tabular or textual forms of presentation.
5. Charts and graphs can bring out hidden facts and relationships and can stimulate, as well as aid, analytical thinking and investigation.

For anyone seriously interested in research, a knowledge of the principles of constructing graphs and charts is indispensable. The average research worker may never actually draw many charts for publication, but he most certainly will have to plan them and direct draftsmen in executing them in their final form.

Although graphic techniques are a powerful and effective medium for presenting statistical data, they are not under all circumstances and for all purposes complete substitutes for tabular and other forms of presentation. The well-trained specialist in this field is one who recognizes not only the advantages but also the limitations of graphic techniques. He knows when to use and when not to use graphic methods, and from his repertoire is able to select the most appropriate form for every purpose. He is thoroughly conversant with the merits of each specific type and form of statistical chart.

Origin of Modern Charting Techniques. The various techniques embodied in this book represent fundamentally a graphic language for presenting statistical data. The origin of statistical charting techniques, as we think of them today, dates back to 1786, when William Playfair published his famous work entitled *The Commercial and Political Atlas.* Two subsequent editions of this book were published in 1787 and 1801. Playfair's other well-known books were *Lineal Arithmetic* (1798), *Statistical Breviary* (1801), and *An Inquiry into the Permanent Causes of the Decline and Fall of Powerful and Wealthy Nations* (1805 and 1807). Playfair, in referring to his "lineal arithmetic," explains that

The advantage proposed by this method, is not that of giving a more accurate statement than by figures, but it is to give a more simple and permanent idea of the gradual progress and comparative amounts, at different periods, by presenting to the eye a figure, the proportions of which correspond with the amount of the sums intended to be expressed.[1]

Furthermore, he states

That I have succeeded in proposing and putting in practice a new and useful mode of stating accounts, has been so generally acknowledged, . . . as much information may be obtained in five minutes as would require whole days to imprint on the memory, in a lasting manner, by a table of figures.[2]

Playfair not only created a new and ingenious technique for analyzing and portraying statistical data, but also delineated the

[1] William Playfair, *The Commercial and Political Atlas* (3d ed.; London: J. Wallis, 1801), pp. ix-x.
[2] *Ibid.*, p. xii.

charts themselves in such expert fashion as to compare favorably with the highest standards of modern graphic presentation. Playfair's contributions include various forms of the rectilinear coordinate graph, areal circle graph, pie diagram, and bar chart. It must be recognized, of course, that in studying the history of graphic techniques many basic developments, such as the principle of coordinates and the invention of analytic geometry, antedate the work of Playfair.[3]

Classification of Charts and Graphs

In examining the literature on charts and graphs, many classifications are to be found. Some of the classifications are clear, logical, and useful, while others are confused and contradictory. In general, one or more of the following criteria might be utilized as a basis for classifying charts and graphs: (1) purpose, (2) circumstance of use, (3) type of comparison to be made, or (4) form.[4]

With respect to purpose, emphasis may be placed either on (1) illustration, (2) analysis, or (3) computation.

In this book, stress will be placed on the design and construction of charts for illustrative purposes. Occasionally, the value of certain charts as analytical tools will be pointed out, but only in the most incidental and cursory fashion will any reference be made to charts for computational purposes.[5]

The second criterion, circumstances under which charts are used, includes (1) wall charts and charts for exhibits; (2) desk charts; (3) charts for administrative and interoffice purposes; (4) charts for stereoptican slides; (5) charts for moving pictures and television; (6) charts for illustrating lectures; (7) charts for

---

[3] For a more detailed discussion of the history of graphic presentation, see H. G. Funkhouser, "Historical Development of the Graphical Representation of Statistical Data," *Osiris*, Vol. 3 (1937), pp. 369-404.

[4] Harry Jerome, *Statistical Method* (New York: Harper & Bros., 1924), pp. 50-51.

[5] The construction and use of computational charts represent a very specialized field which has no place in a book of this kind. See, for example, Frederic T. Mavis, *The Construction of Nomographic Charts* (Scranton, Pa.: International Textbook Co., 1939); Raymond D. Douglass, *Elements of Nomography* (New York: McGraw-Hill Book Co., Inc., 1947); and Harold J. Allcock, *The Nomogram* (New York: Pitman Publishing Co., 1950).

books, magazines, newspapers, and similar types of reproduction. Emphasis in this volume will be on the last type of chart.

On the basis of the third criterion mentioned, type of comparison to be made, charts may be classified as follows: (1) size or magnitude; (2) time, including both absolute and relative changes; (3) space; (4) component facts; and (5) values in the form of frequency and related distributions.

The fourth criterion for classifying charts is the form of the chart. This classification was considered the most appropriate one for organizing the material in this book. In addition to the first two chapters, there are chapters on (1) rectilinear coordinate charts, (2) bar and column charts, (3) semilogarithmic charts, (4) frequency and related distributions, (5) miscellaneous graphic forms, (6) pictorial charts, and (7) charts drawn in projection.

Basic Design Principles

Survey of Problem.[6] The following discussion attempts to describe in a simple, concrete manner certain basic principles that should be used in the design and layout of statistical charts. Frequently, the design of a chart may be worked out by a specialist and the more or less routine drawing completed by a draftsman. On the other hand, it is not uncommon practice for one person to be responsible for both the delineation and the drafting of a chart.

Before the actual work of designing and laying out a chart is begun, it is necessary to complete certain preliminary steps: first, the designer should familiarize himself with the data he wishes to present in graphic form. In successful planning it is assumed that the designer has digested his materials thoroughly and is aware of their major implications. He must be able to select the most salient features of a body of data and translate them into clear, simple, attractive, and meaningful graphic forms. The designer of statistical charts should have a reasonably thorough grasp of statistical methods, as well as an understanding of the

---

[6] A large portion of this section is based on the Report of the Committee on Standards for Graphic Presentation, *Time-Series Charts: A Manual of Design and Construction* (New York: American Society of Mechanical Engineers, 1938), pp. 15-22. Brief quotations have been incorporated from this report.

basic subject matter in which the data happen to lie. Second, a decision must be made concerning the type of chart most appropriate for the purpose at hand. Usually several factors enter into a decision of this kind, such as (1) nature of the data, (2) medium of presentation, (3) purpose of the chart, (4) time available for preparation of the chart, and (5) audience for whom the chart is intended.[7]

Nature of the Data. One should recognize that certain types of statistical data do not lend themselves to satisfactory graphic presentation. In such circumstances, it is advisable to accept this fact readily and not to attempt to construct a chart that would possess no advantage over the original data, which might be in the form of a table or included as part of the text. Effective graphic presentation presumes familiarity with all the basic chart types, as well as their many variations and adaptations. For example, if the data represent a time series, the expert designer will be able to select one of the following types of charts: arithmetic line chart, semilogarithmic chart, column chart, band or stratum chart, or some adaptation of these different forms. On the other hand, data in which the basic classification is in terms of some geographical or areal category might be presented in one of many types of statistical maps.

Medium of Presentation. Statistical charts may be used (1) for reproduction in a book, periodical, or special typewritten or mimeographed report; (2) for exhibit purposes; (3) for lectures; (4) for slides; (5) for administrative purposes in connection with production, distribution, supervision, or other operations; and (6) for moving pictures or television. Occasionally, the chart may be designed so that it can be used for more than one purpose. The author, for example, has been successful in designing charts that have been used both for reproduction in books and also for exhibit purposes and slides. The size and proportions of the chart, as well as the weight of lines, size of lettering, and other features, must be developed and executed with minute care. In

[7] For an excellent discussion of the theory and practice of chart design, see Arthur H. Robinson, *The Look of Maps: An Examination of Cartographic Design* (Madison: University of Wisconsin Press, 1952), *passim*. This book also contains very useful bibliographic material.

this chapter, emphasis will be placed on charts intended for reproduction in books and periodicals.

Purpose of the Chart. Charts of all types should fulfill certain basic objectives: (1) they should be accurate representations of the facts; (2) they should be clear, easily read, and understood; and (3) they should be so designed and constructed as to attract and hold attention. In addition, of course, every chart is designed with one or more specific objectives. If the meaning of a series of figures in textual or tabular form is difficult for the mind to grasp or retain, a statistical chart may clarify the burdensome details and portray the data concisely, logically, and simply. Furthermore, a statistical chart, by emphasizing new and significant relationships, may be of service in discovering new facts and developing hypotheses.

Time Available for Preparation. Time and labor involved in the design and construction of statistical charts are generally of considerable importance. Needless to say, it is shortsighted to emphasize unduly the cost factor. Designing a chart should never be hurried or slipshod. On the other hand, much time can be wasted by indulging in useless details which actually detract from the quality or effectiveness of a chart. If the amount of time needed to do a good job is inadequate because of lack of personnel or funds, or the necessity of meeting a deadline, every effort should be made to simplify and expedite the work, but not at the expense of lowering standards. It would be far more logical, as well as economical in the long run, to construct fewer charts, those to be of the highest quality.

Audience. The educational level and interest of the audience for whom the chart is intended should be given primary consideration. A chart prepared for a popular audience unfamiliar with the more technical type of graphic presentation would be different from one designed for a comparatively small, highly trained group of specialists.

Planning Specifications and Procedures. Without adequate planning, it is seldom possible to achieve either proper emphasis of each component element within the chart or a presentation that is pleasing in its entirety. Too often charts are developed

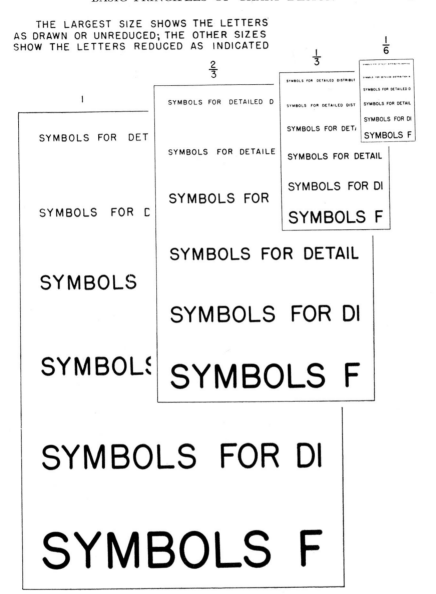

THE LARGEST SIZE SHOWS THE LETTERS
AS DRAWN OR UNREDUCED; THE OTHER SIZES
SHOW THE LETTERS REDUCED AS INDICATED

Figure 1. Reduction of Letters. In the design and layout of a chart for reproduction, allowance should always be made for reduction in size. (From National Resources Committee, *Suggested Symbols for Plans, Maps, and Charts,* Washington, D. C.: Government Printing Office, April, 1937, Plate A-2.)

around a single detail without sufficient regard for the work as a whole. Good chart design requires consideration of these four major factors: (1) size, (2) proportions, (3) position and margins, and (4) composition.

Size. The dimensions of a chart should be related to (1) ease of construction, (2) ease of reading, and (3) harmony with the vehicle of presentation. A chart designed for exhibit or lecture purposes normally should be very much larger than one to be used for reproduction in some publication. There are no absolute rules for determining the original size of a chart. If the chart is too small, it will be difficult to do the drafting work. Moreover, irregularities of execution will be more apparent in the reproduction. As a general rule, the original size of a chart should never be less than twice the size of the reduced chart, and frequently it may be as many as four or eight times as large as the reduced size. In general, a relatively simple chart can be made much smaller than one that is more elaborate and detailed. For example, detailed statistical maps would normally be larger than a simple bar chart. The thickness of the lines and the height of the letters are related to the over-all size of the chart. In designing a chart for reproduction, extreme care must be taken that the lines and lettering are heavy enough and large enough not to fade out or become unreadable in the reduction process. Figure 1 illustrates a series of letter sizes and line weights in original size and in the reduction of two-thirds, one-third, and one-sixth.

Proportions. The proportions of a chart either in original or in reduced form should be such that they conform harmoniously with the medium of presentation. Generally, it will be found that a rectangular form is more esthetically pleasing than a square. It is of special importance to consider the proportions of a chart designed for reproduction. In fact, the size and proportions of the particular book for which the chart is made will obviously influence the proportions of the original chart. Suppose that a full-page chart for a book is to be prepared for a space 4.5 by 7 inches and it is decided that the width of the original drawing is to be 18 inches. Then, according to simple proportion, the height of the original drawing will be

$$4.5 : 7.0 :: 18.0 : x \quad \text{or} \quad \frac{4.5}{7.0} = \frac{18.0}{x},$$

which, when crossmultiplied, gives $4.5x = 126.0$, or 28.0 inches.

Root-two dimensions, representing a ratio of 1 (short side) to 1.414 (long side), are particularly appropriate for statistical charts. In a rectangular page, based on root-two dimensions, the long side is equal to the diagonal of a square constructed on the short side. This rectangle also possesses the unique characteristic that when divided in half widthwise, each resulting rectangle is also of root-two proportions, a characteristic useful in grouping charts on a page. Table I represents the short and long dimensions computed on the basis of root-two ratio.

TABLE I

TABULATION OF ROOT-TWO DIMENSIONS FOR DETERMINING
PROPORTIONS OF CHARTS

Root-Two Dimensions in Inches for Short and Long Sides

Short	Long	Short	Long	Short	Long	Short	Long	Short	Long
1.0	1.4	3.0	4.2	5.0	7.1	7.0	9.9	9.0	12.7
1.1	1.6	3.1	4.4	5.1	7.2	7.1	10.0	9.1	12.9
1.2	1.7	3.2	4.5	5.2	7.4	7.2	10.2	9.2	13.0
1.3	1.8	3.3	4.7	5.3	7.5	7.3	10.3	9.3	13.2
1.4	2.0	3.4	4.8	5.4	7.6	7.4	10.5	9.4	13.3
1.5	2.1	3.5	4.9	5.5	7.8	7.5	10.6	9.5	13.4
1.6	2.3	3.6	5.1	5.6	7.9	7.6	10.8	9.6	13.5
1.7	2.4	3.7	5.2	5.7	8.1	7.7	10.9	9.7	13.7
1.8	2.6	3.8	5.4	5.8	8.2	7.8	11.0	9.8	13.9
1.9	2.7	3.9	5.5	5.9	8.3	7.9	11.2	9.9	14.0
2.0	2.8	4.0	5.7	6.0	8.5	8.0	11.3	10.0	14.1
2.1	3.0	4.1	5.8	6.1	8.6	8.1	11.5	10.1	14.3
2.2	3.1	4.2	5.9	6.2	8.8	8.2	11.6	10.2	14.4
2.3	3.2	4.3	6.1	6.3	8.9	8.3	11.7	10.3	14.6
2.4	3.4	4.4	6.2	6.4	9.1	8.4	11.9	10.4	14.7
2.5	3.5	4.5	6.4	6.5	9.2	8.5	12.0	10.5	14.8
2.6	3.7	4.6	6.5	6.6	9.3	8.6	12.2	10.6	15.0
2.7	3.8	4.7	6.7	6.7	9.5	8.7	12.3	10.7	15.1
2.8	4.0	4.8	6.8	6.8	9.6	8.8	12.4	10.8	15.3
2.9	4.1	4.9	6.9	6.9	9.8	8.9	12.6	10.9	15.4

Positions and Margins. The placing of a chart on a page should conform to the requirements of good design and ease of reading. In order to facilitate reading, charts should be so placed on a page that they can be read from the same position as that from which the other pages are read. Full-page charts which are widthwise on the paper should be so placed that the title is always on the left margin. In this way, the chart can be brought to reading position by a clockwise turn of the paper. The margins of a chart designed for reproduction should be consistent with the format of the publication. In the case of full-page charts, the binding margin should be larger than the other three.

Composition. Good composition is a matter of obtaining a harmonious whole through proper interrelation of component elements. Proper interrelation of components is achieved through adjustment of their size, weight, shape, and position. Since the over-all structure of a chart is more or less inflexible, the greatest opportunity for adjustment is in variation of size and weight of components. The design of various elements of a chart should be determined as it relates to all other elements. This does not mean that an attempt should be made to weight all the elements equally. Sometimes the most important element may dominate the presentation, with other elements emphasized in accordance with their relative importance. Statistical charts should conform as far as possible to the basic principles of artistic design, but at the same time be consistent with clear and accurate portrayal of the data.

In planning a chart, careful consideration also must be given to many other essential features, such as title, subtitle, scales, scale lines, scale figures, scale legends, curves, curve legends, crosshatching, and explanatory notes. Since details of this kind vary with each graphic form, they will be discussed at some length in succeeding chapters.

Layout Techniques and Procedures

In order to demonstrate the actual procedure in laying out a statistical chart, a series of relatively simple data is taken for illustrative purposes (Table II). The most appropriate type of chart for these data is the frequency polygon on a rectilinear coordinate grid. It will be assumed that the chart is to be used for reproduction in a book of more or less standard format, will be full-page in size, and will conform to root-two dimensions. If

TABLE II

FULL-TIME FACULTY SALARIES BY RANK
A MIDWESTERN STATE UNIVERSITY: 1952-53 *

Salary in Dollars	Assistant Professors	Associate Professors	Professors
Total	219	176	233
4,000– 4,499	35	. .	. .
4,500– 4,999	84	3	. .
5,000– 5,499	66	20	. .
5,500– 5,999	30	40	2
6,000– 6,499	2	61	6
6,500– 6,999	. .	32	20
7,000– 7,499	. .	8	32
7,500– 7,999	. .	4	38
8,000– 8,499	2	6	30
8,500– 8,999	. .	1	24
9,000– 9,499	. .	. .	31
9,500– 9,999	. .	1	18
10,000–10,499	. .	. .	12
10,500–10,999	. .	. .	3
11,000–11,499	. .	. .	6
11,500–11,999	. .	. .	7
12,000–12,499	. .	. .	4

* For faculty with rank of assistant professor and above on nine-month appointments.

the original chart is made about three times as large as the reduction, it will be 14 by 20 inches. The procedure will then be as follows:

1. Procure a sheet of drawing paper, tracing cloth, or other suitable material slightly larger than the over-all dimensions of the chart and mount it on a drawing board.[8] (See Figures 2 and 3.)

2. Frame in the working area in which the chart is to be laid out with the widest dimension at the top. Accordingly, a distance of 20 inches is scaled off across the sheet and 14 inches from top to bottom. The plotting points are connected by light pencil lines with a T square and triangle to form a rectangle 14 by 20 inches. When the chart is completed, these lines, if de-

[8] At this stage a knowledge of basic drafting skills will be extremely helpful. For a brief, simple discussion of drafting techniques, see the following chapter.

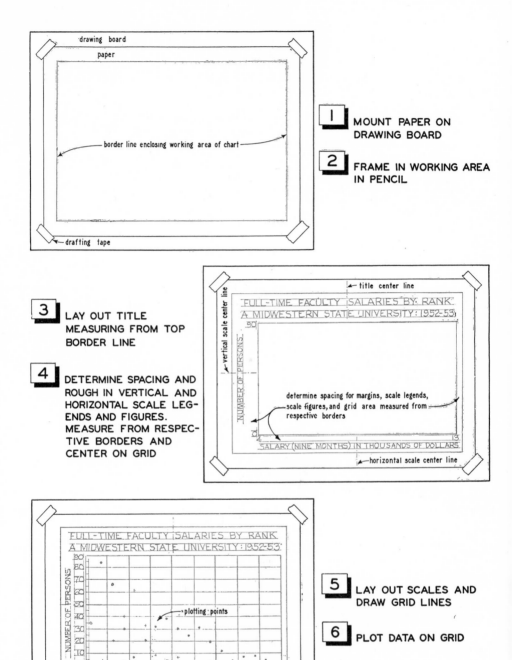

Figure 2. **Steps in Laying Out a Chart.** Illustration based on data in Table II.

14

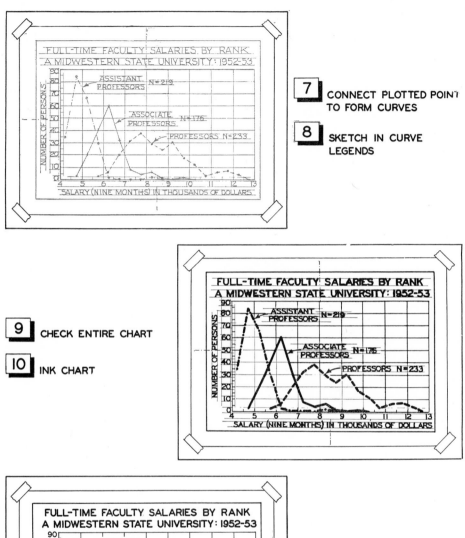

Figure 3. Steps in Laying Out a Chart (*continued*).

15

sired, may be incorporated into a border design. All elements of the chart will be included within the limits of the penciled border lines.

3. The title of the chart is sketched in pencil at the top of the working area in order to determine the exact amount of space required for this purpose. The size of the chart, as well as the amount of reduction, will decide largely the size and spacing of the lettering for the title. Without exception, the lettering for the title is larger than any other lettering on the chart. However, to achieve well-balanced composition, neither the title nor, in fact, any other element should be made too large or conspicuous. In measuring the height of the letters and spacing of lines for the title, measurements are made from the top border line. The arrangement of the title across the chart should be centered between the side borders.

4. The spacing and lettering for the vertical and horizontal scale legends and figures are roughed in. Measurements are made from the respective vertical and horizontal borders, but centered with reference to the grid. Generally, all lettering on the chart, except for the title, is of uniform size. The area remaining after the title, scale figures, scale legends, and necessary spacing have been determined will represent the main body of the chart. The various steps described thus far are applicable to such widely used graphic forms as the rectilinear coordinate charts, bar and column charts, and the semilogarithmic chart.

5. If the chart is a rectilinear line graph, the horizontal and vertical scales are completed, including grid lines and scale points. The lettering for scale figures and scale legends is next completed.

6. The data are plotted on the grid. The plotting points are usually dots or small crosses.

7. The successive plotting points are then connected by straight lines, which are referred to in statistical terminology as "curves." If there are two or more curves, they are differentiated by distinctive line patterns.[9]

8. Curve legends and any necessary explanatory statements are lettered on the chart.

[9] For a detailed presentation of the characteristics, types, and uses of rectilinear coordinate charts, see Chapter 3, "Rectilinear Coordinate Graphs."

9. The chart, which has been drawn entirely in pencil, is carefully checked for completeness, clarity, and accuracy. Particular consideration should be given to the scales, plotting of the data, wording of the title, spelling, and punctuation.

10. The chart is inked in. This should be done with meticulous care with proper materials and equipment.[10]

11. The entire chart is checked again for errors and omissions.

12. The chart is cleaned with Artgum.

[10] See Chapter 2, "Drafting Techniques."

CHAPTER 2

Drafting Techniques

Mastery of at least the basic techniques of drafting is essential if one is to attain a high degree of proficiency in the field of graphic presentation. Manual skill in drafting should be considered as a means to an end—an indispensable tool in the design and construction of statistical charts. As such the student should attempt to develop sufficient skill so that the mechanics of drafting become as automatic as writing. When this level of proficiency is attained, the mind will be free to consider the more important problems of planning and design.

In addition, it should be pointed out that it is a real advantage for the young statistician who is just beginning his professional career to possess drafting ability, since this skill can be put to immediate and practical use. In fact, because of the paucity of capable and well-trained specialists in the field of graphic presentation, drafting skill in combination with an understanding of graphic techniques may mean a higher rate of pay or the difference between obtaining or not obtaining a particular position. Later on, even after advancement to some higher administrative post, the statistician who has had successful experience in delineating and drawing charts will be in a much better position to judge the appropriateness and quality of a chart as well as to supervise intelligently and efficiently the work of others.

There are at least three general criteria in drafting which should be observed carefully by the beginning student. They are accuracy, neatness, and speed. Emphasis must be placed on accuracy and neatness from the very start, since speed can be developed only through practice and experience. One cannot afford to deviate from the highest standards of accuracy and neatness if real proficiency is to be attained in graphic presentation. Careless, slipshod work can only result in lowering the quality, authoritativeness, and effectiveness of a chart.

Drafting Instruments and Materials

In order to do first-class drafting work, it is necessary to have good instruments. Inferior instruments are a handicap. With reasonable care, a good set of drawing instruments will last a lifetime. In purchasing drawing instruments, one can be guided by the recommendations of an experienced friend or place reliance on the trademark of a reputable company. The instruments do not have to be ornate, but should be of high quality both in material and workmanship. In general the beginner should be advised to purchase the best instruments that he can afford.

Drawing instruments may be purchased separately or in sets. If one can afford it, it is recommended that a complete set of drawing instruments be purchased, including not only the ruling pen but compasses and dividers as well.

It is possible to construct many types of charts with relatively few instruments, but eventually the lack of adequate equipment may prove a serious handicap. A minimal list of instruments and equipment for the construction of charts should include the following items: (1) drawing board, (2) T square, (3) ruling pen, (4) civil engineer's scale, (5) triangle, 45°, (6) drawing pencil, (7) eraser, (8) Artgum, (9) black waterproof ink, (10) penholder, (11) at least two lettering pens, (12) Scotch masking tape, (13) can of tracing cloth powder, and (14) penwiper. A more complete listing of materials and equipment would include: (1) 30° by 60° triangle, (2) one French curve and two or three ship curves, (3) drafting table brush, (4) percentage protractor, (5) pencil pointer, (6) thumbtacks, (7) erasing shield, (8) mechanical lettering set, (9) 6-inch compass with extension bar, (10) 6-inch hairspring divider, (11) 3½-inch bow pencil, bow pen, and bow divider, and (12) one extra ruling pen or detail pen.

Drawing Board. The drawing board should be constructed of well-seasoned, straight-grained wood with perfectly straight edges so that an accurate and smooth working surface will be provided for the T square head. Drawing boards are usually made from softwood strips, such as white pine, basswood, or cedar, glued together and reinforced by cleats on the left and right sides. Drawing boards vary in size from 12 by 17 inches to 60 by 120 inches. In addition, there are drawing tables as large as 42 by 90 inches. For ordinary work, the smaller drawing boards are adequate, although if display charts or maps are contemplated, it would be advisable to procure a larger board at the start. In order to insure a smooth, clean surface, it is advisable to cover the drawing board with buff or a pastel-green detail paper. The detail paper can be readily mounted on the drawing board either with rubber cement or with thin wire staples.

Papers and Tracing Cloth. Paper, poster-board, or other materials which are to be used for statistical charts should have a smooth finish, should take ink readily, should stand some erasing, and should be free of loose fibers that might clog the ruling or lettering pen. For preliminary work drawings, detail paper or vellum paper may be used. For finished drawings, a high quality rag content bond paper, 20 or 24 pound, should be suitable. Whatman's HP (hot press) drawing paper is very satisfactory. A good grade of Bristol board or poster-board also may be found to be very suitable. In addition, tracing cloth has many advantages over some of the drawing papers. Charts drawn on tracing cloth can be reproduced by such relatively inexpensive processes as blueprinting, ozalid printing, and other similar processes. Also, because of its translucence, it is possible to trace in ink directly onto tracing cloth a chart from a penciled work drawing.

In mounting drawing paper or tracing cloth on a board, it is suggested that the sheet be placed well up on the board and close to the left-hand edge (Figure 4). The top edge of the paper should be aligned along the working edge of a T square and fastened down securely to the board with thumbtacks, staples, or Scotch tape. For most papers, Scotch tape is preferable to thumbtacks or staples.

Drawing Pencils. Drawing pencils are similar to writing pencils in that they are composed of finely ground emulsified graphite mixed with clay and binding materials in varying proportions, which determine the degrees of hardness. It is recom-

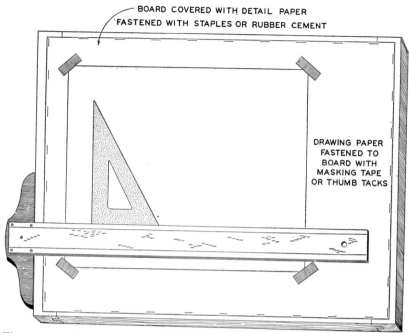

Figure 4. Technique in Mounting Paper or Other Material on Drawing Board.

mended that drawing pencils be used for graphic presentation since they are superior in quality to the average writing pencil. The relative hardness of drawing pencils is indicated by symbols ranging from 7B to 9H. The 7B is extremely soft and black. The next gradations are as follows: 6B, 5B, 4B, 3B, 2B, B, HB (medium), F, H, 2H and on up to 9H, which is relatively very hard. In selecting a pencil, consideration should be given to the type of paper to be used. For general, all-around purposes in graphic presentation, the pencil should range between HB and H. Occasionally a 2H might be found especially satisfactory for preparation of work drawings on detail paper. Some specialists in the field prefer artists' automatic mechanical pencils to the wood-covered pencils because they are always of uniform length and the length of lead can be adjusted without cutting away the wood. Leads of any degree of hardness can be purchased for this type of pencil.

In order to make firm, accurate, and clear-cut lines, it is necessary to have drawing pencils well sharpened at all times. For

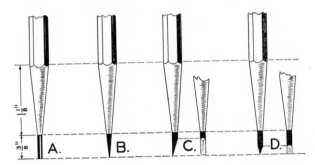

Figure 5. Preparing Pencil for Drawing Charts. *A,* Use sharp knife or draftsman's pencil sharpener to remove wood. Shape point with sandpaper or file. *B,* Conical point. *C,* Chisel point. *D,* Wedge point.

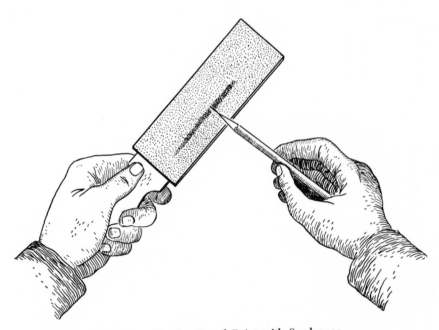

Figure 6. Shaping Pencil Point with Sandpaper.

convenience and to save time it is suggested that a supply of four or five well-sharpened pencils be readily at hand. The pencils can be sharpened either with a knife or with a draftsman's mechanical sharpener and then pointed properly with fine sandpaper or a file. The conical point will be found especially useful for plotting measurements and for lettering. The chisel point and wedge point are customarily used for drawing lines with a straight-edge. Figure 5 illustrates the three types of pencil points as well as their preparation. Figure 6 indicates the sharpening of the lead with a pencil pointer.

Scales. The purpose of scales is to make measurements on the drawing. The scale should never, under any circumstances, be used as a straightedge for drawing lines. There are two main types of scales used for laying out statistical charts—the civil engineer's scale and the statistician's scale. The faces of the civil engineer's scale are subdivided into 10, 20, 30, 40, 50, and 60 parts to an inch.

Scales are manufactured usually in 6-inch and 12-inch lengths, either flat with two or four bevels or in triangular form. All types will be found very satisfactory. The triangular scale has the advantage of being less expensive and includes six different faces (Figure 7). Although the statistician's scale has been designed for statistical work, the civil engineer's scale will be found much more flexible for the preparation of statistical charts. The statistician's scale contains logarithmic divisions as well as some decimal divisions similar to the civil engineer's scale.

Figure 8 illustrates one of the most important and frequent uses of the scale. The distance between any two parallel lines can be divided into any size units desired by first setting the scale on a particular point on one line and merely moving it at different angles.

Protractor. The protractor is used for laying out angles which cannot be made with triangles. It is used most often in the construction of pie charts. Protractors may be calibrated either in degrees or in percentages. The percentage protractor is much more convenient for statistical charts since it obviates the necessity of converting percentages in tabular distribution to degrees. Most protractors are calibrated, semicircular discs made of brass,

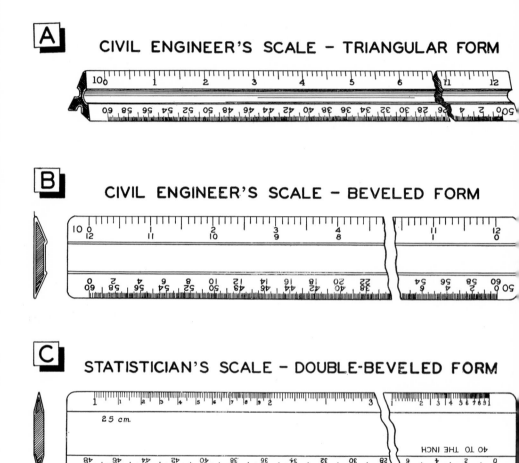

Figure 7.   Illustration of Scales Used in Graphic Presentation.

steel, nickel silver, or a plastic material. The more elaborate protractors frequently have a movable straightedge adjustment.

T Square. The T square is used primarily as a straightedge in drawing horizontal lines and as a base for guiding triangles in drawing vertical or inclined lines. It is also used for "squaring"

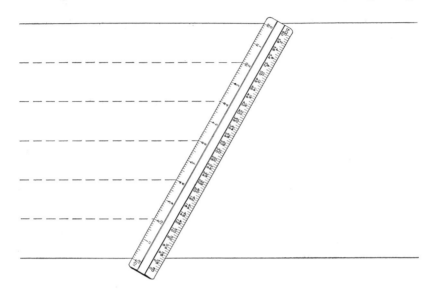

Figure 8. Technique for Dividing Any Given Distance into Equal Units.

paper on the drawing board. It is essential that the upper edge of the blade and the inside edge of the head be perfectly straight. For right-handed persons, the head of the T square is held against the left edge of the drawing board and shifted up or down as required. For left-handed persons, the head of the T square is placed on the right side of the drawing board. Under no circumstances should the lower edge of the T square be used for drawing lines, nor should its head ever be placed on the upper or lower edges of the drawing board.

Perhaps the most suitable and inexpensive type of T square is made with an ebonized hardwood head and a straight-grained maple blade with transparent edges. Some T squares are made of steel. These are more expensive but have the advantage of lying flatter on the drawing board. There are elaborate and expensive drafting machines available which serve the purpose of a T square and other straightedges, but such equipment is not necessary for work in graphic presentation.

Triangles. Triangles which are most commonly used in all types of drafting work are those having angles of 30°, 60°, and 90° and those with two 45° angles and a 90° angle. Triangles are manufactured in different sizes and of different materials. The 8-inch, 45° and 30° by 60° transparent triangles will be found most useful for statistical charts. Occasionally a much smaller triangle or a very large one will be found convenient. The triangles are used to guide the ruling pen, especially in making

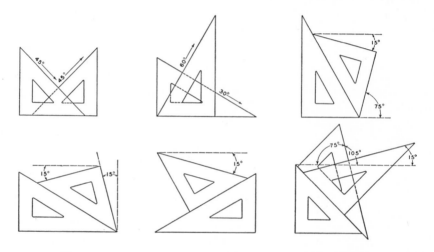

Figure 9. Drawing Lines at Various Degrees with Triangles.

vertical lines or angle lines. In drawing vertical lines, the face of the lower leg of the triangle is held firmly against the T square. Figure 9 illustrates techniques in constructing different size angles by means of the 45° and 30° by 60° triangles. By use of the 45° and 30° by 60° triangles, together with the T square, any angle which is a multiple of 15° can be constructed.

Irregular Curves. Irregular curves such as French curves and ship curves in particular will be found useful in drawing lines which are not part of true circles. In addition to the French curves and ship curves, there are many other types which can be used, particularly railroad curves, mechanical engineer's curves, spline and spline weights, and flexible curves 'which can be formed into different shapes. Figure 10 shows an assortment of different types of curves which will be found particularly useful for almost any type of curve that might be required for a statistical chart.

In laying out a curve, the first step is to sketch freehand the general contour of the curve from the plotting points. The sweep of the curve can be readily determined by the eye. After the preliminary sketch has been completed, certain curves are selected to fit the segments of the sketch so that the final drawing will be firm, smooth, and without kinks. In order to draw a smooth curve, the adjoining segments must be tangent to each other where they connect. This relationship is shown in Figure 11. Any other manner of joining segments of curves will result in jogs or kinks.

Erasers. Erasing both pencil and ink lines is a necessary part of drafting procedure. Accordingly it is important to use the best type of erasers and the proper technique so that the paper will not be injured and the erasures will not be detected. For pencil lines a soft eraser, such as Pink Pearl (Eberhard-Faber), Ellco Pink (B. K. Elliott), Parapink (A. W. Faber), and Carnation (Dixon), should be used. If the pencil line is found especially difficult to erase, then a harder textured eraser, such as Ruby (Eberhard-Faber) or Electric Red (B. K. Elliott), might be used. For ink lines, the Ruby and the Electric Red will be found very effective. Harsh erasers containing abrasive materials should never be used for drafting work. Electric erasers are available at all the larger drafting supply companies and are very valuable and efficient timesaving equipment.

One should be extremely cautious in using a steel knife or razor blade for removing ink lines because of the danger of removing the surface of the drawing paper or tracing cloth. In fact, it is recommended that the beginner avoid knives and other sharp instruments for erasing until he is absolutely certain that he can handle these instruments properly. The erasing shield should always be used for making erasures of ink lines. The best erasing shield is made of very thin, tempered spring steel. Shields made of celluloid, German silver, and soft steel are inferior. For

Figure 10. Samples of French Curves, Copenhagen Ship Curves, and Other Irregular Curves. The French curves, sometimes referred to merely as irregular curves, are represented by the more elaborately scrolled curves in the illustration. The Copenhagen ship curves are characteristically much simpler in form. The relatively straight and long curves at the top and bottom of the illustration are examples of ship curves.

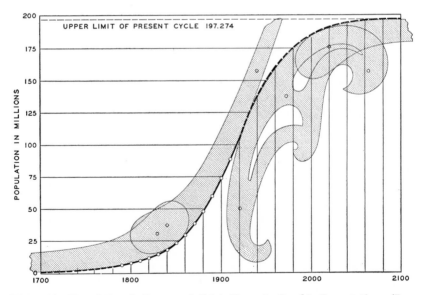

Figure 11. Use of French Curve and Ship's Curve in Graphic Presentation. (Redrawing of a logistic curve showing population trends and forecast for the United States in Raymond Pearl, *The Biology of Population Growth*, 1925, p. 14.)

cleaning drawings, Artgum or some other similar cleaner can be used. To avoid dimming the lines of the drawing, care should be taken to rub the surface of the paper very gently and not too often. Draftsmen sometimes use benzene or some other solvent for cleaning drawings, but this is not recommended because of the danger of fire, and also because such solvents tend to dim the ink lines.

Ruling Pen. The importance of the ruling pen in constructing statistical charts requires that it be of the highest quality. The nibs should be the same length and slightly rounded or parabolic at the ends. They should always be properly sharpened. The inner blade of a well constructed ruling pen is straight, and the outer blade is slightly curved. The handle should be made of hard, ebonized wood or metal so that it will not break easily.

The ruling pen is used to draw lines in ink when guided by the T square, triangle, or irregular curves. It should always be absolutely clean. A lint-free penwiper should be readily available for this purpose. The pen should be wiped occasionally while being used and always immediately after using, since India Ink dries very quickly. In case ink becomes incrusted either on the outside or inside of the pen, it can be removed by the application of a little water and rubbing with a penwiper. Ammonia solution is also useful for this purpose.

The ruling pen should never be dipped into the ink bottle. It is filled by means of a quill or pipette, the upper part of which serves as a stopper for the ink bottle. This stopper should never be removed except for inking the pen, because the bottle may be accidentally tipped over, or the ink, if exposed to the air for any length of time, will thicken and eventually dry up. As another precaution, the ink bottle should not be placed on or very close to the drawing. The purchase of an ink bottle stand will be found to be a good investment, since it will not readily tip over. Or a satisfactory ink bottle stand can be quickly and easily made from a small piece of stiff cardboard, such as a manila file folder or some similar material, and a circle about four inches in diameter cut from it. The ink bottle is placed on the center of the circular piece of cardboard and another circle is drawn by tracing around the bottom of the bottle. Four or five cuts are then made across the bottle-sized circle, and the triangular tabs resulting from these cuts are folded upward. The bottle can then be placed in the hole and the tabs fastened to its sides with Scotch tape or a rubber band.

Figure 12 illustrates how the ruling pen should be filled. Care should be taken not to fill the pen too full. Frequently, it will be found necessary to refill the pen before a line is completed. In

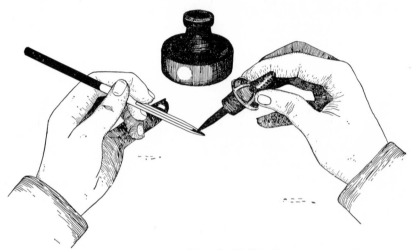

Figure 12. Inking the Ruling Pen.

case of interruptions of this kind, the line can be completed so that the connecting point is not at all noticeable.

The width of the ruling pen line is readily determined by the regulator screw. If a wide line is desired, say, one more than one-sixteenth of an inch, it is best to draw two thinner lines for the outer edges and then fill in the space between with the ruling pen. The blades of the pen should never be screwed tightly together. When not in use, the regulator screw should be loosened so that all tension on the blades will be released.

Using the Pen. In drawing lines, the ruling pen should be held between thumb and forefinger against the straightedge, while the other hand is used to hold the straightedge in a firm position. The pen is inclined slightly in the direction the line is to be drawn. The pen is "pulled" along the straightedge, with the third and fourth fingers being used for stabilizing the hand (Figure 13). Figure 14 illustrates correct and incorrect positions of the ruling pen in relation to the straightedge. If the pen slopes away from the straightedge at too sharp an angle, the resulting line will be irregular in width. Similarly, if the pen is squeezed too tightly against the straightedge, the resulting line will be of irregular width. When the pen slopes inward at too sharp an angle, there is always the danger of ink running underneath the straightedge. Figure 14 also shows what might happen if ink

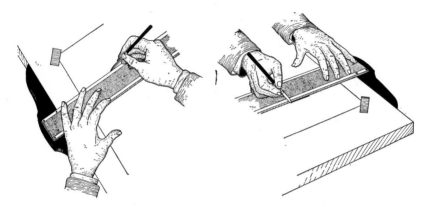

Figure 13. Technique in Holding the Ruling Pen and T Square.

collects on the outside of the pen, if there is insufficient ink in the pen, or if the straightedge slips into a wet line.

Drawing ink is different from writing ink in that it does not readily penetrate the paper but rather lies more on the surface. It is more opaque and has certain waterproof qualities so that it will not readily redissolve in water or be affected by moisture as much as writing ink. A blotter should never be used on drawing ink, since the carbon particles of the ink are absorbed by the blotter, leaving a dull, grayish line on the paper. Of course, when a mistake is made, the line may be blotted immediately and can be erased after it has dried thoroughly.

The beginner may become impatient, especially on humid days, when the ink dries slowly. Therefore, it is essential to follow some systematic order in inking the lines so it will not be necessary to

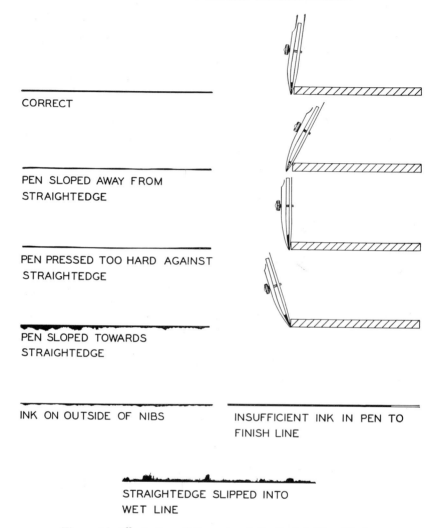

CORRECT

PEN SLOPED AWAY FROM
STRAIGHTEDGE

PEN PRESSED TOO HARD AGAINST
STRAIGHTEDGE

PEN SLOPED TOWARDS
STRAIGHTEDGE

INK ON OUTSIDE OF NIBS

INSUFFICIENT INK IN PEN TO
FINISH LINE

STRAIGHTEDGE SLIPPED INTO
WET LINE

Figure 14. Illustration of Correct and Faulty Ink Line Work.

wait each time for a line to dry. For example, one should begin at the top of a drawing and move downward in successive stages, or begin at one side and move toward the other side.

Compass. In all standard drawing sets there are two types of compasses. The larger one is approximately 6 inches in length, with a free-moving headpiece, a needle point, a pencil leg, a pen leg, and an extension bar. The two smaller ones are known as a bow pen and bow pencil. Each has a spring head and adjusting screws. In using the pencil compass or bow pencil, it is important that the lead be sharpened to form a wedge point. In adjusting the lead in the compass, the flat side of the wedge should be placed perpendicular to the radius of the circle. The pen leg of the compass and the bow pen are, of course, similar to the drafting pen and should be operated in much the same manner. Both the small and large compasses are used for drawing circles and arcs. If the arc or circle is less than approximately an inch in radius, then the bow pencil and bow pen should be employed. In constructing circles or arcs with relatively large radii the extension bar can be readily inserted into the leg of the compass. Beam compasses with bars of as much as 24 inches or more in length can be used for drawing large display charts.

Optical Illusions

The beginning student should be aware of the dangers that inhere in the various types of lines, shades, and shapes. For example, Figure 15 illustrates many of the more common forms of optical illusions in mechanical drawing. The implications of these illustrations are clearly explained in the accompanying annotations.

Lettering

The importance of good lettering in the construction of statistical charts cannot be overemphasized. Lettering on a chart may spell the difference between an expert and an amateur production. Poor lettering can seriously reduce the effectiveness of an otherwise well-designed chart and even cast reflection upon the ability of the designer. In graphic presentation, there are four types of lettering techniques: (1) freehand, (2) mechanical, (3) typewriter, and (4) stick-up or cut-and-paste. Type 4 is either commercially available or specially prepared.

Lettering for statistical charts, regardless of how the work is done, should be considered primarily in terms of (1) legibility, (2) appropriateness, and (3) artistic appeal. From a secondary point of view, the following factors should be taken into account: (1) time available, (2) ease of execution, and (3) cost.

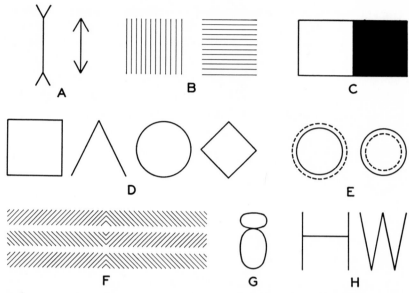

Figure 15. Optical Illusions. *A,* The two vertical lines are of the same length, although the one at the left seems to be longer. *B,* Both shaded sections are identical in height and width. *C,* The white portion of the rectangle appears larger than the black portion, yet actually the two are identical in size. *D,* At their widest point the four geometric forms are exactly equal. *E,* The diameters of the two circles represented by full lines are identical. *F,* The three crosshatched bars are parallel and of identical width from end to end. The bending impression is an optical illusion resulting from this particular type of hatching. *G,* The upper and lower parts of this symbol are of the same width. *H,* The distances between the vertical lines of the letter "H" and the two upper points of the "W" are equal.

Freehand Lettering. There are many specialists in the field of graphic presentation who prefer freehand lettering to any other form. In order to become proficient in freehand lettering, it is essential to know the characteristics of each letter and figure, to understand the order and direction of each stroke in forming the letters, to develop a sense of composition and balance, and to devote the required amount of practice in developing the necessary skills. The most suitable style of lettering for statistical charts is the simple, vertical, commercial Gothic. Occasionally slanting capital letters are used, as well as lower-case letters. In freehand lettering, there is a certain amount of individuality that naturally develops, but one should be careful not to indulge in any ornate or unorthodox styles.

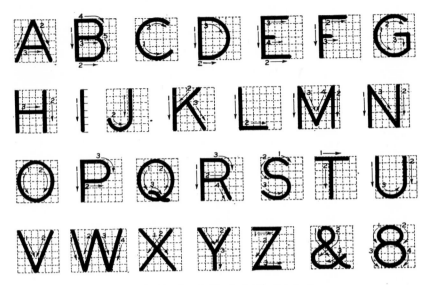

Figure 16. Freehand Vertical Capital Letters.

Figures 16, 17, and 18 portray the essential details and arrangement of vertical capital letters, figures, and fractions. It will be observed that the relative widths of figures and letters show characteristic variations. The W, for example, is approximately seven spaces wide, as compared to approximately four spaces for many of the other letters. Also, the letter M is appreciably larger than most of the other letters. It will be observed further that, as a general rule, the vertical lines are made first, the horizontal lines are made second, and the curved lines last. It is

Figure 17. Freehand Vertical Figures.

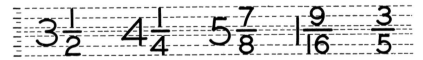

Figure 18. Freehand Vertical Fractions.

essential not only to form letters and figures carefully but also to space them properly. In order to attain proper balance, the individual letters in a word are not spaced at equal distances. Rather, they must appear to be spaced at equal distances. This is true not only for freehand lettering but also for lettering by mechanical means as well as by other techniques. The actual space, for example, between *A* and *L* or *T* is much less than between, say, *B* and *H* or *I*. Figure 19 is an illustration of block letters and numbers which will be found particularly appropriate for titles of large-scale charts.

In selecting freehand lettering pens, one should, of course, take into consideration the style and size of letters to be made. Lettering pens are manufactured with extremely fine points for very small lettering and with very heavy points for relatively large letters. There are also special types of lettering pens in many sizes. The following represents a sample list of pens for different weights of lines:

> *Very Fine:* Gillott 170, 290, and 1000, Crowquill, Esterbrook 355 and 356
> *Fine:* Gillott 303 and 404, Spencerian 1, Esterbrook 1000
> *Medium:* Leonardt 506F and 516F, Hunt 512, Esterbrook 968, Henry Tank
> *Special:* Barch-Payzant, Speedball, Edco, Leroy, Wrico

As a general practice, it is advisable to have several different kinds of pens available. Each pen should be placed in a separate penholder. The regular, inexpensive, cork-end penholder is suitable for most lettering pens.

The first step in lettering is to determine the height of the letters. The over-all size of the drawing, as well as the amount of reduction, if the chart is to be reproduced by some photographic or printing process, is a primary consideration. It is a common mistake for the beginner to make the lettering on a chart too small, so that when the chart is reduced in size the lettering may be difficult to read. After the correct size has been selected, guide lines are then laid out in accordance with the predetermined height of the letters. This may be done by measuring with a scale, estimating, or with a metal or transparent triangular frame with holes in it, such as the Ames or Braddock

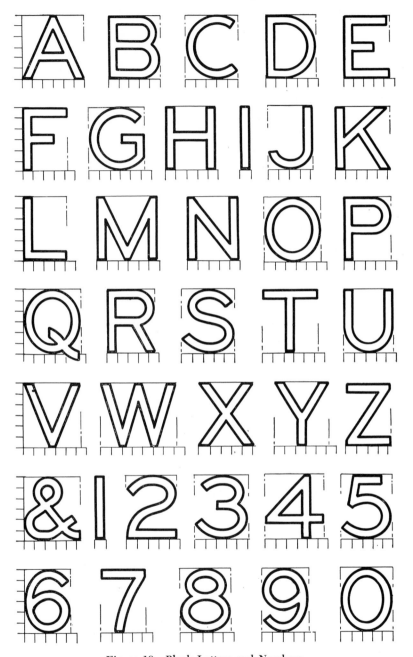

Figure 19. Block Letters and Numbers.

lettering devices or lettering triangles manufactured by Wood-Regan, Keuffel and Esser, Dietzgen, Alteneder, Bruning, and other companies. The beginner may wish to do all the lettering very carefully in pencil and then ink in the lines with the proper pen.

The width of the lines should be consistent with the size of the letters. Relatively large letters, for example, should not be made with a fine, delicate line. Care should be taken to see that the pen is always clean. A pen should be filled on the underside with a quill or dropper. With extreme care, one can dip the pen into the bottle, but there is always the danger of getting too much ink on the pen, which causes too heavy a flow, especially where lines intersect.

Mechanical Type of Letters. Various mechanical lettering devices may be found to be more efficient and economical in the construction of statistical charts than freehand lettering. The best known American-made instruments of this kind are Wrico, Leroy, and Varigraph. Wrico is made in two different types, the standard and the scriber. The standard Wrico lettering equipment consists of guides made of transparent plastic with a series of openings so shaped that when the point of a Wrico pen is moved in contact with their sides, the letters of the alphabet, numerals, and various designs are formed (Figure 20). The Wrico pen is not part of a machine, but is held in the hand and moved in various directions according to the patterns on the guide. The guide is placed directly over that portion of the layout on which the lettering is to be done. The guides are grooved on the undersides so that the ink will not be smeared when they are moved from one character to another. The set of the pen varies with the size and style of letters. There are seven different types for the standard pen, in addition to five for the brush pen. The styles of letters include vertical Gothic, standard slant, condensed vertical Gothic, architectural, Roman, and other types.

The scriber type of mechanical lettering devices can be procured from three different manufacturers: Wood-Regan (Wrico); Keuffel and Esser (Leroy); and Varigraph Company (Varigraph). The basic structural and mechanical features of the Wrico, Leroy, and Varigraph are similar. Each possesses certain

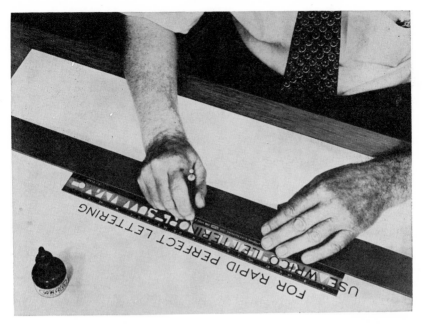

Figure 20. Illustrating Use of Standard Wrico Lettering Pen and Guide.

advantages with respect to original cost, type and variety of letters, and ease and speed of operation. The Leroy has been on the market for a number of years. The Varigraph, a more recent development, and the Wrico scriber set have been on the market only a few years. An inexpensive, scriber-type set similar to the Leroy is available for modest budgets. This set, called the Doric, is also produced by Keuffel and Esser.

In the scriber type of lettering device, the scriber follows the outline of a letter in a templet. The pen, which is attached to a separate arm, reproduces the letter on the drawing. There are several sizes and styles of letters with corresponding pens of varying widths.

Stick-Up and Cut-and-Paste Letters. The commercially prepared stick-up letters possess certain advantages over both freehand lettering and lettering with mechanical guides. In the first place, no special drafting skill is required. Second, there is greater flexibility in the type and style of available letters. Third, it is possible to attain a uniformity and consistency that are difficult to achieve in the other methods, especially in freehand lettering. The best-known commercially prepared letters are Artype, Foto-type, and Visitype. These are printed on acetate with a paraffin adhesive backing. Fototype is also available on heavy, opaque paper. Almost any style or size of letter used in present-day typography is available in these prepared letters.

In applying Artype, for example, to a chart, a sheet of letters of appropriate size and style is first selected. Guide lines are drawn in blue pencil on the layout. Individual letters are cut out of the sheet and placed in the proper position on the chart. When each letter is in correct position, it is rubbed down firmly with the handle of the cutter, which also serves as a burnisher. It is important that the edges of each letter be rubbed down tightly so there is no danger of its peeling off. After all the lettering has been completed for the chart, the blue guide lines are removed. In addition to various styles and sizes of letters, arrows, brackets, patterns, and mathematical and other types of symbols are available in Artype and Visitype. Fototype is in some ways similar to Artype, except that the letters are printed separately in pads with perforated edges and are aligned by means of a composing stick. This technique is superior to cutting out and placing in position each individual letter merely by means of guide lines. Figure 21 shows how Fototype is used.

Gummed paper letters, figures, and symbols are sometimes used for chart work, especially large charts designed for exhibit purposes. Each letter is applied individually to the layout after moistening the gummed side.

Another common paste-up technique is to print with a proof press all the words and figures for a particular chart on a good quality white paper. The words can then be cut out and mounted on the chart with rubber cement. Paper with adhesive backing, such as "Kleen Stik," is also used, and requires no rubber cement. Charles Stott Company (Visitype) prints words to order on acetate with a paraffin adhesive.

Typewriter. Occasionally the typewriter or some similar machine, such as the Vari-Typer, is used for lettering statistical charts. This method perhaps is most acceptable for administra-

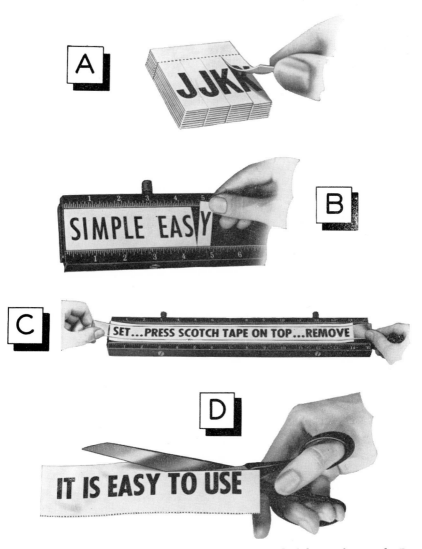

Figure 21. How to Use Fototype. *A,* Tear off individual letters from pad. *B,* Place letters in composing stick. *C,* After line is set, press transparent Scotch tape across letters. *D,* Remove line from composing stick, trim surplus edges, apply rubber cement, and mount in proper position on chart.

tive graphs used within an organization, but unsatisfactory for general exhibit purposes and for reproduction in publications. Perhaps the main shortcoming of lettering made with the typewriter or Vari-Typer is that it is not as attractive as lettering made with mechanical lettering sets or with the stick-up type of letters. Also, because it does not vary much in size, it lacks flexibility for general use in the construction of statistical charts.

CHAPTER 3

Rectilinear Coordinate Charts

Perhaps the best known and certainly one of the most frequently used type of chart is the simple arithmetic line chart. The arithmetic line chart is one of several types of rectilinear coordinate charts. In addition to the simple arithmetic line chart, there are such variations as the cumulative curve chart, staircase curve chart, simple-surface or silhouette chart, staircase surface chart, multiple-surface or band chart, and one-hundred percent surface chart.[1]

The rectilinear coordinate chart is also referred to as a rectangular or Cartesian coordinate graph. The basic form of this type of graph is derived by plotting one or more series of figures on a coordinate surface in which the successive plotting points are joined together in the form of a continuous line, customarily referred to as a "curve."

A curve on a graph of this kind is not necessarily smooth and regular, but rather may be straight and angular. The system of coordinates used in the rectilinear chart is laid out in reference to a pair of intersecting lines, called *axes,* which are drawn at right angles. The horizontal line is referred to as the X axis, or *axis of abscissas,* and the vertical, the Y axis, or *axis of ordinates.* These axes divide the region of the plane into four compartments, called *quadrants,* which are numbered counterclockwise, beginning with the upper-right quadrant. Figure 22 indicates the basic structural characteristics of a rectangular coordinate system. It will be observed further that the point where the two axes intersect is referred to as the *origin of coordinates.* Measurements to the right and above the origin are positive (plus),

---

[1] The various forms of arithmetic line charts discussed in this chapter pertain to time series. The graphic presentation of frequency distributions is covered in Chapter 6, "Frequency Graphs and Related Charts."

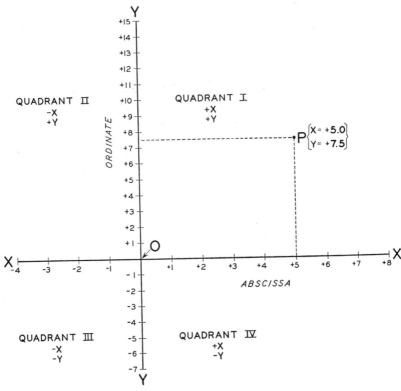

Figure 22. Axes for Constructing Rectangular Coordinate Graph.

whereas measurements to the left and below the origin are negative (minus). In quadrant I, the values on both the X and Y axes
are positive; in quadrant II, the values are negative on the X axis
and positive on the Y axis; in quadrant III, the values are negative
on both axes; and in quadrant IV, the values are positive on the
X axis and negative on the Y axis. The X and Y axes, respectively, can be divided into any desired units of measurement,
beginning with the point of origin as zero. Any point plotted in
the field of coordinates is determined by distances on both the
X and Y axes. In Figure 22, for example, point P has been located
in relation to the following values: $Y = +7.5$ and $X = +5.0$.
In descriptive graphic presentation, quadrant I is used almost
exclusively. Occasionally quadrant IV may be used along with

quadrant I to portray both positive and negative values. Quadrant II is used occasionally, and quadrant III rarely, because two negative scales are involved.

When To Use an Arithmetic Line Chart

The arithmetic line chart is particularly effective in portraying time series such as movements or trends over a period of years or variations covering shorter periods—days, weeks, or months. There are, of course, other techniques for charting time series, such as the semilogarithmic graph and the column chart.

In portraying time series, or in fact any kind of statistics, consideration should be given to the meaning of the data, the purpose of the chart, and the audience to whom the chart is directed.

With respect to the nature of the data and objectives of the chart, the arithmetic line chart is specifically adapted to the following types of data and purposes:

1. For a series where there are many successive values to be pictured
2. Where several series are shown for comparison on the same chart
3. For close reading or interpolation
4. When the emphasis should be on the movement rather than on the actual amounts

Conversely, this type of chart may not be the best for the following cases:

1. Where there are relatively few plotted values in the series
2. When the emphasis should be on the change in amounts rather than on the movement of the series
3. To emphasize the difference between values or amounts on different dates
4. When the movement of the data is extremely violent or irregular
5. When the presentation is designed for popular appeal [2]

[2] Committee on Standards for Graphic Presentation, *Time-Series Charts: A Manual of Design and Construction* (New York: American Society of Mechanical Engineers, 1938), p. 14.

Essential Components of Arithmetic Line Chart

Figure 23 indicates the characteristic components of the arithmetic line chart. Many of the elements and standards required for the arithmetic line chart also are generally applicable to other graphic forms. These facts will be brought out more clearly in succeeding chapters.

Title. The title of a chart is generally placed at the top. This is true not only of the rectilinear coordinate chart but of other types as well. As a working principle, the chart should answer clearly and simply the following three basic questions: What?

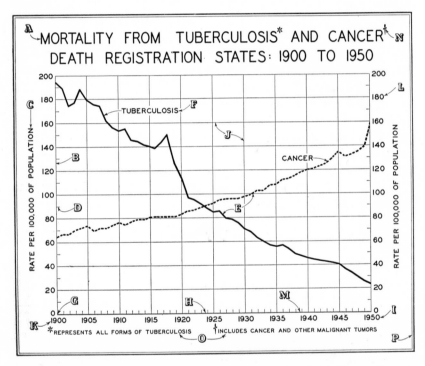

Figure 23. Illustration of Essential Characteristics and Rules for an Arithmetic Coordinate Chart. A, Title at top. B, Axis of ordinates or Y axis. C, Scale legend for Y axis. D, Scale points. E, Curves differentiated—solid and dashed. F, Contiguous legend for curves. G, Origin. H, Zero line heavier than other coordinated lines. I, Lettering heads horizontally whenever possible. J, Grid or coordinate lines—no more should be shown than are necessary. K, Scale figures for X axis. L, Scale figures for Y axis. M, Axis of abscissae or X axis. N, Reference symbol. O, Explanatory note. P, Border—optional.

Where? When? Care should be taken to eliminate all super-fluous words. A title that is too long may take valuable space which should be used for the main part of the graph. A succinct, catchy title, free of journalistic or sensational coloring, will be found especially appropriate for most charts. The title, as well as the basic design of the chart itself, should be compatible with the audience it is designed to serve. Accordingly, titles, as well as the charts themselves, for the popular lecture group would differ from those prepared for technical and scholarly journals.

Scales. The zero base line should be shown on all rectilinear coordinate charts. The only exception occurs when the data represent index or other numbers where the reference value is 100 or some other special number. As a matter of emphasis, the zero base line is usually made a little heavier than other grid lines. Where the values of a series are such that a large part of the grid would be superfluous, it is the practice to break the grid, thus eliminating the unused portion of the scale, but at the same time indicating the zero line. Failure to include zero in the vertical scale is a very common omission which distorts the data and gives an erroneous visual impression. Figures 31 and 32 are illustrations of rectilinear coordinate charts in which the zero base lines have been omitted. Figure 24 illustrates why a large portion of a grid is sometimes superfluous. All of the values for the series of birth rates in the United States from 1915 to 1950 range between approximately 16 and 25. The vertical scale between zero and 15 is not required and, as indicated by *B*, may properly be omitted by means of a broken scale.

In rectilinear coordinate charts the horizontal scale usually represents the so-called independent variable, and the vertical scale, the dependent variable. The usual practice, for example, is to consider time as the independent variable. Accordingly, the divisions on this scale will be determined by the time units in the original data. The unit of time may be represented by hours, days, weeks, months, years, decades. The divisions on the *X* scale are indicated by both scale lines and scale points, or ticks.

Scale Figures and Legends. Both vertical and horizontal scales should carry proper explanatory figures and legends. In Figure 23, for example, the horizontal scale lines are drawn at

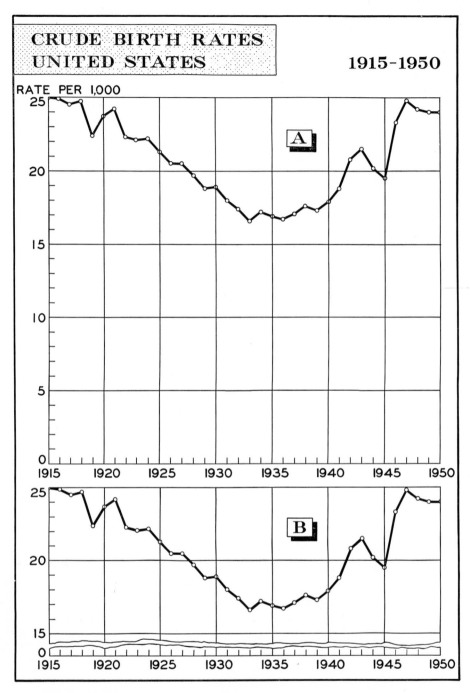

Figure 24. Arithmetic Line Chart with Unbroken and Broken Ordinal Scales. In A, the vertical scale is complete, but only the upper portion of the grid is actually used. In B, the vertical scale is broken and the part of the grid covering only slightly more than the range of the values on the curve is portrayed. (Chart drawn from original data published by the U. S. Bureau of the Census and the Federal Security Agency.)

five-year intervals with specific designations, whereas between the respective scale lines intervening values are indicated by scale points. Where the meaning of the scale designation is obvious, as in Figure 23, there is no need for a scale legend. In laying out the scales for arithmetic charts, it should always be remembered that equal distances represent equal values.

In determining the divisions for the vertical scale, it is essential that the entire range of the data be included. For example, if the data represent population growth ranging from 1,000 to 96,000, it would be appropriate to lay out values on the vertical scale from zero to 100,000. The coordinate lines may then be drawn at intervals of 5,000 or 10,000, and the scale points also can represent even units of, say, 1,000 or some equal decimal division of a thousand. It is nearly always essential to include a scale legend for the vertical axis. The scale legend should describe succinctly what the data represent and, where necessary, the unit of measurement. In Figure 23, for example, the scale legend for the ordinal axis represents rates per 100,000 of population. As indicated in the title and on the curves, there are two series of death rates, one for tuberculosis and the other for cancer.

The scale legend for the vertical axis, when possible, should be placed directly above the scale. Frequently it will be found that the scale legend in this position greatly interferes with the title and, therefore, it may be necessary to place the legend parallel to the scale. As a general rule, all lettering on a chart should be arranged horizontally.

Grid Lines. The number of grid lines should be kept to a minimum. This means that there should be just enough coordinate lines in the field so that the eye can readily interpret the values at any point on the curve. No definite rule can be specified as to the optimum number of lines in a grid. This must be left to the discretion of the chart-maker and can come only from experience. The size of the chart, the type and range of the data, the number of curves, the length and detail of the period covered, as well as other factors, will help to determine the number of grid lines.

Figure 25 illustrates three different coordinate patterns. A shows a grid with a relatively large number of coordinate lines.

Some specialists in the field of graphic presentation might consider some of the rulings superfluous. On the commercially printed graph paper coordinate lines are actually spaced much closer together. This is one reason that printed chart paper is not recommended. One is forced to adapt the design of his graph to an arbitrary and rigid system of coordinates without regard to the type of data that is to be presented. It will be observed further that illustration *B* contains no grid lines, except the 100 per cent base line, all other values on both axes being indicated by scale points or ticks. Some chart-makers prefer this design, although to others it would seem that there are not sufficient grid lines to measure even approximately the values on the respective scales. *C* represents a more balanced pattern in which both grid lines and ticks are used.[3]

Grid Proportions. In laying out a grid for a rectangular coordinate chart, care should be taken to keep the scales in proper balance. It is extremely difficult, if not impossible, to specify hard and fast rules concerning the technique for determining the most appropriate proportions for any given chart. Experimentation will help to solve problems of this kind. Figure 26 illustrates how contracting or expanding either or both the vertical and horizontal scales can radically alter the configuration of the curves, and consequently convey entirely different visual impressions.

Plotting Points. In plotting data on the *X* axis of a rectangular coordinate chart, the points may be located either on scale lines or on the spaces between the scale lines, depending on the design of the chart, which is usually determined by the type of data to be portrayed. When data represent specific points of time, they are known as *point data,* and when they refer to periods of time they are described as *period data.* Point data should be plotted on specific lines, and period data, midway between specific point-of-time rulings. The distinction between point data and period data is not always followed in actual practice. It is more common to plot both kinds of data on specific lines rather than in

[3] The basic idea for Figure 25 was taken from R. R. Lutz, *Graphic Presentation Simplified* (New York: Funk & Wagnalls Co., 1949), p. 16.

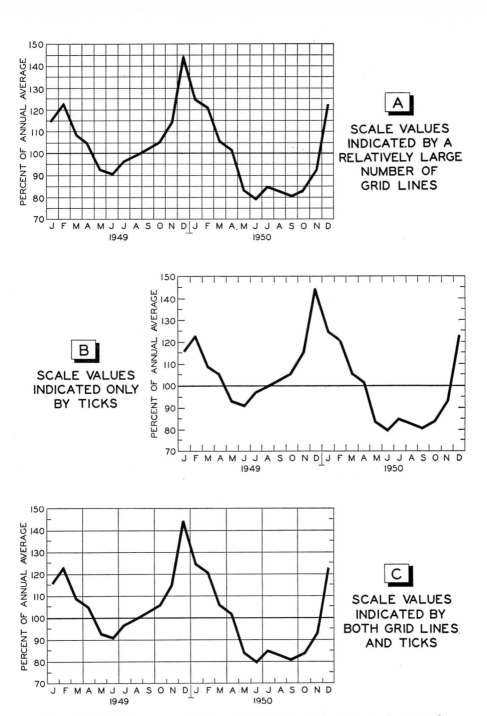

Figure 25. The Frequency of Rulings for Both the Horizontal and the Vertical Axes Should Be Sufficient to Guide the Eye to an Approximate Reading of the Curve Values. See text for further discussion of this point. (Data on chart represent monthly variation of robberies in urban communities. Data taken from Federal Bureau of Investigation, *Uniform Crime Reports* for 1949 and 1950.)

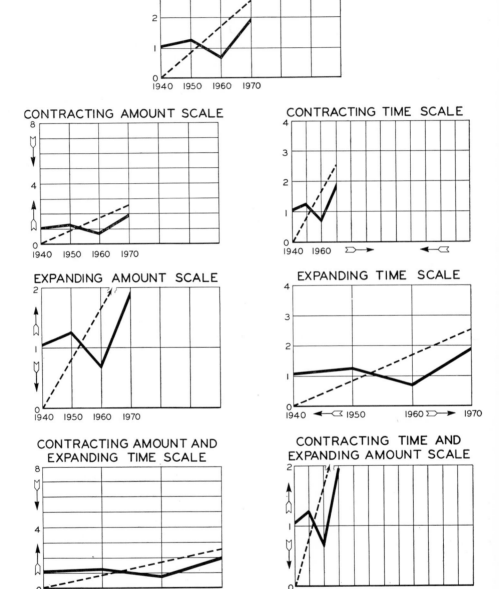

Figure 26. Effect of Scale Alteration on Shape and Slope of Curve. The solid curve represents movement; the dashed curve, trends. (Extracted from Committee on Standards for Graphic Presentation, *Time-Series Charts: A Manual of Design and Construction,* 1938, p. 36, with the permission of the publisher, The American Society of Mechanical Engineers, New York.)

spaces between grid lines. Figure 27 illustrates the plotting of data according to points of time and periods of time.[4] An examination of the other charts in this chapter will reveal both types of plotting.

Differentiating Curves. Curves for any kind of line chart should stand out prominently and be clearly differentiated from one another. The problem of differentiation may be especially difficult when there are several curves that are close together and cross one another. The use of colors to differentiate curves may be found to be satisfactory if the chart is to be used for exhibit purposes only and not for reproduction. The cost of reproduction in color is usually prohibitive. Moreover, colored lines cannot be effectively reproduced in such inexpensive processes as ozalid, blueprint, vandyke, and photostat. Colored lines reproduced in this way show such slight difference in shading tones that they are virtually indistinguishable.

From almost every point of view, a more practical technique in differentiating curves is by means of single-pattern designs. For example, curves may be represented by a full line, dashed line, dot-and-dash line, or some other pattern such as is illustrated in Figure 28.

In differentiating a series of curves on a line chart, consideration also must be given to the number of curves as well as their distribution on the grid. At times it may be found extremely difficult to differentiate these curves properly, especially if there is a tendency for several of them to be distributed on a relatively narrow portion of the grid with frequent crossing or overlapping. When this situation occurs, one of three alternatives may be selected: (1) enlarge the overcrowded portion of the grid, (2) use some other form of graphic presentation, or (3) abandon altogether any attempt to chart such data. Charts at all times should be unambiguous and easily interpreted.

Figure 29 depicts three series of monthly venereal-disease morbidity rates for Navy personnel, Caucasian and Negro, respectively. The top panel is for Caucasians and the lower panel is for Negroes. The curves for early syphilis are shown by a dotted pattern; those for acute gonococcus infections, by a

[4] The basic design of Figure 27 was taken from Lutz, *op. cit.*, p. 25.

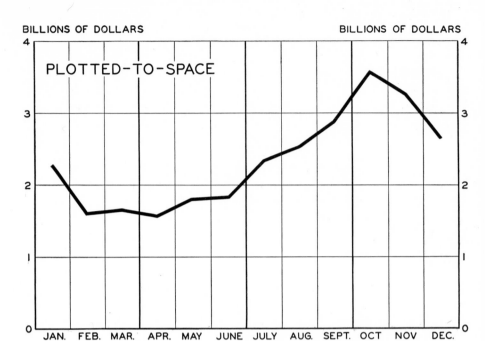

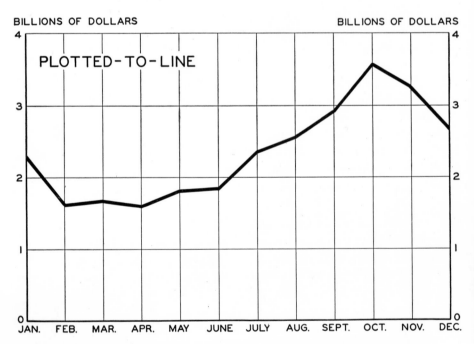

Figure 27. In Practice, Data of This Kind Are Plotted Either to Space or to Line. Theoretically, "point data" (values as of specific points of time) should be plotted on point-of-time rulings and "period data" (values for periods of time) should be plotted midway between point-of-time ruling. (Data represent Farm Income for 1950. See Council of Economic Advisers, *Economic Indicators, May, 1951*, p. 28.)

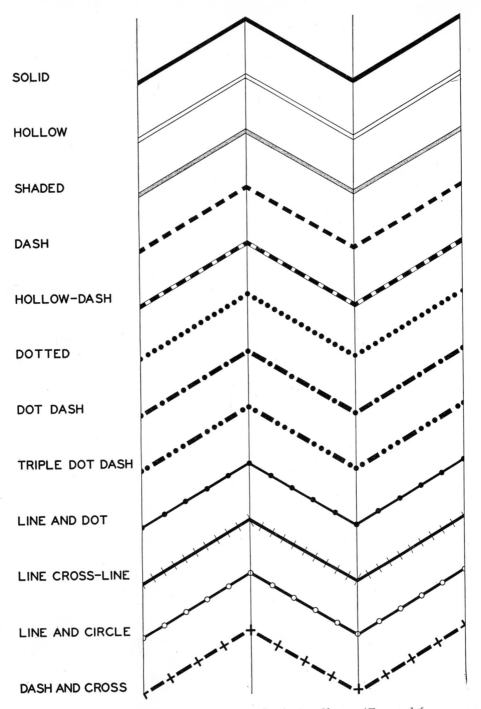

SOLID

HOLLOW

SHADED

DASH

HOLLOW-DASH

DOTTED

DOT DASH

TRIPLE DOT DASH

LINE AND DOT

LINE CROSS-LINE

LINE AND CIRCLE

DASH AND CROSS

Figure 28. Curve Patterns for Various Kinds of Line Charts. (Extracted from Committee on Standards for Graphic Presentation, *Time Series Charts: A Manual of Design and Construction,* 1938, p. 48, with the permission of the publisher, The American Society of Mechanical Engineers, New York.)

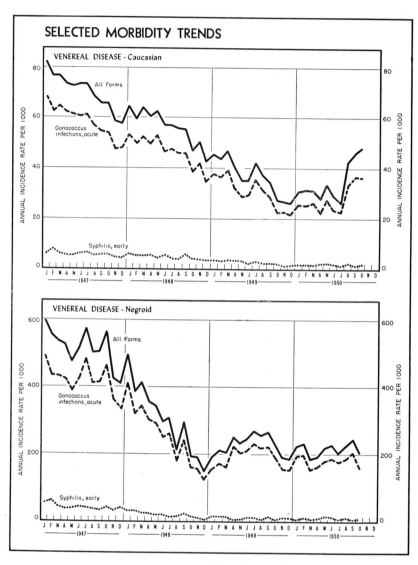

Figure 29. Rectilinear Coordinate Chart Showing Comparative Trends of Venereal Diseases for Navy Personnel, White and Negro. Note three types of curves in each panel as well as differences in vertical scales. (From *Statistics of Navy Medicine,* January, 1951, p. 35.)

dashed pattern; and all forms, by a full line. Each curve is properly labeled by a contiguous legend. Also, other features of the chart such as the following should be pointed out: main title and subtitles, different vertical scales, vertical legend, horizontal scale legend, grid lines, and ticks.

In order to facilitate interpretation, each curve should be labeled clearly and unmistakably. Labels or designations can either be located contiguous to the curves, usually with arrows pointing to them, or listed along with the corresponding curve patterns in a boxed-in legend or key. Curve legends should be located in such a manner as not to interfere with the interpretation of the chart. Contiguous curve labels are much more easily read, since they require less movement of the eye. When contiguous labels are used, they should be (1) brief, (2) easily read, (3) reasonably close to the curve, but never directly on the curve, (4) arranged so as to effect a balanced composition of the chart, and (5) in horizontal position.

Portraying Trend Lines. It is frequent practice in analyzing and presenting temporal series to derive trend lines. A procedure of this kind is generally referred to as *curve fitting.* Curve fitting requires not only a thorough understanding of necessary analytical techniques but also good judgment. Under appropriate conditions, there are two good reasons to describe the trend of a series by some kind of curve:

First, it may be desired to measure the deviations from trend. These deviations consist of cyclical, seasonal, and accidental movements. Frequently the obtaining of these deviations is but one step in attempting to isolate cycles, in order to study them. Second, it may be desired to study the trend itself, in order to note the effect of factors bearing on the trend, to compare one trend with another, to discover what effect trend movements have on cyclical fluctuations, or to forecast future trend movements.[5]

Trend lines may be developed by freehand estimation or by mathematical techniques such as a simple moving average, a weighted moving average, a semiaverage, the method of least squares, a second or higher degree equation, an asymptotic growth curve, or a Gompertz curve. After the values for the

[5] By permission from Frederick E. Croxton and Dudley J. Cowden, *Applied General Statistics* (Copyright, 1945, by Prentice-Hall, Inc., New York), p. 385.

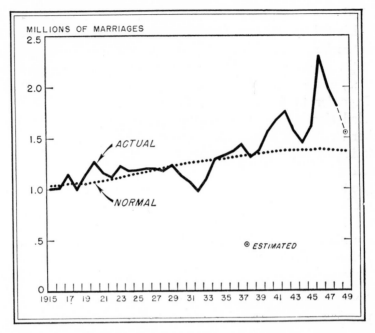

Figure 30. A Common Technique for Portraying Actual Data as Well as a More Generalized Trend. Heavy curve portrays actual annual number of marriages in the United States through 1948 and the dotted curve the "normal" number. "Normal" marriages represent the number that would have occurred in each year if the marriage rates for the various age classifications had been the same as the average for the years 1920 to 1939. The figure for 1949 is based on an estimate. (From S. Morris Livingston, "Family Formation and the Demand for Residential Construction," *Survey of Current Business,* March, 1950, pp. 8-15.)

various points of a trend line have been determined, they are connected either freehand or by means of a straightedge. A finished "smoothed" trend line that manifests some degree of curvature is customarily drawn with a French curve or ship curve.

Figures 30, 31, and 32 illustrate the superimposing of trend lines on arithmetic line charts. In Figure 30, the plotted data are indicated by a relatively heavy full line and the "normal" trend by a dotted line. "Normal" in this instance is defined as the number of marriages that would have occurred in each year if the marriage rates for the various age classifications had been the same as the average for the years 1920 to 1939. Figure 31 shows a straight line trend fitted to actual data up to 1950 and then

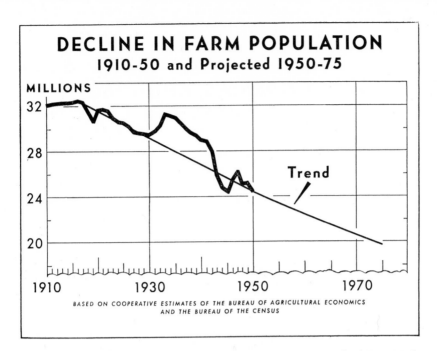

Figure 31. Arithmetic Line Graph with Trend Line Superimposed. (From U. S. Bureau of Agricultural Economics, *1952 Agricultural Outlook Charts*, p. 21.)

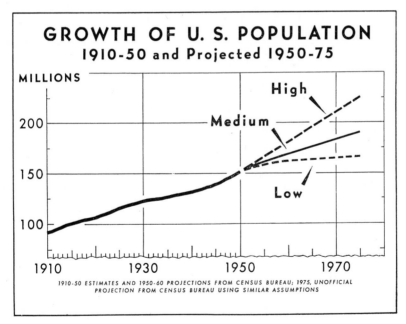

Figure 32. Rectilinear Coordinate Line Graph with Zero Line Omitted. Note the wavy line which symbolizes a break in the scale. Also, it will be observed that the three curves from 1950 to 1975 represent high, medium, and low population forecasts derived in accordance with certain alternate sets of assumptions. (From U. S. Bureau of Agricultural Economics, *1952 Agricultural Outlook Charts*, p. 2.)

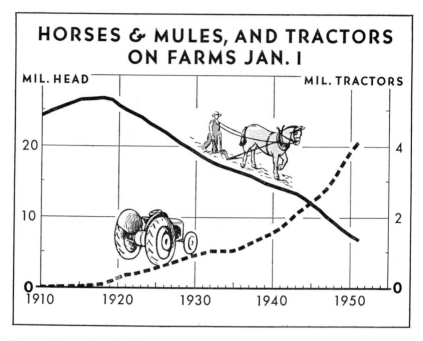

Figure 33. A Multiple-Scale Arithmetic Line Chart. Scale on left indicates millions of head of horses and mules, and the scale on the right, millions of tractors. Extreme caution must be used in interpreting charts of this kind. (From U. S. Bureau of Agricultural Economics, *1952 Agricultural Outlook Charts*, p. 28.)

extended to 1975. In Figure 32 the trend lines are in the form of extrapolations, representing "high," "medium," and "low" population forecasts for the United States from 1950 to 1975.

Multiple Scales. Although as a general principle it is inadvisable to include more than one scale on an arithmetic chart, occasionally there are times when a multiple-scale arrangement possesses certain advantages. It is important, however, for the beginner to be aware of the pitfalls inherent in this arrangement. Figure 33 illustrates an arithmetic line chart with two scales, the one on the left representing horses and mules and the one on the right, tractors. The trends of the two curves are clear, but unless extreme caution is taken in examining and interpreting the chart, an entirely false message may be conveyed to the mind of the unwary reader. This fact was convincingly illustrated when several university students were asked to indicate what the chart showed. Visually the chart may seem to indicate that after 1944 there were more tractors than horses, but when the values for the respective scales are examined more carefully, this actually is not the case. In 1951, for example, there were approximately four million tractors, as compared to approximately six million horses and mules.

When multiple scales are used, they normally should be limited to two scales. More are likely to cause confusion. Except in extraordinary circumstances, zero values for multiple scales should never be omitted. If zero values are omitted, the scales should be so adjusted that the zero lines would coincide if the scales were extended to zero.

Arithmetic Line Charts with Special Features and Applications

Charts with Special Annotations, Symbols, or Other Similar Features. Frequently an arithmetic line chart can be made more effective by additional explanatory or descriptive data in the form of annotations or pictorial symbols. Besides the curve on Figure 34, which shows the monthly variation of the marriage rate in the United States from 1939 through 1950, there are a series of light-dashed lines indicating yearly averages and numerous explanatory notes interpreting specific trends and fluctuations during this period. The implications for the marriage rate of such facts as the enactment of the Selective Service law, the events at Pearl Harbor, extensive overseas movement of armed forces, and the beginning of large-scale demobilization are clearly revealed by the supplementary data on the chart.

Arithmetic Line Charts with Positive and Negative Values. Figure 35 illustrates the use of a simple arithmetic line chart to portray net positive and negative values, such as imports and exports, profits and losses, and assets and liabilities over a period of time. The use of stippling and crosshatching in Figure 35 to emphasize the differentials of supply and production of tallow expressed as net imports and exports further enhances the effec-

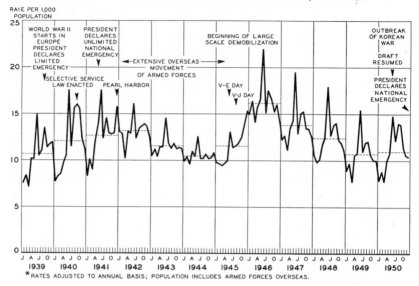

MONTHLY MARRIAGE RATE*: UNITED STATES, 1939-1950

Figure 34. An Arithmetic Line Chart Showing Seasonal Variation. (Redrawn from Metropolitan Life Insurance Co., *Statistical Bulletin,* Vol. 31, December, 1950, p. 2.)

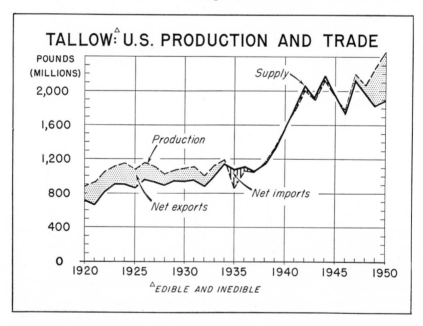

TALLOW△: U.S. PRODUCTION AND TRADE

Figure 35. Net Changes Frequently Can Be Portrayed Effectively by Different Hatchings on Line Charts. (From U. S. Office of Foreign Agricultural Relations, *Foreign Agricultural Outlook Charts, 1952,* p. 58.)

tiveness of a chart of this kind. The basic design of Figure 36 is the same as that of Figure 35, although, of course, the data are entirely different. The two curves on the chart indicate federal receipts and expenditures, respectively. The differentials between these two categories are clearly portrayed as "deficits" and "surpluses." The threefold shading scheme adds emphasis and clarity to the chart.

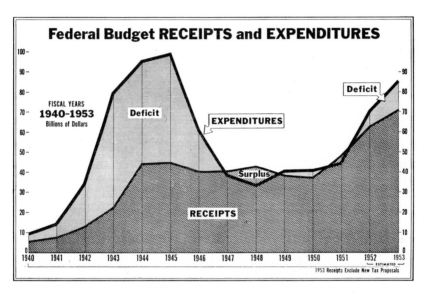

Figure 36. The Use of Crosshatching to Portray Net Changes for a Time Series on an Arithmetic Line Chart. This chart has some of the characteristics of the multiple-surface or band chart, which is discussed in a later section of this chapter. (From the President's *Budget Message* for 1953.)

Arithmetic Charts with Special Referent Lines. In portraying index numbers covering a relatively long period of time, the arithmetic line chart is used almost invariably. Instead of a base line representing zero, charts of this kind contain a referent line normally expressed as 100, which indicates the "base period." The values of a series of index numbers may deviate above or below the main referent line. Figure 37 portrays a cost-of-living index for the University of Washington faculty for the period 1935 to 1950. The base period for this index is 1935 to 1939, which is indicated by 100. The month-by-month course of living costs for the fifteen-year period 1935 to 1950 is clearly depicted on the chart. In addition, the figures and pictorial fillers superimposed on the grid show the differential rates of increase for the major groupings of items that comprise the index.

Another application of the arithmetic line chart in portraying both positive and negative values is illustrated in Figure 38. This

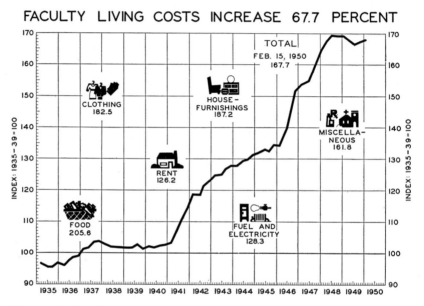

FACULTY LIVING COSTS INCREASE 67.7 PERCENT

Figure 37. An Illustration of an Arithmetic Chart Showing Index Numbers. It will be observed that the base line is 100. Note also pictorial fillers representing major components of index. The index number for each pictured component has been derived as of February 15, 1950. (From special report by Calvin F. Schmid to University of Washington Budget Committee.)

chart shows the seasonal variation of pneumonia and tuberculosis mortality in the state of Minnesota. The three-year means for the respective causes of death are indicated by a zero base line, and the deviations are shown by percentage values above and below the base line.

Plotting Two or More Curves for Different Periods on the Same Grid. Another special application of the arithmetic line chart is to superimpose on the same grid two or more curves representing data for different periods of time. This technique

SEASONAL DISTRIBUTION, PNEUMONIA AND TUBERCULOSIS MORTALITY, MINNESOTA: 1929-31

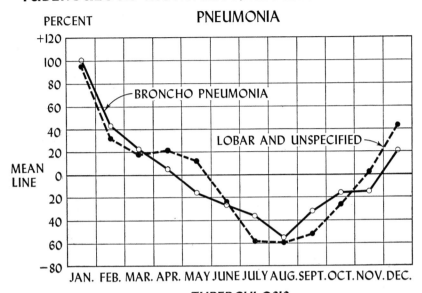

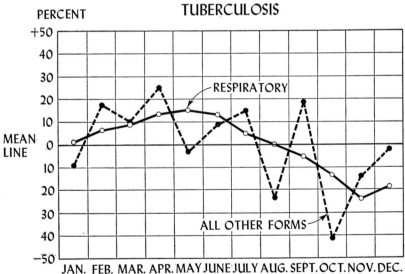

Figure 38. Another Technique for Showing Seasonal Variations by Means of an Arithmetic Line Chart. Ordinal values represent percentage deviations from annual average. (From Calvin F. Schmid, *Mortality Trends in the State of Minnesota*, 1937, p. 170.)

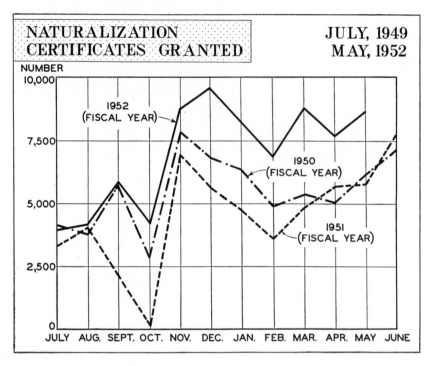

Figure 39. Arithmetic Line Chart Showing How Two or More Curves Representing Different Years or Periods Can Be Superimposed on the Same Grid for Comparative Purposes. (Chart redrawn from U. S. Department of Justice, Immigration and Naturalization Service, Helen F. Eckerson, "Current Statistics," *The I. and N. Reporter*, Vol. I, July, 1952, pp. 7-9.)

makes it possible to compare different series of data by bringing them into close juxtaposition. Figure 39 brings out the similarity in the monthly pattern of naturalization certificates granted for the fiscal years 1950, 1951, and 1952. It also shows unmistakably that, except for a short period early in July, the year 1952 surpassed the other two in the number of certificates granted. If the data had been plotted on a grid as a single continuous curve, with the three years arranged in chronological succession, it would have been extremely difficult if not impossible to make the same clear and accurate comparisons.

Cumulative Curve Chart. Thus far all the examples of arithmetic line charts in this chapter have portrayed trends and fluctuations of values for specified dates or periods. A slightly different application of the arithmetic line chart is to depict cumulative values over a period of time. The dashed curve in Figure 40 shows the year-by-year accumulation of the number of Jewish immigrants to Israel and Palestine from 1919 to 1952. It will be readily observed that the cumulative curve emphasizes a very significant set of facts which could not be revealed by a curve depicting annual numerical variations. The relationship between total population trends and immigration is also clearly indicated in this chart.

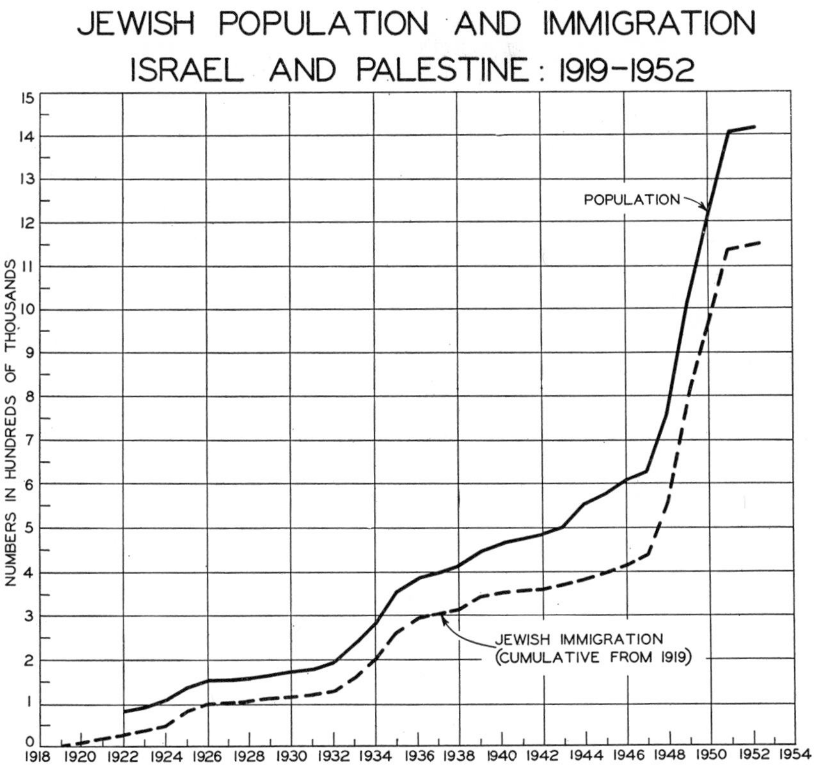

JEWISH POPULATION AND IMMIGRATION
ISRAEL AND PALESTINE : 1919-1952

Figure 40. An Arithmetic Line Chart on Which Is Plotted Values for Particular Intervals of Time as Well as for Cumulative Totals. (From Norman Lawrence, *Israel: Jewish Population and Immigration*, 1952, p. 4.)

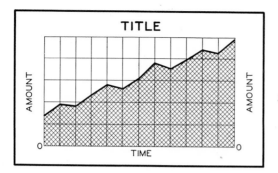

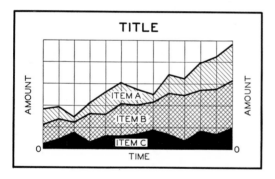

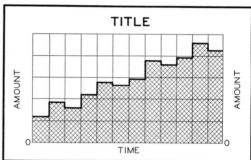

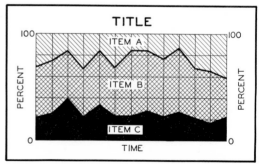

Figure 41. Illustrations of Basic Types of Surface Charts. (Redrawn from Statistics and Progress Branch, Army Service Forces, *Standards of Presentation*, 1944, p. 35.)

Surface Charts

Surface charts, sometimes called *band* or *stratum* charts, are relatively common forms of the rectilinear coordinate graphs. Figure 41 illustrates the four basic types of surface charts: (1) single-surface or silhouette, (2) staircase, (3) multiple-surface or band, and (4) one-hundred percent.

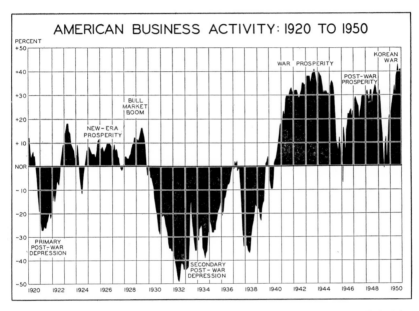

Figure 42. **Silhouette Chart.** (Chart prepared from data in circular published by Cleveland Trust Co., "American Business Activity Since 1790.")

Single-Surface or Silhouette Chart. An example of the single-surface or silhouette chart is shown in Figure 42. It will be readily observed that this chart is merely a line graph in which the area between the curve and the base line has been stippled, crosshatched, or blacked in, thus giving a silhouette effect. The basic data are in the form of index numbers which show monthly fluctuations in the business cycle between 1920 and 1950.

Staircase Chart. The second type of surface chart, the staircase chart, is shown in *B* in Figure 41, as well as in Figure 43. The staircase surface chart is similar to a connected column chart,

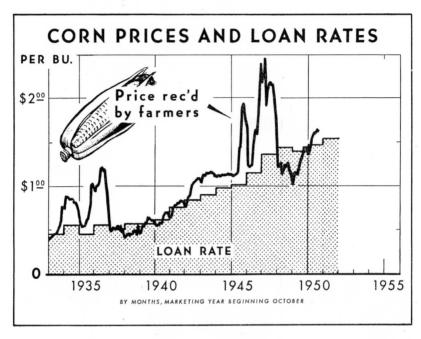

Figure 43. A Time Series Portrayed on an Arithmetic Grid by Means of Shaded Staircase Technique. A typical curve pattern indicating another series of data also is shown on the chart. (From U. S. Bureau of Agricultural Economics, 1952 *Agricultural Outlook Charts*, p. 51.)

but there are no vertical lines separating the values for the individual time units indicated on the X axis. It will also be observed that the staircase chart is very much like the single-surface or silhouette chart. The staircase surface chart in Figure 43 indicates the loan rates and a superimposed curve shows the corn prices received by farmers during the period from 1933 to 1951.

Multiple-Surface or Band Chart. The multiple-surface or band chart is shown in Figure 44. Characteristically, a chart of this kind portrays components of a total expressed in absolute values. In this illustration, for example, trends in the volume of tobacco products, expressed in millions of pounds, are shown by a series of four strata or bands, each one representing a special category. The bottom band indicates cigars; the next, snuff; the third, smoking and chewing tobacco; and the top, cigarettes. This

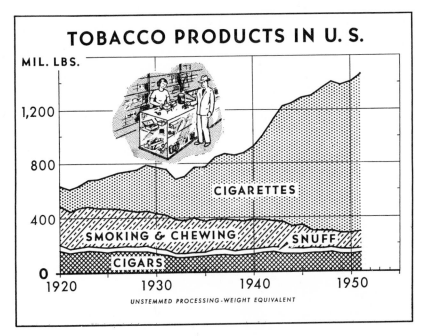

Figure 44. Another Illustration of the Band or Stratum Chart Showing Absolute Change. (From U. S. Bureau of Agricultural Economics, *1952 Agricultural Outlook Charts*, p. 67.)

chart clearly differentiates the trends in both the total and component values of the series. The rapid growth in cigarette production and a noticeable decline in the production of smoking and chewing tobacco are graphically revealed by this chart.

The multiple-surface chart is a valuable tool when properly used. If there are more than five or six components, however, there is danger of making the chart ambiguous and difficult to interpret. Also, in a series where the amplitude of the fluctuation is wide and sharp, the values for the curves may be badly distorted. It should be emphasized further that the interpretation of charts of this kind is based on the width of the bands rather than the values indicated by the upper edge of each band.

One-Hundred Percent Surface Chart. The one-hundred percent band chart is shown in Figure 45. Like the preceding type of surface chart, it is used to portray components of a total, but the values are in percentages rather than in absolute numbers. The ordinal scale, of course, extends from zero to 100 percent. The data for this figure indicate the proportional trends in the legal grounds for divorce in the state of Minnesota from 1870 to 1932. Each of the major categories—cruelty, adultery, desertion, drunkenness, and all other—is represented by a distinctive type of stippling or crosshatching.

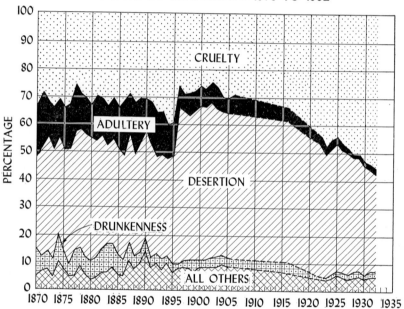

Figure 45. An Illustration of a One-Hundred Percent Surface Chart. (From Calvin F. Schmid, *Social Saga of Two Cities*, 1937, p. 318.)

CHAPTER 4

Bar and Column Charts

The bar chart is one of the most useful, simple, adaptable, and popular techniques in graphic presentation. The simple bar chart, with its many variations, is particularly appropriate for comparing the magnitude, or size, of coordinate items or of parts of a total. The basis of comparison in the bar chart is linear, or one-dimensional. The length of each bar or of its components is proportional to the quantity or amount of each category represented. In comparing size or in comparing component parts, three basic geometrical forms can be utilized. In addition to one-dimensional or linear forms, there are two-dimensional or areal comparisons and three-dimensional or cubic comparisons.[1]

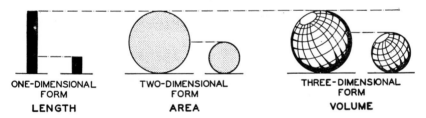

ONE-DIMENSIONAL FORM	TWO-DIMENSIONAL FORM	THREE-DIMENSIONAL FORM
LENGTH	AREA	VOLUME

Figure 46. **Three Basic Types of Geometric Forms for Comparing Sizes.** It will be noted that in each form the smaller figure is one-fourth the larger.

Figure 46 illustrates the three basic geometrical forms. In each instance, the larger figure is four times that of the smaller one. The eye can readily appraise this basic difference in the case of the bar chart, but it is much more difficult and uncertain for the areal and cubic forms. Also, it should be pointed

[1] In addition to one-, two-, and three-dimensional forms, angles are sometimes used for comparing component parts. The various sectors, for example, of a pie chart represent parts of a total. The number of degrees of each sector is drawn in proportion to the size of each component category.

73

POPULATION GROWTH
NEW YORK STATE : 1900 TO 1950

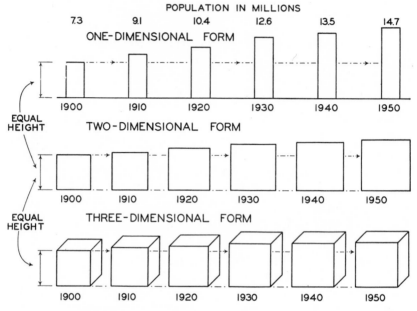

Figure 47. Application and Comparison of Linear, Areal, and Cubic Forms.
Data represent population growth of New York State from 1900 to 1950.

out, when two- and three-dimensional forms are irregular in shape, the problems of comparison become more complicated. Although the bars necessarily possess width, it is the respective length of each bar that determines the magnitude or value of a series of categories.

Figure 47 was prepared to demonstrate in more detail the implications of the three basic geometrical forms in graphic presentation. The data portrayed by this chart represent population statistics for New York State from 1900 to 1950. A column chart for a series of this kind would be entirely appropriate, but, of course, the vertical scale as well as the spacing of the columns would be different from that indicated in Figure 47. For the sake of comparability, however, the height of each geometrical form representing the 1900 data is identical. It will be observed that the height of the columns from 1900 to 1950 more than doubled, since the population increased from 7.3 million to 14.7 million. On the other hand, the two-dimensional symbols doubled in area, and the three-dimensional symbols doubled in volume, but these changes are much more difficult to visualize.

For comparisons of magnitudes, the geometric form that provides the simplest and most graphic, as well as the most correct, impressions should be used. On the basis of these criteria, one-dimensional or linear forms are usually superior. Sometimes, of course, it may be advisable or even necessary to use areal or cubic forms, especially where there are space or other restrictions, or where areal or cubic symbols seem to be more appropriate. In graphic presentation, the two most common one-dimensional forms are the bar chart and the column chart. Basically they are identical. In the bar chart, the bars are arranged horizontally, whereas in the column chart the bars are arranged vertically. As will be indicated in this chapter, there are many variations and combinations of both the bar and column charts.

Bar Charts

Types of Bar Charts. Eight different types of bar charts are portrayed in Figures 48 and 49. The more common designations and brief descriptions of each type follow.[2]

Simple Bar Chart. This is one of the most useful and most widely used forms of graphic presentation. The simple bar chart is used to compare two or more coordinate items. Comparison is based on direct linear values; the length of the bars is determined by the value or amount of each category. The bars are usually arranged according to relative magnitude of items.

Bar-and-Symbol Chart. This is merely a simple bar chart with supplementary information indicated by a cross-line, circle, diamond, or some other symbol.

Subdivided-Bar Chart. This type of bar chart, like the one-hundred percent bar chart below, is also referred to as a *segmented-bar* or *component-bar* chart. The scale values of the subdivided-bar chart are shown in absolute numbers. In order to portray per-

---

[2] Army Services Forces, *Standards of Presentation* (Washington, D. C.: War Department, 1944), pp. 38-39.

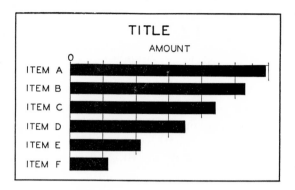

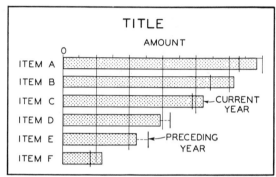

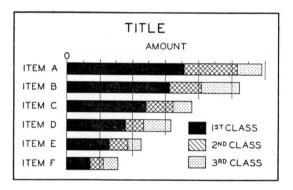

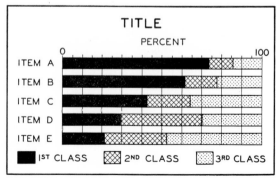

Figure 48. Illustrations of Different Types of Bar Charts.

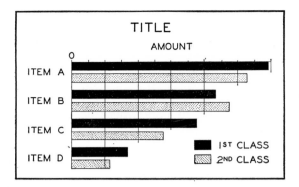

GROUPED BAR CHART

PAIRED-BAR CHART

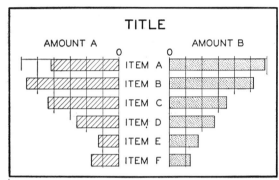

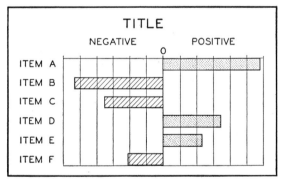

C
DEVIATION-BAR CHART

SLIDING-BAR CHART

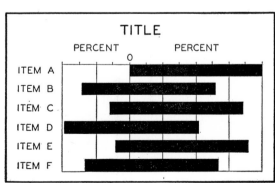

Figure 49. Illustrations of Different Types of Bar Charts.

77

centage distribution of components, the one-hundred percent bar chart should be used.

Subdivided One-Hundred Percent Bar Chart. This type of chart consists of one or more segmented bars where each bar totals 100 percent. The various divisions of the bars represent percentages of the whole.

Grouped-Bar Chart. This type of chart is also referred to as a *multiple* or *multiple-unit* bar chart. Comparison of items in two, and sometimes three, respects can be made by this type of chart.

Paired-Bar Chart. This chart, along with the deviation-bar chart and the sliding-bar chart below, is a special type of *bilateral, two-way,* or *two-directional* chart. Different units and scales can be used for each set of bars.

Deviation-Bar Chart. Note that bars extend either to left or to the right of the same base line. This type of bar chart is especially valuable for presentation of positive-and-negative and profit-and-loss data.

Sliding-Bar Chart. This is a bilateral chart in which each bar represents the total of two main components. One part of the bar is left and the other part is right of a base line. The scale may represent either percentages or absolute numbers.

Standards of Design for Simple Bar Chart

Detailed consideration will be given first of all to the simple bar chart, since it is the most widely used, as well as basic to all other forms. The characteristics and standards suggested for the simple bar chart are generally applicable to the several adaptations and variations already discussed.

Arrangement of Bars. The arrangement of the bars should be adapted to the objectives of the study. Usually the bars are arranged in order of size, starting with the largest. Sometimes, of course, an alphabetical, geographical, or other systematic ordering of data may be more appropriate to the purposes at hand.

Width of Bars and Spacing. The width of the bars and of the intervening spaces has no special significance. The width of the bars should be uniform. The number of bars and the size and proportions of the chart are the determining factors in the width of the bars, as well as the spacing between them. A good general working rule is that the spacing between the bars should be one-half the width of the bars. Sometimes, however, it may be more appropriate to lay out the spaces as little as one-fourth the width of the bars, or as much as their entire width. In any case, the bars should be of uniform width and evenly spaced. Also in a well-designed chart of this kind, the bars should not be disproportionately long and narrow, or short and wide.

Characteristics of Bars. It is customary practice to blacken in the bars in a simple bar chart. Various colors, of course, can be used in the preparation of charts for exhibit purposes and certain types of popular publications, where an additional expenditure of funds may be warranted, since color reproduction is more expensive. Stippling and crosshatching also may be used instead of full black bars. Mere outline bars are not generally recommended. If crosshatching is used, care should be taken not to create optical illusions.

Scale. As a general practice, it is recommended that a carefully planned scale be included on every bar chart.[3] The scale enables one to gauge the length of bars with a reasonable degree of accuracy. The scale can be arranged to coincide with the top of the first bar or drawn as an independent line just above the top bar. If the latter type of scale is used, the spacing between the top bar and the line should be equivalent to about one-half the width of the bar. The scale for the simple bar chart should always begin with zero. The zero line usually is the main referent point, and it should be emphasized by making it slightly heavier than the other scale lines. The scale for a horizontal bar chart should never be broken except under the most unusual circumstances. No doubt the reader has seen bar charts in which this has been done, especially when one category is dispropor-

---

[3] It has been argued that for committee and conference purposes a bar chart without a scale, but with the essential data clearly indicated, is preferable, since it may be difficult or impossible to read the scale. The precise data, if required, are readily available on the chart. Also, in subdivided-bar charts it is easier to label the segments if there is no scale. See R. R. Lutz, *Graphic Presentation Simplified* (New York: Funk & Wagnalls Co., 1949), pp. 55-58.

tionately larger than the others on the graph. If one is compelled to resort to this practice, extreme care should be taken to indicate the break in the scale as well as in the bar.

The number of intervals on the scale should be adequate for measuring distances but not numerous enough to cause confusion. The intervals should be indicated in round numbers, preferably in such units as 5's, 10's, 25's, 50's, 100's, and 1,000's. Odd-number units such as 3's, 7's, and 13's should be avoided. The intervals on the scales are marked off by lines and ticks. The scale lines and ticks are similar to those described in connection with the rectilinear coordinate chart. They should be drawn relatively light but of sufficient weight to remain sharp and clear in case the chart is reduced in size. Scale figures and a scale legend are also essential parts of a bar chart.

Data. Sometimes it is desirable that data on which the chart is based be included directly on the chart. Optical illusions and confusion may result if the accompanying data are not placed in the proper position. Normally, it is not good usage to place the figures inside the bars or at the right end of the bars. When data are placed inside the bars, there is a tendency to compare only the parts of the bars in which there are no figures, rather than the entire length of the bars, and if the data are placed at the end of the bars, the resulting tendency is to add the figures to the bars with respect to comparative lengths. If for some reason it seems necessary to letter within the bar, the lettering should be small enough to leave a strip of shading on all sides. If lettering is placed at the end of the bar, it should be relatively small in size and separated from the bar. Generally, basic data should be placed at the left of the zero line outside the grid.

Examples of Bar Charts

Simple Bar Chart. A careful examination of Figure 50 will assist the reader to understand more fully the essential principles and characteristics of the simple bar chart. The data represent the educational status of the population twenty-five years of age

(*Figure 50.*) The bar representing the city of Seattle is stippled for emphasis. Also, note numbers in bars for indicating rank order. (From Calvin F. Schmid, *Social Trends in Seattle*, 1944, p. 106.)

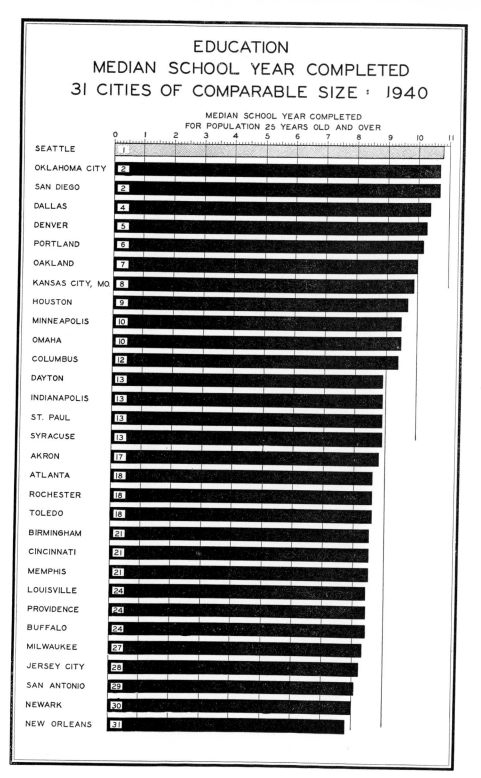

Figure 50. A Simple Bar Chart.

81

and over as measured by the median school year completed for thirty-one cities of comparable size in 1940. These cities are included in a population range from 250,000 to 500,000. Because of the relatively large number of items, the rank order of each city is indicated by a figure on the respective bar. This particular feature is not a customary one, since most charts of this kind have fewer items to compare, say not more than ten or twelve, and it is not necessary to number them. The spacing between the bars is relatively close, about one-third the width of a single bar. Since the chart was originally designed for a monograph on Seattle, the bar representing that city was emphasized by stippling. The range of the scale is from zero to eleven, adequately covering the maximum value of the data, which is 10.8 years. Each major division is indicated by a line, and the minor divisions are shown by scale points or ticks. The scale figures and scale legend also are clearly indicated. The titles and stubs comprise the other essential components of the chart.

A special adaptation of the simple bar chart is shown in Figure 51. This is not a common type of chart, but it illustrates how certain basic principles and techniques can be adapted to special problems. First, because of the unusual length of the stubs for each of the six categories, the lettering is placed above the respective bars rather than in the conventional location to the left of the zero referent line. Second, the data are expressed in terms of index numbers, with the first bar representing 100. Third, the arrangement of the bars is determined by certain defined stages in the family life cycle, and not by magnitudinal rank order. Fourth, scale lines have been omitted, since they would have interfered with the lettering of the stubs. The fact that the scale figures are placed at the bottom has no special significance; the customary practice is to place the scale figures at the top.

Subdivided- or Component-Bar Chart. The subdivided- or component-bar chart may be developed either from absolute figures or percentages. With this type of chart it is possible not only to present graphically the component parts of several items in a series of data, but also to compare the component parts one with another. When numerical data are involved, the design and procedure in constructing subdivided-bar charts are identical to

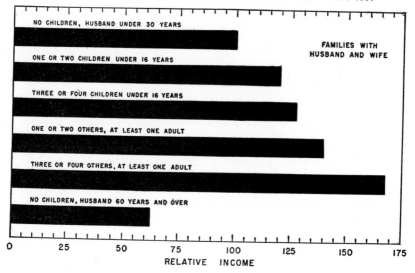

MEDIAN INCOMES OF CITY FAMILIES AT DIFFERENT STAGES IN THE
FAMILY LIFE CYCLE, 1944
(INCOME OF FAMILIES WITH NO CHILDREN, AND HUSBAND UNDER 30 YEARS = 100)

NO CHILDREN, HUSBAND UNDER 30 YEARS

FAMILIES WITH
HUSBAND AND WIFE

ONE OR TWO CHILDREN UNDER 16 YEARS

THREE OR FOUR CHILDREN UNDER 16 YEARS

ONE OR TWO OTHERS, AT LEAST ONE ADULT

THREE OR FOUR OTHERS, AT LEAST ONE ADULT

NO CHILDREN, HUSBAND 60 YEARS AND OVER

0   25   50   75   100   125   150   175
RELATIVE INCOME

Figure 51. **Stubs Lettered Above Bars.** Sometimes in order to save space it may be found expedient to letter stubs within bars or above bars. (From U. S. Department of Agriculture, *How Families Use Their Incomes,* Misc. Publ. No. 653, p. 16.)

that of a simple bar chart except that each of the bars is subdivided into its component categories. In the case of data expressed in percentage, a percentage scale is used; that is, the component parts for each bar are shown as relative proportions of 100 percent.[4] In each instance the primary purpose is to compare for a single category the individual parts in their relationship to the whole.

The segments of bars in this type of chart should be arranged in accordance with a logical or analytical sequence. The most common arrangement is by order of size. When segments are used in more than one chart, it is good practice to follow the same order, although the quantities may differ from one chart to another. To assist in differentiating the various segments of the

[4] It should be pointed out that a percentage-component bar chart may consist of only one bar. This type of subdivided-bar chart is similar in application to the pie chart. For a detailed discussion of this type of chart see Chapter 7, "Miscellaneous Graphic Forms."

bars, crosshatching is used. Whenever two or more patterns of crosshatching are used, a key or legend is normally required. The key or legend consists of small blocks of hatching with short explanatory labels indicating the meaning of each category. Unless there is some special reason, the crosshatching should follow an intensity gradation, beginning with the darkest on the left.

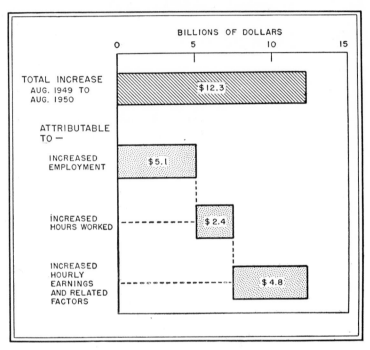

Figure 52. An Illustration of a Step-Bar Chart. The various components of a total are shown by separate bars in step form. This technique is particularly effective in showing a relatively large number of subdivisions. Chart shows factors contributing to the increase in wage and salary payments for private nonagricultural industries from August, 1949, to August, 1950. (From *Survey of Current Business,* October, 1950, p. 7.)

Parts *C* and *D* of Figure 48 illustrate the essential features of the subdivided-bar chart. Part *C* represents numerical data, and Part *D*, percentage data.

Step-Bar Chart. A very useful means of portraying component categories is the step-bar chart. The various components are shown as separate bars in step form. The largest section is usually shown at the top, followed by the remaining sections in order of size. The miscellaneous category is placed at the bottom, although it may be larger than many of the other specific categories. Figure 52 is an illustration of the step-bar chart. It shows the factors contributing to the increase in wage and salary payments for private nonagricultural industries from August, 1949, to August, 1950.

Area-Bar Chart. Another variation of the one-hundred per cent component-bar chart includes area as an essential factor. The areas of the bars for the major categories are drawn in proportion to the over-all values which they represent; the areas of the subdivisions of the bars are based on the respective values of the subcategories. For example, the respective areas of the three bars in Figure 53 have been drawn in proportion to the amount of money expended on the Spanish-American War, World War I, and World War II. The comparative costs of the three wars are clearly reflected by the areas of the bars. The subdivisions, in turn, also indicate the size of expenditures. The title, subtitles, labels, and figures for each subdivision, as well as the crosshatching, are also essential features of this type of chart.

Component-Bar Chart with Horizontal and Vertical Subdivisions. Figure 54 shows a one-hundred per cent component-bar chart with both horizontal and vertical subdivisions. The horizontal divisions indicate number of dwelling units in eight different rental categories for Minneapolis and St. Paul, respectively. The vertical subdivisions show the condition of the dwelling units in terms of four categories: "good condition," "minor repairs," "major repairs," and "unfit for use." The chart shows at a glance three major comparisons: (a) the number and proportion of dwelling units in each rental category; (b) the relationship between the condition of the dwelling units and rental level; and (c) the similarities and differences of these patterns between Minneapolis and St. Paul.

Grouped-Bar Charts. In comparing several magnitudes for each of two or three periods of time or for two or three categories, the grouped-bar chart may be found very appropriate. This type of chart is also referred to as the "multiple-bar" or "compound-bar" chart. It is shown in Figure 55, in which the methods of

COST OF WARS, UNITED STATES

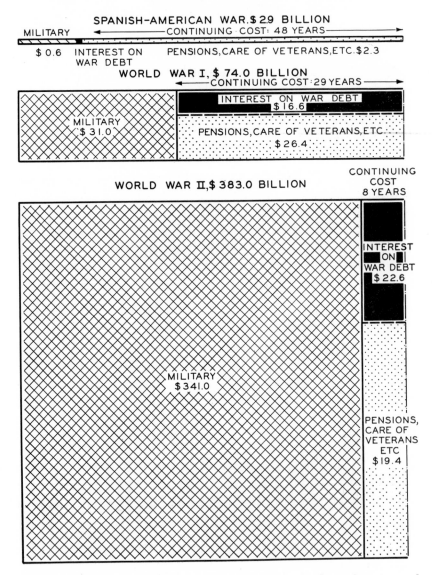

Figure 53. **Another Illustration of the Area Bar Chart.** (Redrawn from National Industrial Conference Board, *America's Resources for World Leadership*, 1947, p. 27.)

CONDITION OF RENTED DWELLING UNITS BY MONTHLY RENT MINNEAPOLIS AND ST.PAUL : 1934

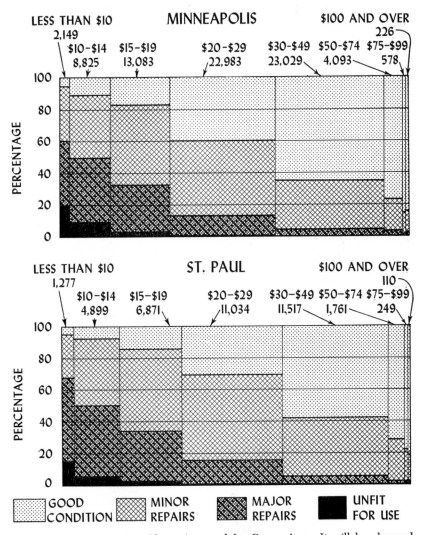

Figure 54. Two Area Bar Charts Arranged for Comparison. It will be observed that the vertical scales indicate the percentage of dwelling units in each of the four categories—(1) "good condition," (2) "minor repairs," (3) "major repairs," and (4) "unfit for use"—according to the proportion of dwelling units in each of eight rental categories for Minneapolis and St. Paul, respectively. (From Calvin F. Schmid, *Social Saga of Two Cities,* 1937, p. 216.)

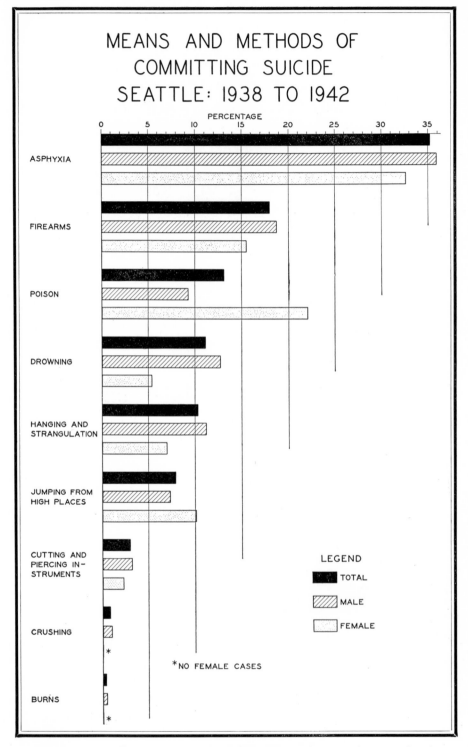

Figure 55. An Illustration of a Grouped-Bar Chart. (From Calvin F. Schmid, *Social Trends in Seattle,* 1944, p. 212.)

committing suicide are differentiated according to sex. As will
be observed from the legend, the crosshatched bars indicate
males, and the stippled bars, females. The black bars represent
both sexes combined. By placing the bars in close juxtaposition
the values for each sex and for each category are readily compar-

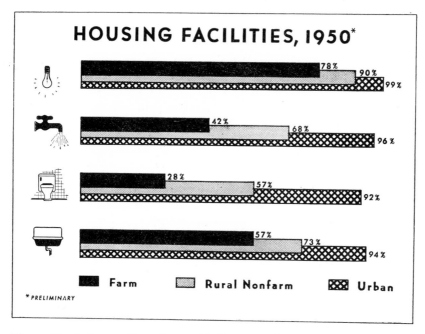

Figure 56. A Grouped-Bar Chart with Bars Partially Superimposed on Each
Other in Order to Save Space. Pictorial symbols rather than words describe the
four major categories. Also, note lack of scale. (From U. S. Bureau of Human
Nutrition and Home Economics, *Rural Family Living Charts*, p. 44.)

able. The rank order of the nine different categories was determined by relative size of the total. In this kind of chart the bars
are sometimes joined laterally, but the more common practice
is to leave a small space between them. There is always a relatively wide uniform spacing between the groups of bars.

Figure 56 is another illustration of the component-bar chart
with certain distinctive features. To save space it is not an
uncommon practice to overlap the bars in each of the major
categories. The bars are readily differentiated by a system of
crosshatching. The black bar indicates farm; stippled bar, rural

nonfarm; and crosshatched bar, urban. Although it is very effective for this chart, the use of various symbols signifying such household facilities as electricity, running water, toilets, and kitchen sinks is not a common practice. This particular chart contains no base line or scale, but the comparative values in terms of length of the respective bars and percentages can be clearly interpreted. The basic design of this chart could be improved if the bars for the four major categories were arranged in a logical rank order of relative values.

Bilateral-Bar Charts. The paired-bar, deviation-bar, and sliding-bar charts represent different forms of two-way or bilateral charts. In this type of chart the bars extend to the left and to the right of a common reference line or division. Bilateral-bar charts are well adapted to the presentation of positive and negative deviations from normal, increases and decreases, gains and losses, or the comparison of two contrasting attributes.

Paired-Bar Chart. The amount of population migration to and from farms from 1940 to 1948, inclusive, is portrayed in the form of a paired-bar chart in Figure 57. There is a pair of bars for each year, one bar extending to the left, which shows the volume of migration to farms, and one to the right, which portrays migration from farms. The data, expressed in millions of people, are lettered directly on the bars. The arrowheads and pictorial fillers help to emphasize the signification of the chart and add to its attractiveness.

Another illustration of a multiple bilateral-bar chart is shown in Figure 58. The basic comparisons are not gains or losses, increases or decreases, but two contrasting indices of rice production—acreage and tonnage—for the nine principal rice-producing countries of the world. This type of bilateral-bar chart is also known as a paired-bar chart. Acreage (millions of acres) devoted to the growing of rice is shown on the left, and rice production (millions of short tons of milled rice), on the right. Since there are two paired bars for each of the nine major categories, this chart represents a combination of both the grouped- and paired-bar chart. In order to differentiate the data for the two periods, the average for 1936-40 and 1949, one bar is crosshatched and the other is black.

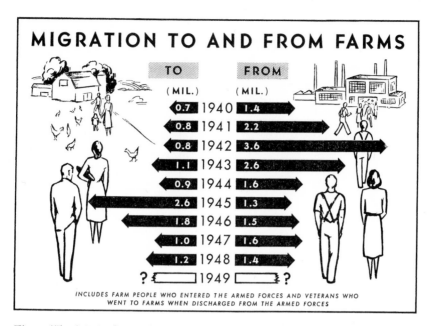

Figure 57. A Paired-Bar Chart. (From U. S. Bureau of Agricultural Economics, *Agricultural Outlook Charts, 1950,* p. 31.)

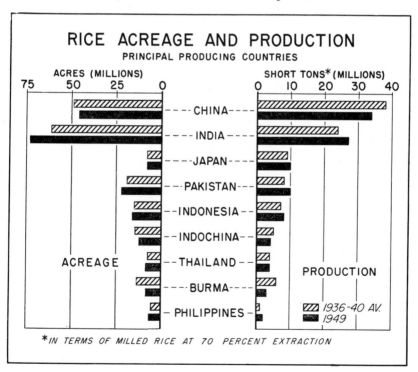

Figure 58. A Combination of the Grouped- and Paired-Bar Chart. (From U. S. Office of Foreign Agricultural Relations, *Foreign Agricultural Outlook Charts, 1951,* p. 27.)

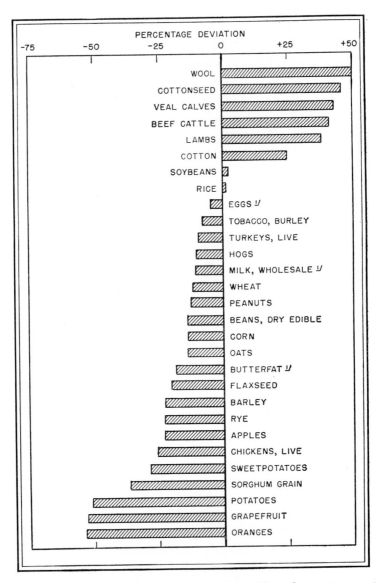

Figure 59. **An Illustration of a Deviation-Bar Chart.** Chart shows prices received by farmers in terms of percentage deviation from parity, December, 1950. (From *Survey of Current Business,* January, 1951, p. 3.)

MORTALITY CHANGES-RESPIRATORY TUBERCULOSIS
MINNESOTA: 1910-1920 AND 1920-1930

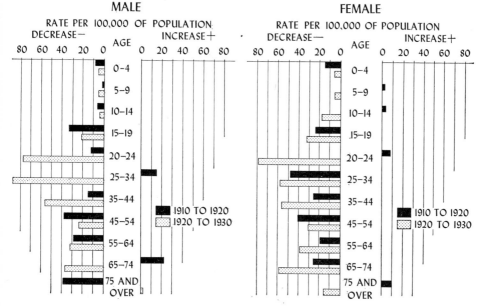

Figure 60. Another Illustration of a Deviation-Bar Chart Expressed in Ratios. Figures represent decennial increases and decreases in respiratory tuberculosis mortality expressed in rates per 100,000 of population according to age and sex. (From Calvin F. Schmid, *Mortality Trends in the State of Minnesota,* 1937, p. 119.)

Deviation-Bar Chart. A bilateral chart showing percentage deviations is portrayed in Figure 59. The values on the scale indicate percentage deviations of prices from parity received by farmers in December 1950. The items are arranged in percentage rank order beginning with the highest positive deviation. The last item on the chart is the highest negative deviation. The scale on either side of the zero line covers the range of plus and minus values. The stubs for the positive bars are indicated in the blank space to the left of the zero line. Similarly, the stubs for the items with negative values are shown on the positive side of the scale.

Figure 60, in the form of two multiple deviation-bar charts, portrays increases and decreases in tuberculosis mortality by sex and age between 1910 and 1920 and between 1920 and 1930. The chart on the left portion of the page depicts tuberculosis mortality trends for males, and the one on the right, similar data for females. The bars to the left of the zero line indicate decreases, and bars to the right, increases. The black bars represent data for 1910 to 1920, and the stippled bars, data for 1920 to 1930. The scale figures are expressed as death rates per 100,000 of population.

Sliding-Bar Chart. An illustration of a sliding-bar chart is shown in Figure 61. The chart portrays the relationship between

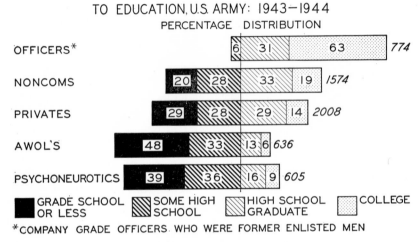

Figure 61. **Illustration of a Sliding-Bar Chart.** (Redrawn from *The American Soldier,* Vol. I, 1949, p. 114.)

educational level and advancement, and maladjustment in the United States Army during World War II. The basic design consists of five one-hundred percent component-bar charts subdivided according to the following educational levels: (1) grade school or less, (2) some high school, (3) high school graduate, and (4) college. There is one bar for each of five specially defined classes—officers, noncommissioned officers, privates, AWOL's, and psychoneurotics. The referent line separates high school graduates from those with only "some high school." It can be readily observed that proportions of the men to the right and to the left of the referent line show a close correspondence to their status, position, and maladjustment.

Column Charts

As has been pointed out previously, the only significant difference between the bar chart and the column chart is the arrangement of bars; the bars are arranged horizontally in the bar chart and vertically in the column chart. With respect to emphasis and application, the column chart is valuable in portraying time series, especially if the number of plotted values is not very large. The arithmetic line chart is more appropriate than the column chart if the period covers many years and plotting points.

Types of Column Charts. Eight different forms of the column chart are illustrated in Figures 62 and 63. The following statements summarize the names and salient characteristics of these eight variations of the column chart.[5]

Simple Column Chart. In several basic features the simple column chart has much in common with the simple bar chart. The base line of the column chart is drawn horizontally, and under no circumstances should it be omitted. The simple column chart is particularly valuable for showing time series.

Connected-Column Chart. This type of chart possesses characteristics of both the simple column chart and staircase surface chart. Although all the columns are distinct, there is no space between them. The connected-column chart may be particularly valuable as a space-saving device.

Grouped-Column Chart. This chart is comparable to the grouped-bar, multiple-bar, or compound-bar chart. Two or occasionally three columns representing different series or different classes in the same series can be grouped together, as illustrated in Figure 17. In grouping the columns they may be joined together or separated by a narrow space.

Subdivided-Column Chart. The subdivided-column chart, like the subdivided-bar, segmented-bar, or component-bar chart, is used to show a series of values with respect to their component parts. The subdivided-column chart is also similar to the subdivided-surface chart. Crosshatching is ordinarily used to differentiate the various subdivisions of the columns. The scale is characteristically expressed in terms of absolute values.

[5] Army Service Forces, War Department, *op. cit.*, pp. 38-39.

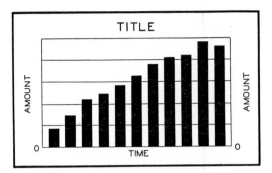

SIMPLE COLUMN CHART

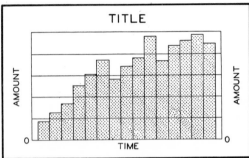

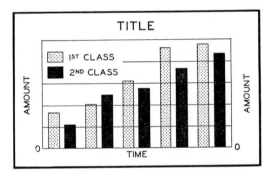

GROUPED-COLUMN CHART

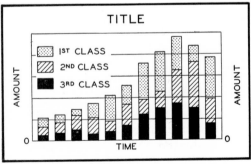

Figure 62. Illustrations of Different Types of Column Charts.

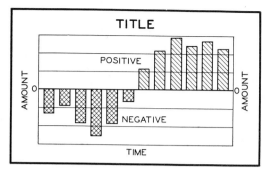

A

NET–DEVIATION
COLUMN CHART

B

GROSS–DEVIATION
COLUMN CHART

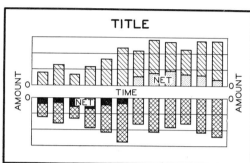

C

FLOATING–COLUMN CHART

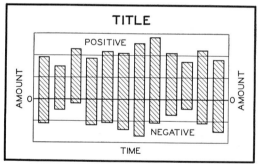

D

RANGE CHART

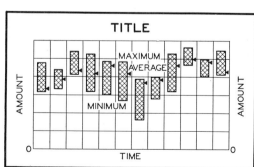

Figure 63. Illustrations of Different Types of Column Charts.

Net-Deviation Column Chart. The net-deviation and the gross-deviation column charts are similar to the bilateral-bar charts. They emphasize positive and negative numbers, increases and decreases, and gains and losses. In the net-deviation chart the column extends either above or below the referent line, but not in both directions.

Gross-Deviation Column Chart. The columns in this type of chart extend in both directions from the referent line. By means of crosshatching, both gross and net changes can be readily portrayed.

Floating-Column Chart. The floating-column chart is a deviational or bilateral chart with one-hundred per cent component columns. The deviations from the referent line represent positive and negative values or differential attributes.

Range Chart. The range chart shows maximal and minimal values in time series. This chart has been referred to as a "stock-price" chart, since it is extensively used in plotting highest and lowest daily stock quotations. Average values also can be readily indicated on the columns.

Standards of Design. The standards as well as most of the characteristics and procedures discussed in connection with the bar chart are directly applicable to the column chart. The columns should be of uniform width and evenly spaced. The spacing between columns is generally larger than the spacing between bars, and varies from one-half the width to one and one-half times the width of the columns. In the simple column chart the columns are usually blackened in, although stippling and crosshatching sometimes may be found appropriate. The vertical scale always begins with zero and covers the range of the data to be plotted.

Figure 64 clearly demonstrates the consequences of omitting the zero base line. The column graph on the right (*B*) is drawn correctly with an ordinal scale running from zero to 6,000. The graph on the left side (*A*) has a vertical scale ranging from 4,000 to 6,000. The differences in the relative size of the columns give a grossly exaggerated and distorted impression. In *A*, the height of the largest column is approximately three times that of the

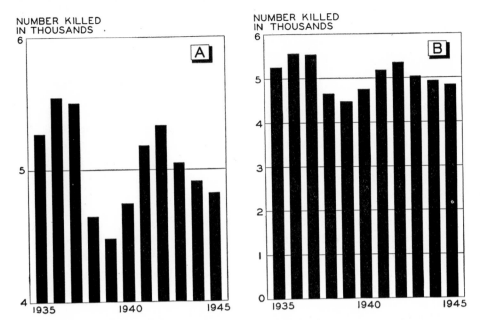

NUMBER KILLED
IN THOUSANDS

A

NUMBER KILLED
IN THOUSANDS

B

Figure 64. Column Chart With and Without Zero Base Line. *A*, Erroneous Omission of Zero Base Line. *B*, Correct Technique in Designing an Arithmetic Scale for Bar Chart. Data represent annual number of railroad fatalities (passengers, employees, trespassers, and others). (From U. S. Bureau of the Census, *Historical Statistics of the United States: 1789-1945*, 1949, p. 206.)

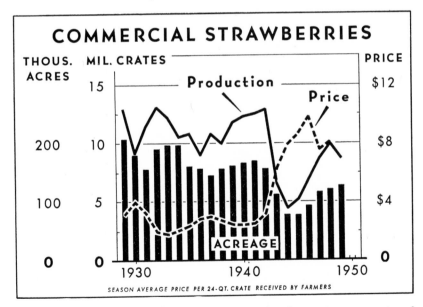

Figure 65. Another Illustration of a Multiple-Scale Chart. Note two series of scale figures on left and one on right. The two curves portray production and price, respectively, and columns indicate acreage. (From U. S. Bureau of Agricultural Economics, *Agricultural Outlook Charts, 1950*, p. 87.)

99

smallest. Actually, the differences between the minimal and maximal values are a little over one scale interval on the correctly drawn chart. Unlike the bar chart, a completely boxed-in grid seems more desirable for the column chart. This fact is shown clearly in Figures 65, 66, and 67, as well as in other accompanying illustrations. Other essential features of the column chart, such as scale intervals, scale figures, legends, accompanying data and hatching, are similar to those discussed in connection with bar charts.

Combining Features of Two or More Types of Charts. It is common practice to combine features of two or more types of graphs on the same chart. Whatever techniques are most appropriate in portraying a set of data should be utilized. An illustration of the simple column chart used in combination with the arithmetic line chart will be found in Figure 65. The three ordinal scales are another distinctive feature of this chart. These scales show (1) the number of acres devoted to the growing of strawberries, (2) the amount of strawberry production expressed in millions of crates, and (3) the price of strawberries per crate. The columns represent acreage, and the curves show price and production, respectively. The period covered is from 1929 to 1949, inclusive. In designing charts of this kind, the hazards of multiple scales should be kept in mind.[6]

Figure 66 is a combination of two types of column charts—the grouped-column chart and the subdivided-column chart. Figure 66 shows world coffee production and distribution from 1946 to 1951. In each pair of columns the one on the left shows visible coffee stocks and total production, and the one on the right shows the amount of coffee consumed and destroyed. Averages for these various categories, based on data covering several years, are shown by two relatively wide bars on the left side of the grid. There is no special significance in the width of the columns except for emphasis, since they represent an average based on several years of data.

Subdivided-Column Chart. Figure 67 is an illustration of a subdivided-column chart. This chart shows annual tobacco ex-

[6] See Chapter 3, "Rectilinear Coordinate Charts," for a more detailed discussion of the use of multiple scales.

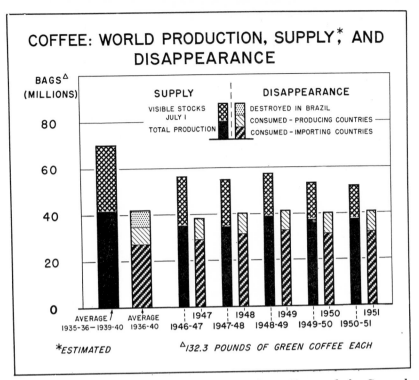

Figure 66. A Combination of the Subdivided-Column Chart and the Grouped-Column Chart. (From U. S. Office of Foreign Agricultural Relations, *Foreign Agricultural Outlook Charts, 1952*, p. 97.)

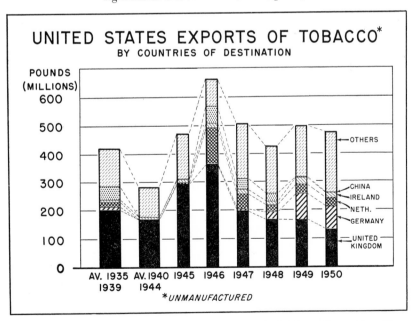

Figure 67. A Subdivided-Column Chart with Dashed Lines Connecting Component Parts to Emphasize Trends. Five-year averages for 1935-39 and 1940-44 are represented by relatively wide columns. (From U. S. Office of Foreign Agricultural Relations, *Foreign Agricultural Outlook Charts 1952*, p. 91.)

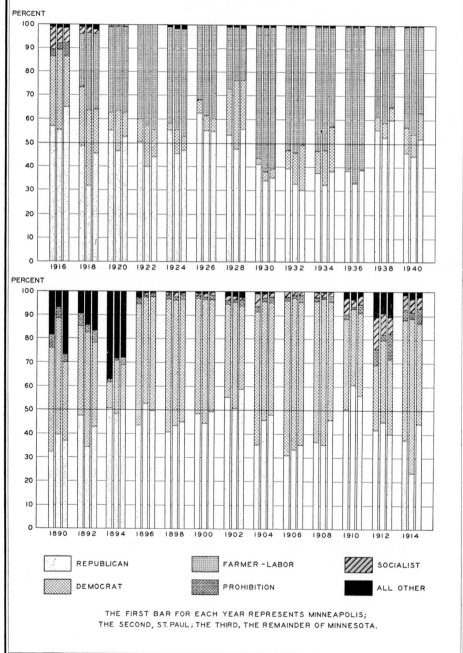

POLITICAL PARTY MOVEMENTS
GUBERNATORIAL ELECTIONS
MINNEAPOLIS, ST. PAUL AND REMAINDER OF MINNESOTA
1890 TO 1940

REPUBLICAN

DEMOCRAT

FARMER-LABOR

PROHIBITION

SOCIALIST

ALL OTHER

THE FIRST BAR FOR EACH YEAR REPRESENTS MINNEAPOLIS;
THE SECOND, ST. PAUL; THE THIRD, THE REMAINDER OF MINNESOTA.

Figure 68. Grouped One-Hundred Percent Column Chart Portraying Time Series.

102

ports from the United States for the period 1945 to 1950, with averages for two earlier periods, 1935 to 1939 and 1940 to 1944. Each column is subdivided into several categories representing amounts exported to certain specified countries. The dashed lines connecting the components of the several columns help to emphasize trends. Like the subdivided-bar chart, the subdivided-column chart may be designed either for numerical data or percentage data. Figure 67 of course, is based on numerical data. When percentages are used, the chart customarily assumes the form of a series of one-hundred percent component columns.

Figure 68 illustrates a one-hundred percent column chart. Since there are three columns for each year, it can be classified more specifically as a one-hundred percent grouped-column chart. The similarity of this type of chart and the one-hundred percent grouped-bar chart is apparent. The vertical scale extends from zero to 100 percent. The six hatchings indicate six

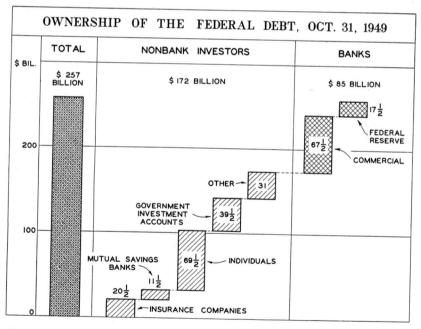

Figure 69. Step-Column Chart. This type of chart is the same as the step-bar chart except for the vertical arrangement on the page. The seven components and their proportionate values are clearly indicated by this technique. (From *1950 Annual Report of the Secretary of the Treasury*, p. 170.)

groups of political parties. The chart shows the proportions of votes received by the various political parties in the gubernatorial elections in Minnesota from 1890 to 1940. The first bar for each year represents Minneapolis; the second, St. Paul; and the third, the remainder of Minnesota.

DISTRIBUTION OF CONSUMER FOOD DOLLAR
1935

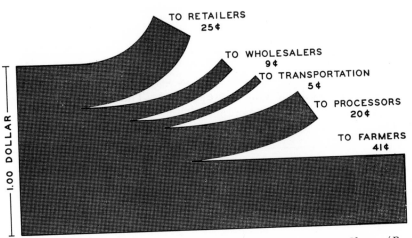

Figure 70. **Another Variation of the One-Hundred Percent Column Chart.** (Redrawn from National Resources Committee, *Structure of the American Economy,* Part I, 1939-40, p. 68.)

A variation of the one-hundred percent subdivided chart is the step-column chart shown in Figure 69. The total federal debt is indicated by a single column representing 257 billion dollars. This total is broken down into seven separate segments arranged in the form of steps, five segments being classified as "nonbank investors" and two as "banks." The hatching, explanatory labels, vertical scale, and amounts for each category and larger grouping make it possible to derive clear and precise comparisons.

Figure 70 is another example of a special type of the one-hundred percent column chart. It shows how the consumer dollar is distributed. The width of the component divisions are drawn in proportion to the amount indicated for each of the five

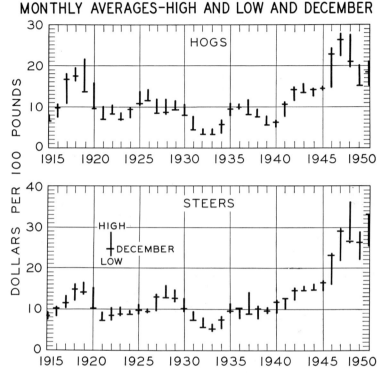

WHOLESALE PRICES OF STEERS & HOGS
CHICAGO : 1915 TO 1950
MONTHLY AVERAGES-HIGH AND LOW AND DECEMBER

Figure 71. **Range Chart.** (Redrawn from Board of Governors of the Federal Reserve System, *Federal Reserve Charts on Bank Credit, Money Rates and Business,* Historical Supplement, April, 1951, p. 106.)

categories. The length of each component in this figure possesses no particular significance.

Range Chart. The range chart is particularly effective in showing fluctuations of monthly, weekly, or daily prices, or stock quotations. For example, Figure 71 portrays the range of the monthly average prices of steers and hogs at Chicago from 1915 to 1950. The length of the column indicates the relative fluctuation from the high and low of monthly averages for each year shown on the chart. The cross-line indicates the average for December of each year.

Figure 72 is another variation of the range chart showing treasury bond prices for the Fourth Liberty Loan after World War I as compared to the Victory Loan after World War II. The monthly price fluctuation, as well as the trends of treasury bonds during the postwar periods for both loans, are clearly indicated by this chart.

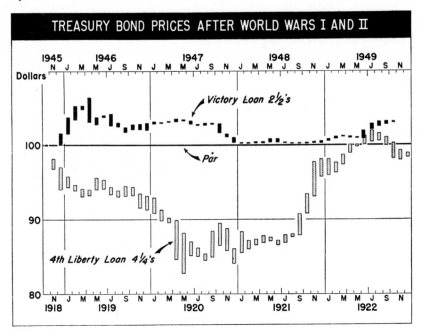

Figure 72. **Another Illustration of a Range Chart.** (From *1950 Annual Report of the Secretary of the Treasury*, p. 171.)

A range chart in which the temporal factor is only of incidental significance is shown in Figure 73. The chart portrays the range of earnings of salesmen in twelve different industries in 1948. The average range of all the industries is indicated by a separate division of the grid and by a stippled area extending across the chart. The range of earnings of the respective categories can be compared readily with the over-all average as well as with one another.

Column Chart with Circular Base Line. In order to attract attention or achieve popular appeal it is common practice to incorporate symbolic or pictorial features with basic graphic

EARNINGS OF "AVERAGE" SALESMEN IN 1948
234 UNITED STATES COMPANIES

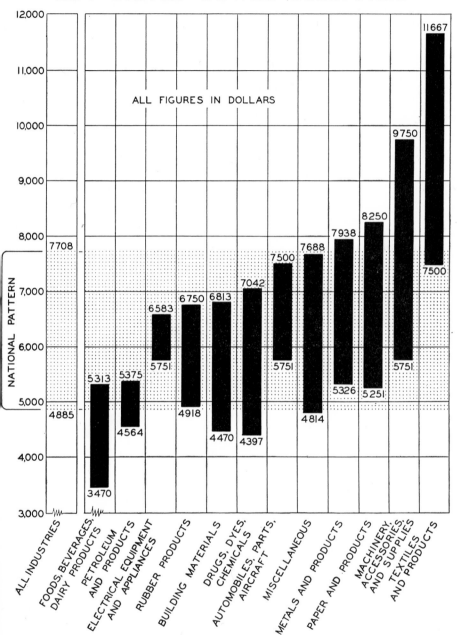

Figure 73. **Another Application of the Range Chart.** Chart shows 1948 earning ranges of salesmen for the various industries indicated on the chart. The average for all industries is represented by a stippled band and bracket. (Redrawn from National Industrial Conference Board, *Road Maps of Industry*, March 18, 1949, No. 690.)

forms.[7] Figure 74 shows the number of accidents in the lumber industry of California by hour of occurrence. A simple column chart with a horizontal base line indicating the hour of data could have been used. Instead, a circular base line calibrated pictorially in the form of a clock was used. The scale lines are represented by a series of concentric circles drawn equidistant from the base line. The length of the columns, of course, shows the number of accidents.

INJURIES IN LUMBER INDUSTRY BY HOUR OF OCCURRENCE CALIFORNIA: JULY AND AUGUST,1948

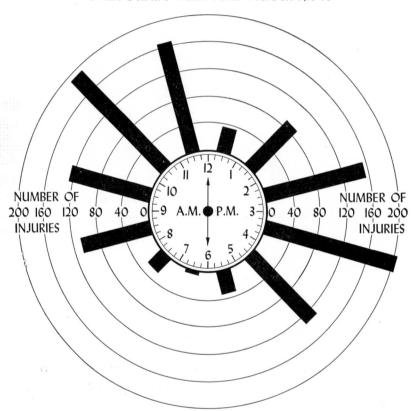

Figure 74. Another Variation of the Simple Column Chart with Circumference of Circle as Base Line and Series of Concentric Circles as Scale Lines. (Redrawn from chart prepared under direction of M. I. Gershenson, Director, Division of Labor Statistics and Research, California Department of Industrial Relations.)

[7] See Chapter 9, "Pictorial Charts," for further discussion.

CHAPTER 5

Semilogarithmic or Ratio Charts

The purpose of this chapter is to describe the theory, construction, and use of the semilogarithmic chart. The semilogarithmic chart is unequaled for many purposes, especially in portraying proportional and percentage relationships. In comparison with the arithmetic line chart, it possesses most of the advantages without the disadvantages. This type of chart not only correctly represents relative changes but also indicates absolute amounts at the same time. Because of its distinctive structure, it is referred to as a semilogarithmic or arith-log chart. The vertical axis is ruled logarithmically, and the horizontal axis, arithmetically. The continued narrowing of the spacings of the scale divisions on the vertical axis is characteristic of logarithmic ruling, whereas the equal intervals on the horizontal axis are indicative of arithmetic ruling. Because of its emphasis on proportional relationships, the semilogarithmic chart is sometimes referred to as a ratio chart.[1]

For the uninitiated, the term "semilogarithmic," as well as the characteristic ruling of the vertical axis, may seem formidable; but actually the theoretical principles on which this chart is based, and also its construction and use, are comparatively simple. Prejudice and general lack of understanding unfortunately have resulted in considerable resistance to the use of semilogarithmic charts. Generally, rates of change are more significant than absolute amounts of change in statistical analysis and presentation. In using the ratio chart, one can have confidence that relative changes are portrayed without distortion and uncertainty. An effective use of the semilogarithmic chart requires knowledge of

[1] The semilogarithmic chart must not be confused with the chart in which both axes are ruled logarithmically.

109

only one or two elementary principles. Moreover, an understanding of logarithms is not at all necessary.

Comparison of Semilogarithmic and Arithmetic Charts

Thus far only charts with arithmetic scales have been discussed. In such charts equal spaces represent equal values—that is, equal amounts of change. In the semilogarithmic chart, the vertical scale is divided logarithmically so that relative changes can be represented accurately. The arithmetic chart emphasizes absolute changes; the semilogarithmic chart emphasizes rates of change. Although the semilogarithmic chart is extremely valuable in graphic presentation, it is not a complete substitute for the arithmetic graph.

The essential differences between arithmetic and semilogarithmic charts can be clarified readily by plotting two simple pairs of figures on each type of grid: in the first pair the value for one period is 90 and that for the succeeding period is 99; in the second pair the corresponding change is from 10 to 11. In each instance there has been an increase of 10 per cent. On an arithmetic chart the amount or increment of change for the first pair would be nine units, and for the second pair, one unit. In other words, the upward movement of the curve for the first pair on an arithmetic grid would be nine times as great as the upward movement of the curve for the second pair of figures. By contrast, the curves for these data when plotted on a semilogarithmic chart would have identical slopes, because the relative or percentage changes are the same.

Figure 75 illustrates more specifically the basic characteristics of both the arithmetic and semilogarithmic charts.[2] A series increasing at a constant amount—10,000 dollars per decade—is shown by a straight line on an arithmetic grid. This fact, of course, is readily understandable, since equal increments of change are represented by equal distances on an arithmetic scale, and accordingly the upward slope of the curve is constant at each period. The corresponding curve on a semilogarithmic grid is convex upward, which indicates an increase but at a decreasing

    [2] William Addison Neiswanger, *Elementary Statistical Methods* (New York: The Macmillan Co., 1943), pp. 186-89.

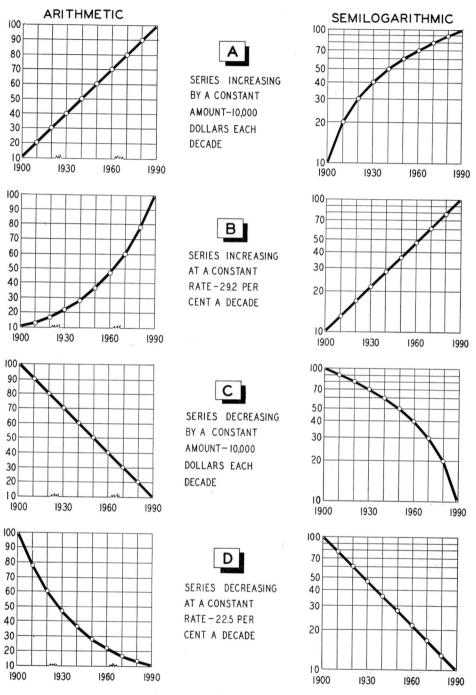

Figure 75. Comparison of Arithmetic and Semilogarithmic Charts Showing Constant Increments of Change and Rates of Change, Respectively.

111

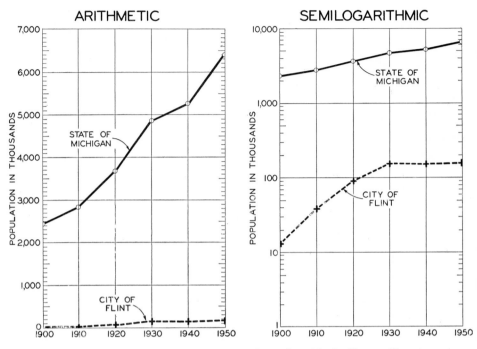

Figure 76. A Comparison of Arithmetic and Semilogarithmic Charts. Note especially effectiveness of semilogarithmic chart in portraying rate of change.

rate. This series is known as an arithmetic progression. It shows an increase by equal amounts from one period to another, but the rate of increase is a declining one. A series increasing at a constant rate is indicated by a curve showing a constant slope on the semilogarithmic grid, but on an arithmetic grid the curve is concave upward. This type of series is known as a geometric progression, since each value differs from the preceding one by a constant ratio (rate, percentage, multiplier, or divisor). The two remaining illustrations on this chart indicate declining arithmetic and geometric series. A series decreasing by a constant amount is represented by a straight line on an arithmetic grid, whereas on a semilogarithmic grid it is convex downward, which reflects a decrease at an increasing rate. A constant rate of decrease is indicated by a straight line on a semilogarithmic chart and a concave downward line on an arithmetic chart.

Figure 76 further illustrates the advantages of the semilogarithmic chart and the limitations of the arithmetic chart, especially in the comparison of changes where relatively large and small quantities are involved. The arithmetic chart may be satisfactory for portraying comparative fluctuations if the quantities compared are of approximately the same value or size. On an arithmetic chart, the wider the range of scale, the greater the division between actual and relative changes. In a semilogarithmic graph, on the other hand, it is possible to compare relatively small numbers with large ones without producing any misleading or inaccurate implications. It will be noted from Figure 76 that the ordinal axis on the arithmetic scale has a range from zero to 7,000,000, and the corresponding axis on the semilogarithmic grid ranges from 1,000 to 10,000,000. Between 1900 and 1910, the population of the city of Flint increased from 13,103 to 38,550, or 294.2 percent. On the arithmetic chart this increment is represented by approximately one-fourth of a scale unit, which is hardly detectable. The corresponding growth for the same decennial period for the entire state of Michigan was from 2,420,982 to 2,810,173, or 11.6 percent. It will be observed that this increment of growth is registered by almost four units of the arithmetic scale. However, in comparing the differential rates of population growth for the two series, it is unmistakably indicated that the city of Flint greatly surpassed the entire state of Michigan. The relative increases in the two series are authentically portrayed on the semilogarithmic grid. On the arithmetic grid, one is left with inaccurate and deceptive impressions. A comparison of the slopes of the two curves on the semilogarithmic chart for any decennial period correctly indicates rates of growth.

Construction of the Semilogarithmic Chart

There are several different procedures that can be followed in constructing a semilogarithmic chart. Each procedure will be discussed briefly, indicating its particular advantages and disadvantages. As pointed out in the foregoing discussion, equal vertical distances on a semilogarithmic chart always indicate equal percentages or rates of change. In other words, if the percentage change between two or more pairs of figures is constant, it will be found that the differences between the logarithms of these figures will be the same. Accordingly, a chart of this kind can be constructed either by plotting the logarithms of the items in a series on a natural scale or by laying out a logarithmic scale and plotting the natural numbers of the items in a series. The first method is not used very often, since it is cumbersome and, of course, requires familiarity with the handling of logarithms. Moreover, since it is relatively simple to construct a logarithmic scale or to obtain specially prepared printed semilogarithmic paper, there seems to be no particular advantage in plotting logarithms of a series on plain coordinate paper or natural scale. Plotting data on a logarithmic scale is just as simple as plotting data on an arithmetic one.

Meaning of Logarithms. For those who are not familiar with logarithms, the following brief explanation may help to clarify a few points that will be discussed below. A logarithm (common system of logarithms) is the power to which 10 must be raised to obtain a given number. For example, the logarithm of 10 is 1; of 100, 2; of 1,000, 3; and of 10,000, 4. In other words, 100 is the second power of 10 (10^2); 1,000 is the third power of 10 (10^3); and 10,000 is the fourth power of 10 (10^4). In case a number is not an exact power of 10, its logarithm will be expressed as an approximation containing decimals. By consulting a table of logarithms, it will be found that the logarithm of 2 is 0.3010; of 3, 0.4771; of 4, 0.6021; of 20, 1.3010; of 200, 2.3010. There are two separate components of a logarithm: (1) *characteristic* and (2) *mantissa*. The characteristic is the integer of the logarithm and is located to the left of the decimal point. In the logarithm of 20, the characteristic is 1, and in the logarithm of 200, the characteristic is 2, and so on. The characteristic is always the number which is one less than the number of digits in the integer of the number. The mantissa is the decimal part of the logarithm. The antilogarithm is the number corresponding to a given logarithm. For example, since the logarithm of 3 is 0.4771, then 3 is the antilogarithm of 0.4771. It will be observed that in the construction of a semilogarithmic grid only the logarithmic values from 1 to 10 are required.

Additional Characteristics of the Semilogarithmic Chart

In addition to the characteristic logarithmic rulings on the vertical axis and the arithmetic rulings on the horizontal axis, there are other features of the semilogarithmic chart which should be mentioned. No doubt it has been observed already that there is no zero base line on the semilogarithmic scale. The logarithm of zero is minus infinity. Since there is no zero line, the bottom line of a chart on a logarithmic scale may represent any convenient value.[3] In general, it can be slightly less than the smallest value that is to be plotted on the chart. The highest value on a semilogarithmic chart should be a little more than the largest value in the series that is to be portrayed. As a matter of practice, it is recommended that the bottom line begin with 10 or some division or multiple of 10, such as 0.001, 0.01, 0.1, 1, 10, 100, 1,000, or 10,000. The value of each successive figure that might be added is 10 times that of the preceding one. As many figures as are required may be added above or below the original scale. The divisions on a logarithmic scale are referred to as "cycles," "decks," "banks," "phases," or "tiers." In practice it will be found that more than five cycles are seldom needed. The highest and lowest values of the data to be plotted govern the number of cycles to be laid out on a chart.

Specific Techniques in Laying Out the Semilogarithmic Chart. Before discussing the specific techniques in laying out the semilogarithmic chart, some comment should be made on the use of commercially printed semilogarithmic graph paper. In the preparation of charts, this type of graph paper possesses the shortcomings inherent in all graph paper. From a professional point of view, printed graph paper is inflexible and unattractive and should be used rarely in constructing charts for exhibit purposes or publication. The main value of printed graph paper is for

[3] It is possible, of course, to show an arbitrary zero line, as well as relative values, on a semilogarithmic chart by recalibrating the scale. For example, the 100 per cent line can be relabeled 0, and all other values of the scale relabeled correspondingly to represent percentage increase or decrease from this point. This technique is seldom used, since it destroys the uniform labeling of scale values of the various decks, which are characteristic of the semilogarithmic chart. Karl G. Karsten, *Charts and Graphs* (New York: Prentice-Hall, Inc., 1923), pp. 407-11.

administrative purposes and for preliminary and experimental sketching as a basis for ascertaining the more salient features of data and the most appropriate graphic design to be used for the final layout.

The first method of constructing a semilogarithmic scale is by means of a table of logarithms. Figure 77 portrays very simply the three major steps in the logical development of a logarithmic scale.[4] After the height of the scale is determined, the first step,

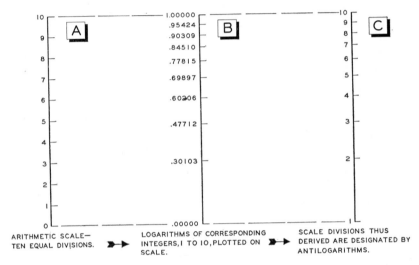

Figure 77. Basic Technique in Constructing a Logarithmic Scale.

A, merely shows a vertical line divided into ten equal spaces from zero to 10. In B, the same distance is divided in proportion to the logarithmic values of 1 to 10. In C, the divisions thus derived are designated by their respective antilogarithms. No matter what the desired height of a scale may be, it is relatively simple to lay out the divisions of the scale in proportion to the logarithmic values of a given height. For example, if the height of a scale is 4 inches, then the first division will be the logarithm of 2 multiplied by 4, or $(0.3010)\,(4) = 1.20$ inches. Similarly, the distance to 3 will be $(0.4771)(4) = 1.91$ inches. A fractional division of the scale can also be derived in the same manner. For

[4] Neiswanger, *op. cit.*, pp. 189-90.

TABLE III

SIZE OF SCALE INTERVALS OF LOGARITHMIC
SCALES OF 3-, 4-, 5-, 6-, AND 7-INCH CYCLES

Scale Value	Logarithm	Cumulative Distance in Inches from Scale Value 1				
		3-Inch Cycle	4-Inch Cycle	5-Inch Cycle	6-Inch Cycle	7-Inch Cycle
1	0.0000	0.00	0.00	0.00	0.00	0.00
1.5	0.1761	0.53	0.70	0.88	1.06	1.23
2	0.3010	0.90	1.20	1.51	1.81	2.11
2.5	0.3979	1.19	1.59	1.99	2.39	2.79
3	0.4771	1.43	1.91	2.39	2.86	3.34
3.5	0.5441	1.63	2.18	2.72	3.26	3.81
4	0.6021	1.81	2.41	3.01	3.61	4.21
4.5	0.6532	1.96	2.61	3.27	3.92	4.57
5	0.6990	2.10	2.80	3.49	4.19	4.89
5.5	0.7404	2.22	2.96	3.70	4.44	5.18
6	0.7782	2.33	3.11	3.89	4.67	5.45
6.5	0.8129	2.44	3.25	4.06	4.88	5.69
7	0.8451	2.54	3.38	4.23	5.07	5.92
7.5	0.8751	2.63	3.50	4.38	5.25	6.13
8	0.9031	2.71	3.61	4.52	5.42	6.32
8.5	0.9294	2.79	3.72	4.65	5.58	6.51
9	0.9542	2.86	3.82	4.77	5.73	6.68
9.5	0.9777	2.93	3.91	4.89	5.87	6.84
10	1.0000	3.00	4.00	5.00	6.00	7.00

example, the distance to 3.5 is $(0.5441)(4) = 2.18$ inches. Table III summarizes the cumulative distances from 1 to the respective divisions on a logarithmic scale 3, 4, 5, 6, and 7 inches in height. In calibrating a scale developed in this manner, a civil engineer's scale will be found useful in plotting the points. In case more than one deck is required for a chart, the original layout can be copied readily on tracing paper or tracing cloth.

A much easier and more practicable technique in laying out a logarithmic scale is to purchase four or five sizes of commercially printed semilogarithmic or logarithmic paper. Complete scales for plotting purposes can be prepared by cutting strips ¾ to 1 inch wide from each of the sheets. Normally these scales will be adequate for virtually all sizes of logarithmic charts that might be constructed. Moreover, a supply of this kind will last for years, since additional strips can be cut from the paper in case any wear out. It is recommended that the strips of printed graph paper be mounted on thin cardboard (a filing folder is excellent for this purpose) to facilitate handling and reading of the scale, and sprayed with a coat of lacquer or plastic to preserve the scale. Each strip of paper prepared in this manner is an effective logarithmic scale. It will be recalled from Chapter 2 that the standard statistician's scale has five logarithmic scales which will be found useful in constructing logarithmic charts. In the light of the author's experience, however, several scales prepared from printed semilogarithmic chart paper are more flexible and efficient.

Figure 78 illustrates how a logarithmic scale is used in laying out the vertical axis of a ratio chart. It will be observed that there are three cycles on this chart, and the procedure in plotting the points is the same as that for plotting points for grid lines on an arithmetic chart with a civil engineer's or some other equal-division scale. It is relatively simple to contract or expand a logarithmic scale with commercially printed graph paper. Figure 78 shows how a scale can be contracted, whereas Figure 79 illustrates how a scale can be expanded.[5] From these illustrations it can be seen how a scale of any size can be constructed readily according to this technique, and also how an assortment of several different sizes of paper will help to simplify work of this kind.

A third technique in constructing logarithmic scales is illustrated in Figure 80. The construction of a flexible scale of this kind is comparatively simple. Two logarithmic scales of different sizes are laid out several inches apart on a piece of paper or tracing cloth. It is necessary to draw a horizontal center line so that the centers of the two scales will be exactly on the same level. The various points on the two logarithmic scales are then joined. If desired, the scale lines can then be extended in either direction to cover virtually any desired height. The flexible scale should be drawn on some relatively tough, transparent ma-

---

[5] Frederick E. Croxton and Dudley J. Cowden, *Applied General Statistics* (New York: Prentice-Hall, Inc., 1945), pp. 120-23.

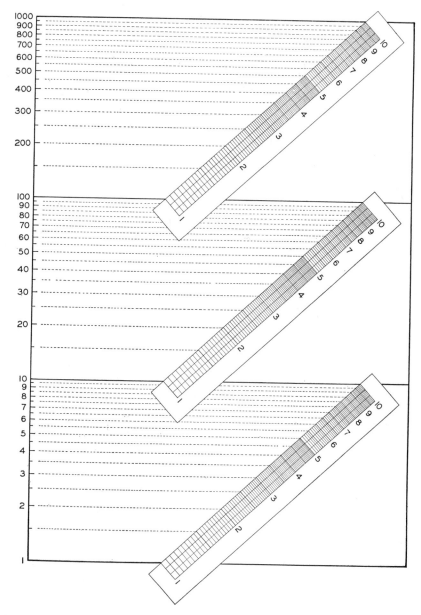

Figure 78. Technique for Constructing Logarithmic Scale from Commercially Printed Graph Paper. Figure also illustrates how plotted scale can readily be reduced in size.

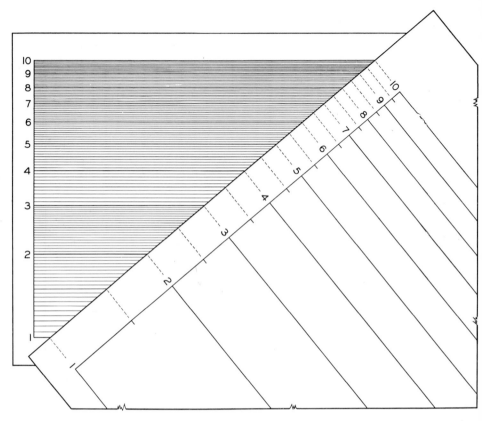

Figure 79. Another Illustration Showing Construction of Logarithmic Scale from Commercially Printed Graph Paper. Note in particular technique for expanding original scale.

terial, such as tracing cloth or heavy rag tracing vellum. The scale can be used directly in the construction of logarithmic charts or can be reproduced first on black line or ozalid prints and then cut into strips according to required sizes. Another method in using the flexible scale is to overlay a strip of tracing cloth on vellum of the same height as the scale to be laid out. The various divisions can be marked directly on the overlay, which can be used as a scale for plotting points.

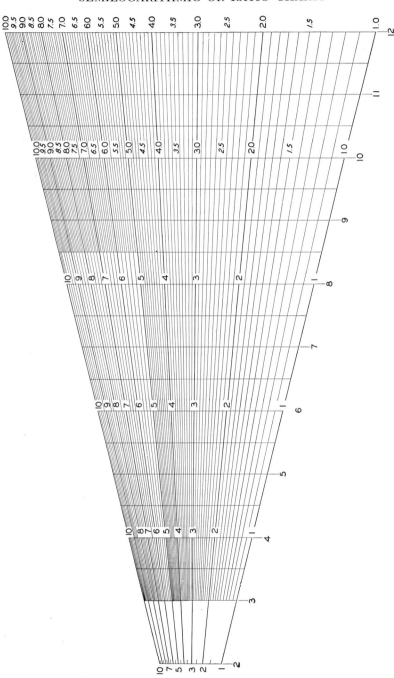

Figure 80. A Flexible Scale for Logarithmic Plotting.

Special Applications of the Semilogarithmic Chart

As a technique for showing proportional rates of change, the semilogarithmic chart is unquestionably the best. This fact has been emphasized throughout the chapter. The semilogarithmic chart makes possible direct and correct comparisons of relative increases and decreases. In addition, this type of chart has other special uses. First, in comparing rates of change among variables not expressed in the same units, the semilogarithmic chart has a unique advantage. In the case of an arithmetic chart, generally only one or possibly two scales can be indicated on the vertical axis. Under very special circumstances, it is possible to use three different scales. In any case, multiple scales on arithmetic charts must be used with extreme caution and only under very limited conditions. There is no restriction of this kind in the case of a semilogarithmic chart, for it is possible to show several scales without complicating the chart or creating wrong impressions. In Figure 81 it will be observed from the grid on the left side that comparisons can be made readily among population growth, the number of telephones, the number of motor vehicles, and streetcar and bus passengers. Similarly, in the center grid, population growth is compared with water meters, electric light accounts, income from the city light department, number of electric ranges served by city current, the mileage of streets, and the mileage of sewers. On the grid on the right side of the chart, population growth is compared with the number of books circulated by public libraries, the number of books in public libraries, and average daily public school attendance.

As indicated in connection with Figure 82, the semilogarithmic chart is particularly valuable in comparing two or more series of widely different magnitudes. The relative changes as indicated by the slopes of the curves are comparable no matter in what position they may be in the field. Equal rise or fall on the same scale represents the same ratio of change. Figure 82 indicates ten different series of data ranging in value from less than 150 to more than 80,000. The relative rates of change for each of these series are correctly indicated on the chart, and it is possible to make comparisons among them, as well as among the

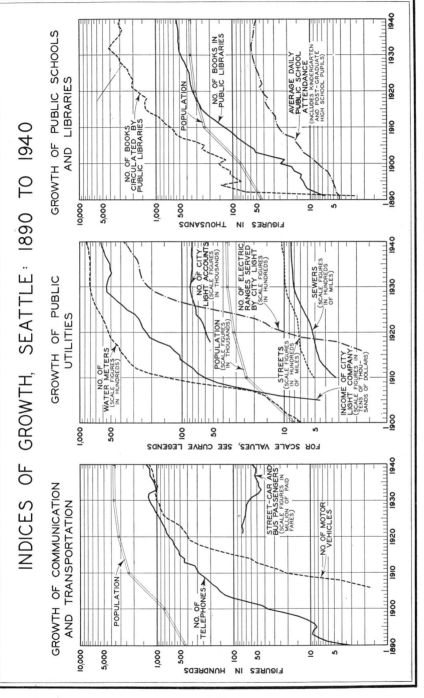

Figure 81. The Semilogarithmic Chart Is a Valuable Technique for Comparing Rates of Change Among Variables Not Expressed in the Same Units. (From Calvin F. Schmid, *Social Trends in Seattle*, 1944, p. 38.)

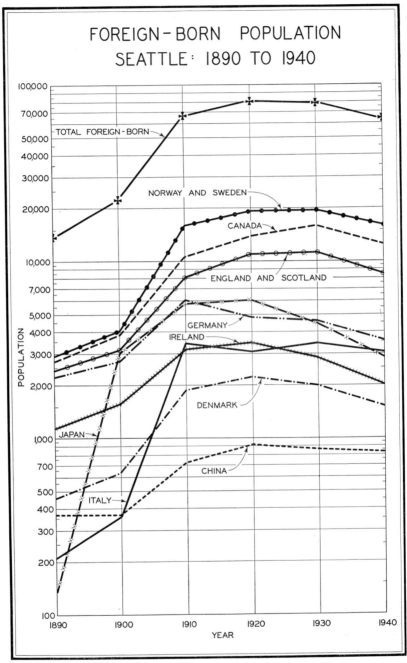

Figure 82. Three-Deck Semilogarithmic Chart. There are ten different curves on this chart with values ranging from less than 200 to over 80,000. (From Calvin F. Schmid, *Social Trends in Seattle,* 1944, p. 98.)

124

segments of the same curve. By contrast, if these data had been plotted on an arithmetic grid, the results would have been worthless or actually worse than worthless, since it would have been impossible to interpret either relative rates of growth or absolute changes for most of the curves.

Another technique for comparing a large number of curves of widely different values is to place sections of a semilogarithmic scale one above the other according to any desired sequence. Figure 83 illustrates how a series of seven age-specific fertility curves arranged chronologically according to age of female can be portrayed clearly by this method. The curve at the top represents the age group 15 to 19 years, followed in successive order by the six remaining age groups covering the entire reproductive period. It will be observed that the fertility rates vary markedly among the several age groups. For example, the rates for the age group 20 to 24 years range from approximately 100 to 250 per 1,000 female population. On the other hand, the rates for the age group 45 to 69 years vary from less than 0.7 to approximately 3.5. Only that portion of the scale covering the range of rates for each respective age group is required. Trends and rates of changes among the various curves are readily reflected by the slope of the curves. This technique also saves space.

It should be pointed out that the arithmetic and semilogarithmic scales approach each other as the maximal and minimal percentage changes among the values become increasingly smaller. If the relative difference between the highest and lowest values is around 25 or 50 percent, or sometimes even more, the arithmetic chart may be more appropriate than a semilogarithmic chart, but where the range of relative difference is much larger, the semilogarithmic chart is superior. Where there are several series of data which lie on different portions of the scale, even though the percentage changes are extremely slight from one pair to another, the semilogarithmic chart is sensitive to these changes and depicts them correctly. The semilogarithmic chart may prove to be particularly valuable in studying relationships between one or more series of temporal data. Curves can be brought into close juxtaposition and readily compared. In this way it is possible to detect direct correlations, as well as the absolute amount of "leads" and "lags." This procedure may fre-

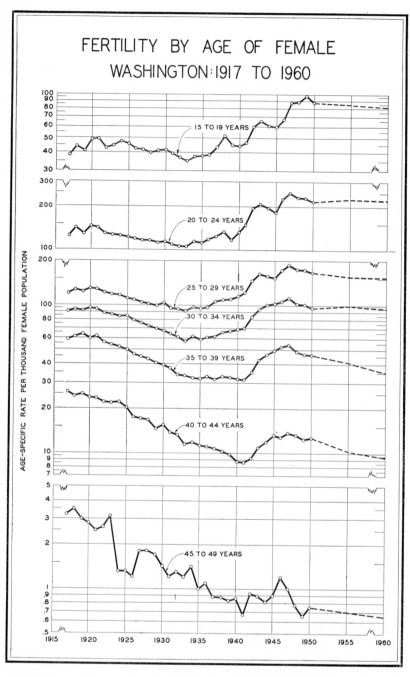

Figure 83. In Order to Conserve Space as Well as to Facilitate Comparison, Several Curves Can Be Placed on One Chart by Including Only Small Sections of a Scale. (From Calvin F. Schmid, Warren E. Kalbach, Vincent A. Miller, and Fred J. Shanley, *Population and Enrollment Trends and Forecasts, State of Washington*, 1953, p. 10.)

quently be a useful device as a preliminary step in the application of more elaborate correlational analyses.

Sometimes attempts are made to use the semilogarithmic charts for developing forecasts. This is done by simple extrapolation. It is possible, of course, to extrapolate from the arithmetic chart as well as the semilogarithmic chart. Extrapolations of this kind may have some justification, if the trend shows marked stability and conformance to a geometric increase. However, extreme caution must be exercised. Arbitrary mechanical or mathematical types of projections are of dubious value. It is recommended that, if one is interested in forecasting, a more analytical type of procedure be used which would take into consideration the various components and basic elements involved, as well as modifying factors.[6]

Measuring Percentage Changes on a Semilogarithmic Chart

After some practice, it is possible to estimate the approximate percentage increase or decrease represented by curves on a semilogarithmic chart. It will be recalled that the vertical distance of a curve on a semilogarithmic chart is indicative of the percentage change regardless of the location of the curve on the grid. For example, the distances from 10 to 20, 100 to 200, and 1,000 to 2,000 represent increases of 100 percent, and all three curves indicating these changes will manifest the same slope.

The most practicable and precise technique for measuring percentage changes is to trace the scale calibrations of the semilogarithmic chart on a strip of durable, transparent material such as tracing cloth, rag tracing vellum, or heavy acetate. It will be necessary, of course, to make a separate percentage scale for each size of chart. Values corresponding to percentage changes should be marked carefully on the scale. The upper part of the scale of Figure 84 represents percentage increases, and the lower part shows percentage decreases. The scaling extends upward

6 See, for example, Calvin F. Schmid *et al.*, *Population and Enrollment Trends and Forecasts, State of Washington* (Seattle: Washington State Census Board, 1953), *passim*.

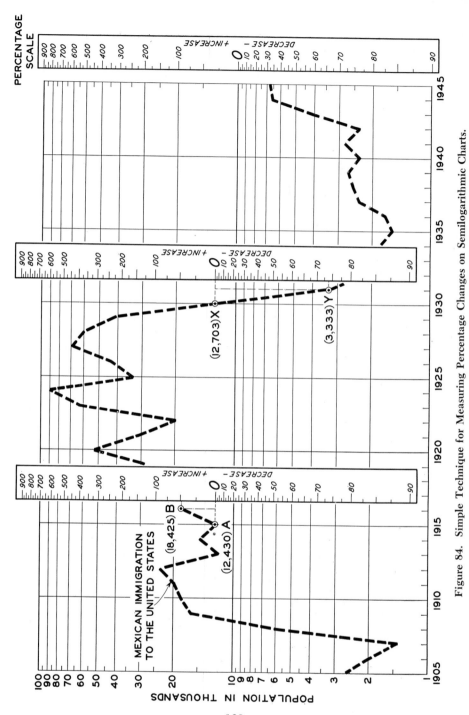

Figure 84. Simple Technique for Measuring Percentage Changes on Semilogarithmic Charts.

128

and downward from zero. The percentage increase from the beginning of a cycle to the first division is 100 percent (1 to 2, 10 to 20, 100 to 200, and so on). The increase from the beginning of the cycle to the third major division is 200 percent (1 to 3, 10 to 30, 100 to 300, and so forth). The percentage increase from the beginning of the cycle to the end is 900 percent (1 to 10, 10 to 100, 100 to 1,000, and so on). The scale values below the zero point represent percentage decreases. For example, the decrease from the top of the scale to the bottom is 90 percent (10 to 1, 100 to 10, and so on). A change from a division to one immediately below, such as from 60 to 50, 3 to 2, 7,000 to 6,000, and so on is 10 percent. Figure 84, which depicts Mexican immigration to the United States from 1905 to 1945, inclusive, illustrates the application of the percentage scale to the semilogarithmic chart. The section of the curve from 1915 to 1916 represents an increase in Mexican immigration from 12,430 to 18,425. The zero point of the percentage scale is placed on the level of the plotting point A. The distance to plotting point B (18,425) represents an increase of 48.2 percent. The percentage decline from 12,703 immigrants in 1930 to 3,333 in 1931 can be read off the scale by placing the zero point on 12,703 and reading down to the scale value opposite 3,333 (73.7 percent).

Interpretation of Curves

Although the foregoing discussion on the characteristics, construction, and application of semilogarithmic charts touches directly on the subject of interpretation, it is the purpose of this section to present in more specific form the implications of typical curve patterns found on charts of this kind. It must not be forgotten that the semilogarithmic chart emphasizes rates of change, the slope of the curve being indicative of the rate of change. Rate-of-change comparisons can be made readily between different parts of a single series or between two or more series.

Figure 85 depicts certain generalized curve patterns found on semilogarithmic charts: (1) A curve increasing at a constant rate

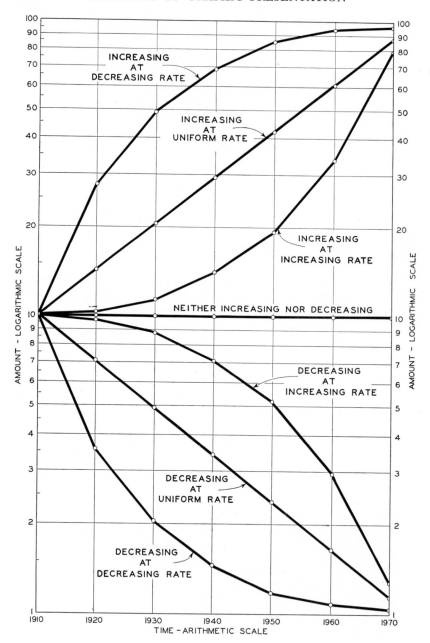

Figure 85. Curves Illustrating the Interpretation of Semilogarithmic Charts.

takes the form of a straight ascending line. Correspondingly, a curve decreasing at a uniform rate is a straight descending line. Two or more curves or segments of curves on a semilogarithmic chart that are parallel indicate the same rate of change. (2) An ascending convex curve indicates an increase at a decreasing rate. This fact can be understood readily, since the relative steepness of the curve is indicative of the rate of change. The slope of the curve is steep at the beginning and becomes progressively less as the curve moves toward the top of the field. The configuration of a curve that is decreasing at a decreasing rate moves downward in concave fashion. Again, the implications of this pattern can be ascertained readily, since the relative slope of the various portions of the curve declines toward the bottom of the chart. (3) A curve increasing at an increasing rate moves upward in concave fashion. It will be observed that the relative slope of the line becomes more pronounced toward the top of the chart. If the curve is decreasing at an increasing rate, the curve pattern is convex downward. This is, of course, in conformity with the basic principle that the greater the slope of the line the greater the rate of change. Since the declivity of the curve increases toward the bottom of the chart, the curve shows an increasing rate of change. (4) When the curve is horizontal, it is neither increasing nor decreasing.

Other Graphic Techniques for Showing Rates of Change

Because of lack of familiarity with the semilogarithmic chart, a desire for simplicity, or for some other reason, a statistician may prefer to use some technique other than the semilogarithmic chart to portray rates of change. This can be done in at least two ways, neither of which is entirely satisfactory. These methods represent only a partial and frequently inadequate solution. Moreover, if simplification is the objective, more problems are actually created than solved. The first method is to portray relative changes by means of a percentage scale. Mere percentages fail to provide any indication of the actual values that are represented by the percentages on the curve. The semilogarithmic scale not only portrays relative changes correctly but also exhibits accurately the numerical values of the series represented by the curve. Moreover, the semilogarithmic chart avoids the inevitable confusion resulting from the arbitrary selection of the base year or base period. The second alternate solution is to construct an arithmetic grid with two different vertical scales. This method is satisfactory if the scales are drawn in proper proportion and if the values do not vary too markedly from one another. Otherwise, the changes indicated by the curves will be distorted and misleading.

CHAPTER 6

Frequency Graphs and Related Charts

The purpose of this chapter is to describe the more important charting techniques for portraying frequency distributions and similar forms of data. The presentation of this material will be organized under the following major headings: (1) simple frequency graphs, (2) ogives, or cumulative frequency charts, (3) probability graphs, and (4) charts relating to distributions of age-specific rates.

Simple Frequency Graphs

Simple arithmetic frequency graphs represent the most common technique for portraying frequency distributions. There are three kinds of simple frequency graphs: (1) frequency polygon, (2) histogram, and (3) smoothed frequency curve. These graphs are illustrated in Figure 86. It will be observed that they are based on data in Table IV.

Simple frequency graphs are usually drawn on rectilinear coordinates. The Y axis always begins with zero and under no circumstances is it broken.[1] The horizontal scale does not have to begin with zero unless, of course, the lower limit of the first class interval is zero. In laying out the vertical scale, the range should be constructed to accommodate the maximum class frequency. Customarily the highest value on the vertical axis is slightly higher than the maximal frequency. The scale intervals for the vertical axis are expressed in some convenient unit of round numbers, such as 5's, 10's, 25's, or some multiple thereof.

---

[1] The practice of breaking the vertical scale is frequently permissible in rectilinear time charts. For a more detailed discussion of this point, as well as the basic theory and practice of constructing rectilinear coordinate charts, see Chapter 3, "Rectilinear Coordinate Charts."

TABLE IV

WEEKLY EARNINGS OF CLASS "A" TYPISTS
SEATTLE, WASHINGTON: 1951

Earnings (in dollars)	Frequency		Cumulative Frequency			
			Number		Percentage	
	Number	Per Cent	"Less Than"	"More Than"	"Less Than"	"More Than"
Total	761	100.0	761	761	100.0	100.0
35.00 to 37.49	9	1.2	9	761	1.2	100.0
37.50 to 39.99	57	7.5	66	752	8.7	98.8
40.00 to 42.49	70	9.2	136	695	17.9	91.3
42.50 to 44.99	120	15.8	256	625	33.7	82.1
45.00 to 47.49	142	18.5	398	505	52.2	66.3
47.50 to 49.99	92	12.1	490	363	64.3	47.8
50.00 to 52.49	99	13.0	589	271	77.3	35.7
52.50 to 54.99 ...	56	7.4	645	172	84.7	22.7
55.00 to 57.49 ...	62	8.1	707	116	92.8	15.3
57.50 to 59.99 ...	29	3.8	736	54	96.6	7.2
60.00 to 62.49 ...	5	.7	741	25	97.3	3.4
62.50 to 64.99	13	1.7	754	20	99.0	2.7
65.00 to 67.49 ...	2	.3	756	7	99.3	1.0
67.50 to 69.99	5	.7	761	5	100.0	.7

Source: United States Bureau of Labor Statistics, *Occupational Wage Survey, Seattle, Washington* (September, 1951), Table A-1.

The number of class intervals in the frequency distribution determines the range, as well as the divisions of the horizontal scale.

In portraying frequency distributions, a distinction should be made between *continuous* and *discontinuous* variables. A continuous variable has an unlimited number of possible values ranging between the lowest and highest; a discontinuous variable represents discrete increments or complete units, and hence is not capable of indefinite refinement. Each value of a discontinuous or discrete variable is distinct and separate, whereas the values of a continuous variable merge into one another by minute gradations. Age, weight, and temperature are examples of continuous variables; people, houses, and automobiles are examples of discontinuous variables.

Frequency Polygon. In laying out a polygon the appropriate frequency of each class is located at the midpoint of the interval, and the plotting points are then connected by straight lines. Figures 86(A), 87, and 88 are illustrations of frequency polygons. As has been pointed out, the frequency polygon in Figure 86(A), and also the histogram, step histogram, and smoothed-frequency graph, are based on the same series of data which will be found in Table IV. The abscissal axis indicates wage intervals extending from $35 to $70, and the ordinal axis shows the frequencies of the class intervals, which range from 2 to 142 typists. Figure 87 portrays the distribution of scores on the Kuhlman-Anderson Intelligence Test for a sample of fifth and sixth grade pupils. The horizontal axis represents intelligence scores, and the vertical axis indicates number of pupils. Figure 88 shows chest measurements for three different age groupings of naval recruits. It will be noted that the vertical axis is calibrated in percentages.

Histogram. The typical histogram is constructed by erecting vertical lines at the limits of the class intervals and forming a series of contiguous rectangles or columns. The area of each rectangle represents the respective class frequencies. If the histogram is constructed over equal class intervals, the heights of the rectangles will be proportional to the areas. In such cases the heights will represent the class frequencies. For this reason histograms based on equal class intervals are much simpler to interpret than are those based on unequal intervals. Unequal class intervals are discussed on pages 145 to 147. Sometimes all the vertical lines except the two at each end of the distribution are omitted, thus giving a step rather than a column effect to the chart. This type of histogram is referred to as a *step-frequency* chart. Occasionally, the rectangles of the histogram are cross-hatched, stippled, or blacked. The histogram is particularly appropriate for depicting discrete series, although it can be used for continuous series. Figures 86, 93, and 94 portray various types of histograms. An examination of Figure 86 will reveal the conventional histogram as well as the step form of histogram. Figure 93 represents a grouped histogram designed to compare two series of discrete data.

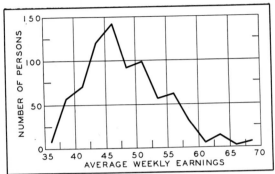

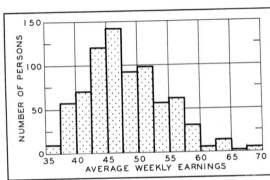

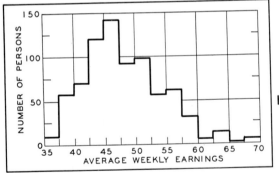

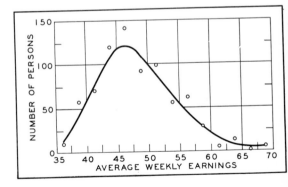

Figure 86. Four Types of Simple Frequency Charts.

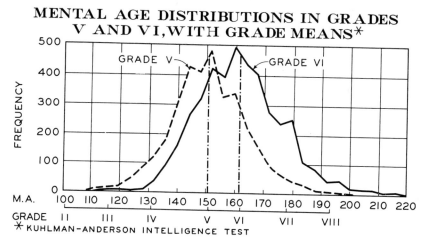

Figure 87. A Comparison of Two Frequency Polygons. Data indicate mental age distribution of children in the fifth and sixth grades based on the Kuhlman-Anderson Intelligence Test. The mean of each grade from the second through the eighth is also shown on the chart. (Redrawn from Gilbert L. Betts, "Test Calibration for Categorical Classification," *Educational and Psychological Measurement,* Vol. 9, Autumn, 1949, pp. 269-79.)

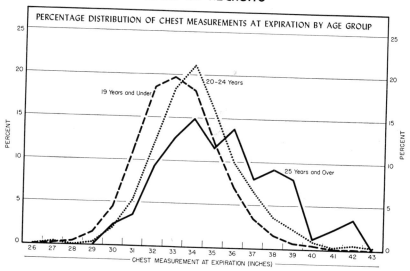

Figure 88. Frequency Polygons. (From *Statistics of Navy Medicine,* January, 1950, p. 4.)

A Variant of the Typical Frequency Histogram; the Age and Sex Pyramid or Triangle. The age and sex pyramid, which is extensively used to portray certain types of population data, is fundamentally a two-way, or bilateral, histogram with the X and Y axes reversed. It will be observed from Figures 89, 90, and 91 that the class intervals are indicated by the vertical axis, and the numerical or percentage frequency, by the horizontal axis. The histogram rectangles to the left of the zero or base line represent the male sex, and those to the right, the female sex. The age divisions read from bottom to top, beginning with the youngest group. In a normally structured population, the general configuration of this type of chart is pyramidal or triangular. This fact is clearly understandable as a consequence of the normal operation of fertility and mortality on the age and sex structure of the population. However, migration or some other factor may be responsible for extreme variations from the symmetrical triangle. The series of nine age and sex pyramids in Figure 89 typify the selective influence of various ecological and other factors on the age and sex structure of the population in different sections of a large city. Figure 90 illustrates a simple technique for showing increases and decreases for the several age categories in an age and sex pyramid. Figure 91 is an adaptation of the grouped-bar chart arranged as an age and sex pyramid in order to compare two different populations.[2]

Smoothed-Frequency Graph. The main purpose of smoothing a frequency graph is to iron out or eliminate the accidental irregularities resulting from sampling errors. As a rule, only frequency distributions based on samples should be smoothed. Accordingly, a smoothed-frequency curve represents a generalized characterization of the universe from which the sample was taken. Of course, only continuous series should be smoothed. In smoothing a curve it is important that the total area under the curve be equal to the area under the original histogram or polygon. Frequently, when a smoothed curve is constructed, the plotting points of the original data are drawn on the grid to facilitate comparison with the original data.

[2] See Chapter 4, "Bar and Column Charts."

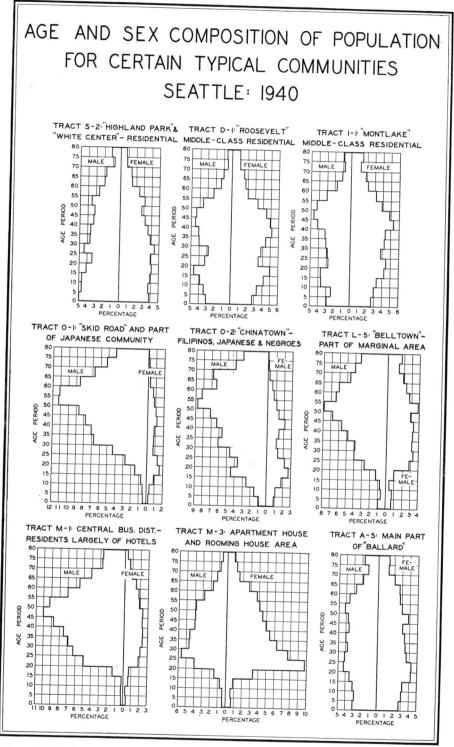

Figure 89. A Series of Age and Sex Pyramids or Triangles. Age and sex pyramids are two-way frequency charts with frequencies represented by the horizontal rather than the vertical axis. (From Calvin F. Schmid, *Social Trends in Seattle*, 1944, p. 92.)

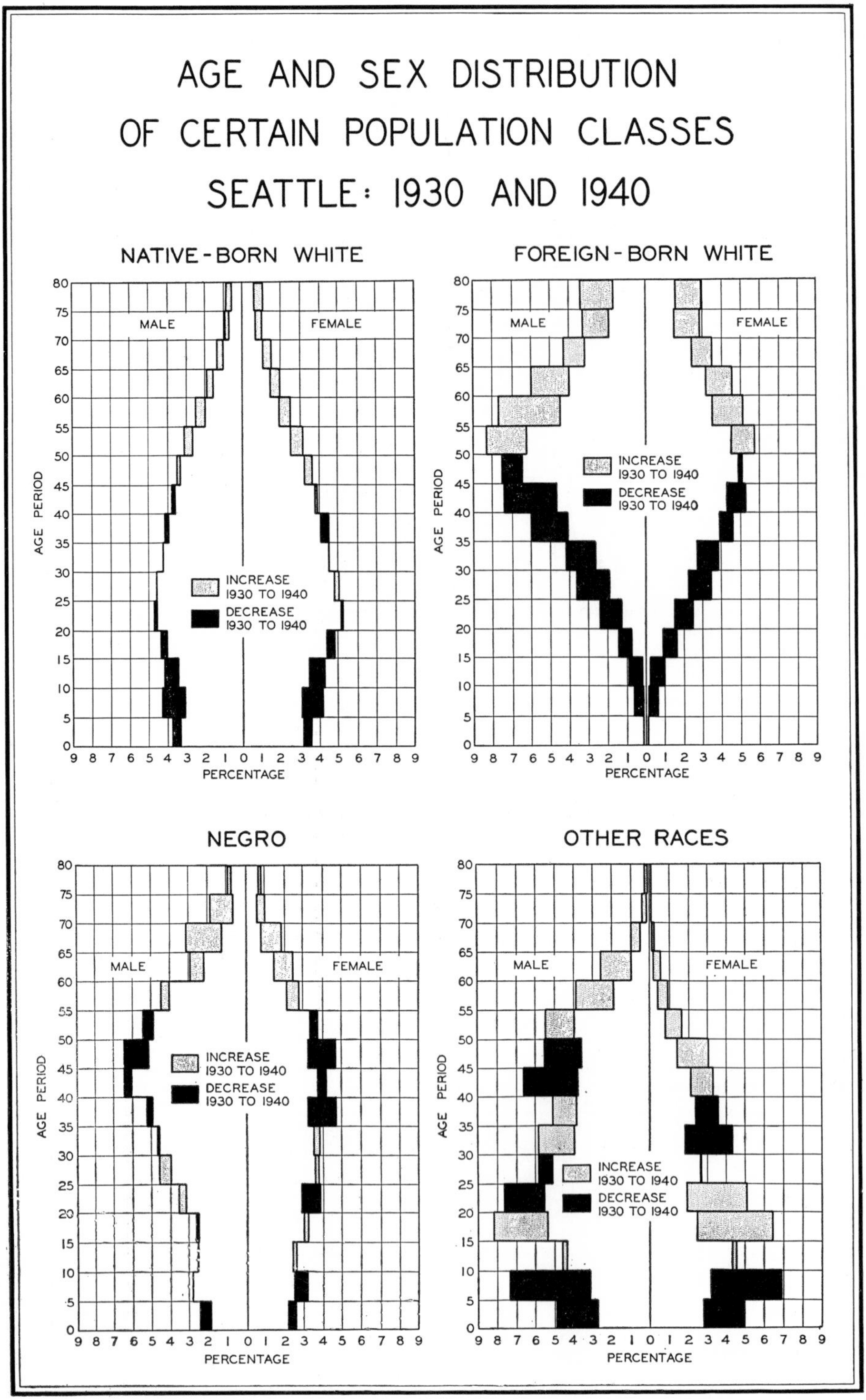

Figure 90. Another Illustration of Age and Sex Pyramids. Changes according to specific age periods by sex for each nativity and racial group are clearly indicated in the chart. (From Calvin F. Schmid, *Social Trends in Seattle*, 1944, p. 83.)

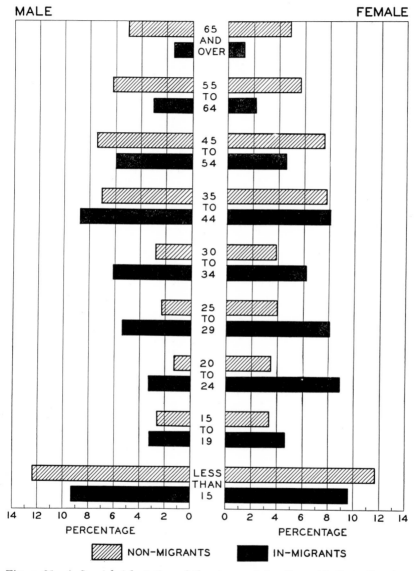

Figure 91. A Special Adaptation of the Age and Sex Pyramid. Basically, this chart represents two grouped-histograms with the class intervals on the vertical axis and frequencies on two horizontal axes. (From Calvin F. Schmid, *Population Trends in the Puget Sound Region: 1940-1950.*)

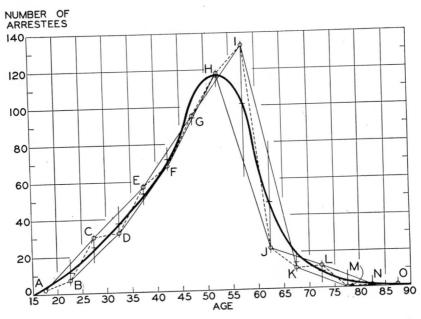

Figure 92. Technique for Smoothing a Frequency Curve. Data represent male arrestees for common drunkenness in the city of Seattle for 1951.

Although there are several different procedures that can be used in smoothing frequency curves, the following simple graphic technique will be found satisfactory for most purposes: [3]

1. Construct a frequency polygon. It will be observed from Figure 92 that the plotting points are shown by small open circles which are connected by light dashed lines. The plotting points are designated in alphabetical order, beginning at the lowest class interval.

2. Connect every other plotting point by straight lines, such as AC, BD, CE, DF, and so on.

3. Draw short lines, perpendicular to the X axis, through each plotting point so that they cut the connecting lines AC, BD, CE, DF, and so on.

4. By inspection, indicate on the perpendicular lines the midpoints of the distance between the plotting points and the connecting lines AC, BD, CE, DF, and so on. The consecutive points thus

[3] L. L. Thurstone, *The Fundamentals of Statistics* (New York: The Macmillan Co., 1938), pp. 39-44.

determined are connected with a smooth freehand curve. The final smoothing is done with a French curve or other similar curve.

The most serious limitation of this technique for smoothing frequency curves is the almost invariable tendency to reduce too much the height of the plotting point coincident with the modal interval. With a little experience and practice, however, adjustment can be made for this tendency.

Graphic Comparison of Frequency Distributions. There are several techniques for comparing graphically two or more frequency distributions. If the variables are continuous, the polygon or smoothed curve is usually most satisfactory. In constructing the polygons or smoothed curves, different line patterns can be used. One curve, for example, may be represented by a full line, another curve by a dashed line, another by a dot-and-dash line, and so on. Illustrations of various curve patterns will be found in Chapter 3. Figure 87 portrays two frequency polygons, and Figure 88 shows three on the same grid.

In comparing two or more series of data by means of frequency polygons or smoothed curves, either numerical or percentage values can be used. Numerical values should be used for comparison only when the total number of cases in each of the distributions are approximately the same. Where the number of cases in each of the series show considerable difference, it is generally advisable to use percentages. In this type of chart, the vertical scale represents percentages rather than absolute frequencies, and the area under each of the polygons or smoothed curves is identical.

The histogram or step diagram also can be used for comparing two or more frequency distributions. Figure 93 illustrates the construction of a histogram comparing two discrete series of data. The chart shows the proportion of different sized dwelling units in Minneapolis and St. Paul as indicated by the number of rooms.

Charting Frequency Distributions with Unequal Class Intervals. It is a basic principle in the graphic presentation of frequency distributions that the frequency between any two points in the distribution is represented by the area under the curve between those points. When the frequency is represented by a percentage of the total, the area under the curve is unity and the mathematical expression of the area is called its *density function*.

Empirical frequency distributions based on data obtained in discrete units may likewise be represented by curves which have

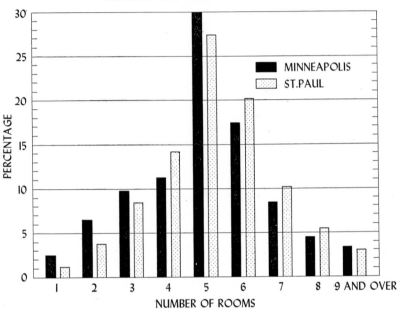

SIZE OF DWELLING UNITS ACCORDING TO NUMBER OF ROOMS MINNEAPOLIS AND ST.PAUL 1934

Figure 93. A Grouped Histogram for Comparing Two Frequency Distributions. In this illustration the vertical axis is expressed in percentages. (From Calvin F. Schmid, *Social Saga of Two Cities*, 1937, p. 245.)

this areal relationship to frequencies between any designated points. If the data are grouped into class intervals, it is assumed that the cases in the interval are evenly distributed, and hence each point between the class boundaries has the same frequency. Accordingly, the area of a rectangle in a histogram formed over any class interval represents the frequency in that interval. Since the area of a rectangle is the product of its width times its height, and since the width is the independent, arbitrarily chosen value, and the frequency depends on the observations, the height may be computed readily by dividing the frequency by the width of the class interval. If the class intervals are all of equal width, the width can be considered to be unity. In such instances, of course, the height of the rectangle is equal to the frequency in the class interval. However, if the class intervals are of unequal width, the same basic principle applies and the proper height is found by dividing the frequency by the width of each class interval. Any convenient interval may be chosen as unity, and the proper divisors can be computed from this interval. Using these divisors, the height for each rectangle of the histogram can then be computed readily for any combination of class width. For example, in part A of Figure 94 equal intervals of $5,000 were used. If $5,000 then is chosen as unity, in order to compute the heights of rectangles of the histogram part C of Figure 94, where the class interval is $1,000, the frequency must be divided by 1/5 (since $1,000 is 1/5 of $5,000); and, where the class interval is $10,000, the frequency must be divided by 2 (since $10,000 is 2 times $5,000); and so on. These data are shown in Table V. To determine the divisor, divide the width of the class interval under consideration by the width of the class interval which has been chosen as unity.

A common error in constructing a histogram with unequal class intervals is to make the heights of the respective rectangles commensurate with the frequencies of the class intervals without taking into consideration the width of the class intervals. This practice leads to extreme distortion and misrepresentation (see part B in Figure 94). Errors of this kind can be readily avoided if the basic principles outlined in the foregoing paragraphs are followed.

Frequency Distribution Plotted on Logarithmic Scale. Sometimes it may be desirable to plot frequency distributions on a logarithmic scale, particularly if there is pronounced skewness. The results of plotting a series of figures on a logarithmic scale are the same as plotting the logarithms of the figures. If, for example, a frequency distribution shows marked positive skewness, it tends to be normalized when plotted on a chart with a logarithmic horizontal axis. This fact is illustrated by Figure 95.[4]

[4] The original data for these frequency distributions were derived from G. Udny Yule, "On Sentence-Length as a Statistical Characteristic of Style in Prose: With Application to Two Cases of Disputed Authorship," *Biometrika,* Vol. 30 (1939), pp. 361-90.

TABLE V

DISTRIBUTION OF NET INCOMES OF MAJOR INDEPENDENT PHYSICIANS,
UNITED STATES: 1949 *

A: Equal Class Intervals		B: Unequal Class Intervals		
Annual Income in Dollars	Number of Physicians	Annual Income in Dollars	Number of Physicians	Height of Histogram Rectangle Adjusted to Preserve Frequency Area **
Total	23,047	Total	23,047	.....
−5,000 to −0,001 ..	206	−5,000 to −0,001 ..	206	206
		0 to 999 ..	726	3,630
		1,000 to 1,999 ..	938	4,690
0 to 4,999 ..	5,267	2,000 to 2,999 ..	1,110	5,550
		3,000 to 3,999 ..	1,177	5,885
		4,000 to 4,999 ..	1,316	6,580
		5,000 to 5,999 ..	1,323	6,615
		6,000 to 6,999 ..	1,353	6,765
5,000 to 9,999 ..	6,514	7,000 to 7,999 ..	1,292	6,460
		8,000 to 8,999 ..	1,395	6,975
		9,000 to 9,999 ..	1,151	5,755
10,000 to 14,999 ..	4,851	10,000 to 14,999 ..	4,851	4,851
15,000 to 19,999 ..	2,839	15,000 to 24,999 ..	4,423	2,211
20,000 to 24,999 ..	1,584			
25,000 to 29,999 ..	795			
30,000 to 34,999 ..	472			
35,000 to 39,999 ..	249	25,000 to 49,999 ..	1,786	357
40,000 to 44,999 ..	173			
45,000 to 49,999 ..	97			

* Unpublished data compiled under direction of William Weinfeld for his study, "Income of Physicians, 1929-1949," *Survey of Current Business* (July, 1951), pp. 9-26. Special transcript of data furnished by Charles F. Schwartz, Assistant Chief, National Income Division, United States Department of Commerce.

In order to keep the table as simple as possible, the two open-ended class intervals, −$5,000 or more (loss) at the lower extreme and $50,000 or more (gain) at the upper extreme, were omitted. There were only two cases in the interval −$5,000 or more, and 164 in the interval $50,000 or more.

** Using interval of 5,000 as unity, divide number of physicians by 1,000/5,000, or 0.2, for intervals of 1,000; 10,000/5,000, or 2, for intervals of 10,000; and for intervals of 25,000, 25,000/5,000, or 5.

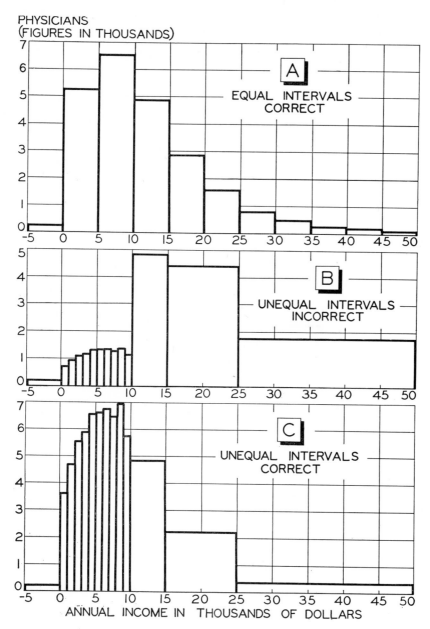

Figure 94. Frequency Histograms with Equal and Unequal Class Intervals.
(Based on Data in Table V.)

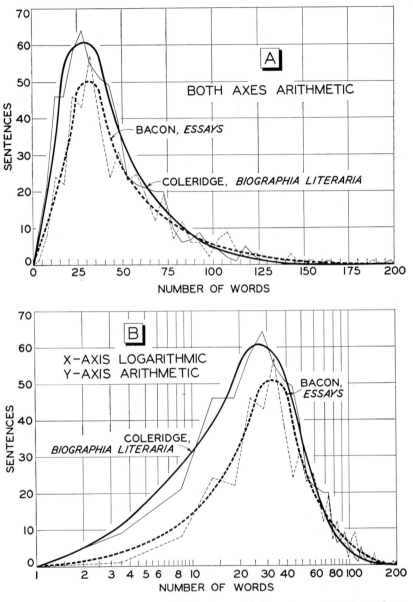

Figure 95. Plotting Frequency Distributions on Arithmetic and Semilogarithmic Scales. In the upper panel both axes of the grid are arithmetic, whereas in the lower panel the horizontal axis is logarithmic and the vertical axis, arithmetic. The data show the numbers of sentences (vertical axis) having a specified length in words (horizontal axis) in Bacon's *Essays* and Coleridge's *Biographia Literaria*. (From G. Udny Yule, "On Sentence-Length as a Statistical Characteristic of Style in Prose: With Application to Two Cases of Disputed Authorship," *Biometrika*, Vol. 30, 1940, pp. 362-90.)

In a subsequent paper C. B. Williams pointed out that,

When I converted some of Yule's tables into diagrams I was struck by their general resemblance to skew distributions with which I have recently been dealing in some entomological problems ... which distributions, I found, became normal and symmetrical if the logarithm of the number was taken as a basis for subdivision into groups instead of the number itself.[5]

Mathematicians have done very little work on this normalizing procedure and at the present time the mathematical implications of logarithmic transformation of frequency distributions are still obscure. Also, it should be pointed out that in plotting frequency distributions the vertical scale rather than the horizontal scale may be ruled logarithmically, or both the horizontal and vertical scales may be calibrated in this manner.

Cumulative-Frequency Graph or Ogive

For some purposes the cumulative-frequency curve, or ogive, is more valuable than the simple frequency graph. In the simple frequency distribution, the number of cases for each class interval is indicated separately. In a cumulative-frequency distribution, the frequencies of the successive class intervals are accumulated, beginning at either end of the distribution. If the cumulation process is from the lesser to the greater, it is referred to as a "less than" type of distribution; if the cumulation proceeds from the greater to the lesser, it is known as a "more than" type of distribution.

In constructing an ogive the cumulative frequencies are represented by the vertical axis and the class intervals by the horizontal axis. Unlike the simple frequency graph, the range of the vertical scale covers the total number of cases in the distribution. In the upper panel of Figure 96, for example, the ordinal scale extends from zero to 800, which is 39 more than the total number of cases.

Instead of plotting the cumulated frequencies at the midpoint of each class interval, as is done in the simple frequency graph, they are plotted either at the lower or upper end of the interval,

[5] "A Note on the Statistical Analysis of Sentence-Length as a Criterion of Literary Style," *Biometrika*, Vol. 31 (1940), pp. 356-61.

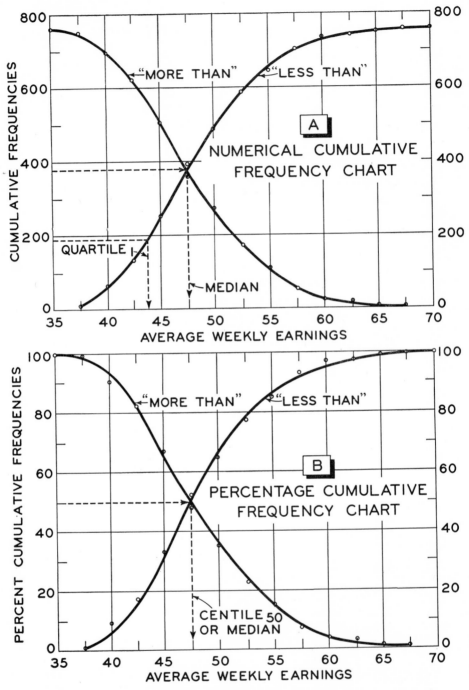

Figure 96. Cumulative Frequency Graphs or Ogives. In the upper panel *A*, the figures on the vertical axis represent actual cumulative frequencies, whereas in the lower panel *B*, the figures on the vertical axis are cumulative percentages. Note especially the plotting points for both the "less than" and "more than" types of ogives and also the interpolation lines.

depending on whether the cumulation is of the "less than" or "more than" type. If the distribution is of the "less than" type, the cumulated frequency for each class is plotted at the upper end of the interval. On the other hand, the plotting procedure for the "more than" types of distribution begins at the lower end of the interval. When the cumulative frequencies are represented as percentages, as is often the case, the vertical axis covers the range from zero to 100 percent, while the horizontal axis is the same as for the numerical frequency graph. The percentage cumulative-frequency chart is also referred to as a *centile graph* or *centile curve.*[6] The lower panel in Figure 96 illustrates this type of chart.

Both the numerical and percentage cumulative-frequency curves are characteristically of the elongated **S** shape. The "less than" type extends from the lower left to the upper right of the grid, and the "more than" type from the upper left to the lower right of the grid. The "less than" and "more than" types of curves intersect at the median value. It should be emphasized that the median, quartiles, deciles, and other similar measures represent values on the X axis.

From the standpoint of graphic presentation, the ogive is especially adapted to the following purposes: (1) To determine as well as to portray the number or proportion of cases above or below a given value. For example, in order to estimate the number of typists receiving weekly wages of $52.50, or less, a vertical line can be plotted at the midpoint of the interval 50-55 on the abscissal scale on Figure 96(A). A horizontal line is then drawn from the intersection of the vertical line and the ogive to the ordinal axis, which indicates that approximately 590 of the workers receive less than $52.50 per week. (2) To compare two or more frequency distributions. Generally there is less overlapping when comparing several ogives on the same grid than when comparing several simple frequency curves in this manner. In comparing ogives, emphasis is placed on the number or proportion of cases above or below a given point, whereas, in com-

[6] In older terminology, the word "percentile" was used instead of "centile." "Centile" seems to be preferable since it is more consistent with general usage of terms which describe other divisions of the scale, such as deciles, quintiles, and quartiles, but not "perdeciles," "perquintiles," or "perquartiles."

paring simple frequency curves, emphasis is placed on maximal concentration and skewness. In this connection, however, it should be remembered that the maximal frequency or concentration of cases on an ogive is indicated by the steepest portion of the curve.

The median, quartiles, deciles, or some other measure of this kind can also be derived by simple interpolation. The first quartile (Q_1), for example, can be found by dividing the number of cases in a distribution by four $(N/4)$; from this value on the vertical axis a horizontal line is drawn to the "less than" type of ogive, and from the point of intersection a vertical line is dropped to the horizontal axis. The point where the vertical line intersects the horizontal axis is Q_1. Figure 96(A) illustrates the procedure in interpolating quartiles and median.

Lorenz Curve. A special type of cumulative-frequency graph known as a *Lorenz curve* [7] can be used effectively to portray such data as the distribution of wealth and income in relation to certain segments of the population, the productivity of farms in terms of cumulative proportions of farms, and the distribution of retail sales as related to various groupings of stores.

The first step in the construction of a Lorenz curve is to transpose the data into percentages and arrange them into "less than" types of cumulative-frequency distributions. The basic data for an illustration of this type of curve are portrayed in Figure 97 and summarized in Table VI.

The next step is to construct a square-shaped grid with both axes ranging in value from zero to 100 percent. The horizontal axis represents the percentage of physicians cumulated from lowest to highest incomes, and the vertical axis represents the percentage of net income cumulated from lowest to highest income. The chart clearly portrays the relative amount of dispersion in frequency distributions. A curve of equal distribution would be a straight line extending diagonally from zero to 100. Such a curve would indicate that any specified proportion of physicians

[7] Named for M. O. Lorenz, who first developed this type of curve. For further details, see his original paper entitled, "Methods of Measuring the Concentration of Wealth," *Journal of the American Statistical Association* (June, 1905), New Series No. 70, pp. 209-19.

TABLE VI

Type of Data Required for Lorenz Curve: Distribution of Net Income of Major Independent Physicians, United States: 1949 *

Net Income (dollars)	Midpoint of Income Class (1)	Number of Physicians (2)	Aggregate Income (000's omitted) (3)	Cumulative Frequencies — Number — Physicians (4)	Cumulative Frequencies — Number — Aggregate Income (000's omitted) (5)	Cumulative Frequencies — Percentage — Physicians (6)	Cumulative Frequencies — Percentage — Aggregate Income (7)
(A) *Loss:*							
2,000 and over	3,500	22	—71	22	—71	.1	**
1,000–1,999	1,500	42	—63	64	—134	.3	.1
1–999	500	144	—72	208	—206	.9	.1
(B) *Gain:*							
1–999	500	726	363	934	157	4.0	.1
1,000–1,999	1,500	938	1,407	1,872	1,564	8.1	.6
2,000–2,999	2,500	1,110	2,775	2,982	4,339	12.8	1.6
3,000–3,999	3,500	1,177	4,120	4,159	8,459	17.9	3.1
4,000–4,999	4,500	1,316	5,922	5,475	14,381	23.6	5.2
5,000–5,999	5,500	1,323	7,276	6,798	21,657	29.3	7.9
6,000–6,999	6,500	1,353	8,794	8,151	30,451	35.1	11.1
7,000–7,999	7,500	1,292	9,690	9,443	40,141	40.7	14.6
8,000–8,999	8,500	1,395	11,858	10,838	51,999	46.7	18.9
9,000–9,999	9,500	1,151	10,934	11,989	62,933	51.6	22.9
10,000–14,999	12,500	4,851	59,574	16,840	122,507	72.5	44.5
15,000–19,999	17,500	2,839	48,790	19,679	171,297	84.8	62.2
20,000–24,999	22,500	1,584	35,118	21,263	206,415	91.6	75.0
25,000–29,999	27,500	795	21,566	22,058	227,981	95.0	82.8
30,000–39,999	35,000	721	24,439	22,779	252,420	98.1	91.7
40,000–49,999	45,000	270	11,960	23,049	264,380	99.3	96.0
50,000–59,999	55,000	91	4,968	23,140	269,348	99.7	97.8
60,000–69,999	65,000	30	1,940	23,170	271,288	99.8	98.5
70,000–99,999	85,000	36	2,900	23,206	274,188	99.97	99.6
100,000 and over	152,364	7	1,067	23,213	275,255	100.00	100.0
Totals	....	23,213	275,255				

* The statistics in this table arranged from unpublished data compiled under direction of William Weinfeld for his study, "Income of Physicians, 1929-49," *Survey of Current Business* (July, 1951), pp. 9-26. Special transcript of data furnished by Charles F. Schwartz, Assistant Chief, National Income Division, United States Department of Commerce.

** Less than 0.5 per cent.

CUMULATIVE PERCENTAGE DISTRIBUTIONS OF INDEPENDENT PHYSICIANS AND THEIR NET INCOME FROM MEDICAL WORK

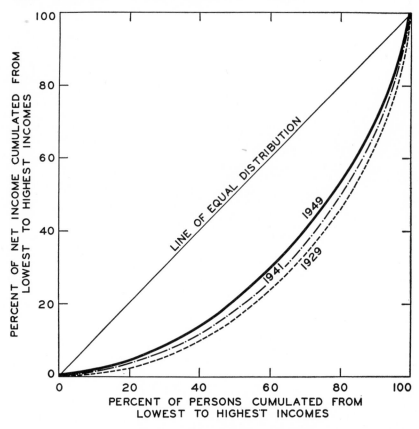

Figure 97. **Lorenz Curve.** (Redrawn from William Weinfeld, "Income of Physicians, 1929-49," *Survey of Current Business,* July, 1951, pp. 9-26.)

would earn precisely the same proportion of income. For example, 20 percent of the physicians would receive 20 percent of the income, 50 percent of the physicians would receive 50 percent of the income, 75 percent of the physicians would receive 75 percent of the income, and so on. Actually, this is not the case. There is a marked deviation from the line of equal

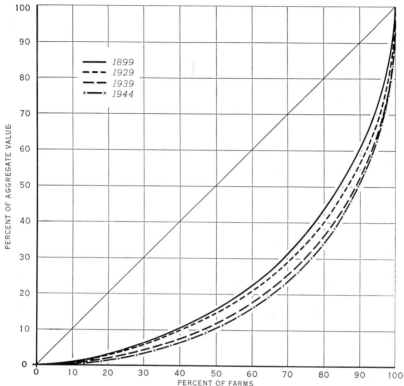

CUMULATIVE DISTRIBUTION OF TOTAL VALUE OF AGRICULTURAL
PRODUCTS, UNITED STATES, 1899, 1929, 1939, AND 1944

Figure 98. Another Application of the Lorenz Curve. The series of four curves shows trends in proportion of total value of agricultural products produced by any specified proportion of farms. (From U. S. Bureau of Agricultural Economics, *Agricultural Outlook Charts, 1950,* p. 92.)

distribution. The distance between the curve and the diagonal line is indicative of the degree of deviation. It will be observed from Figure 97 that 50 percent of the physicians, beginning with those of lowest income, receive less than 20 percent of the income.

Figure 98 is another application of the Lorenz curve. The four curves indicate the total value of agricultural products produced by a specified proportion of farms for 1899, 1929, 1939, and 1944. It will be observed, for example, that 50 percent of the farms, beginning with the least productive, contributed approximately 10 percent to the aggregate value of all agricultural products in the United States in 1944.

Probability Graphs

Probability paper is the name given to the special arrangement of vertical and horizontal spacing of a grid which has the property of representing the cumulative normal function as a straight line. Since probability paper [8] is widely used and represents a special class of grids used on charts for particular purposes, its characteristics and utility should be recognized. It is based on the normal frequency curve. The use of such a grid was early suggested by Francis Galton and later developed by Allen Hazen.[9] Although it is possible to reverse the axes, the usual grid is ruled arithmetically on the vertical axis and the horizontal axis is divided proportionally to the magnitude of cumulative normal ordinates. Since the normal distribution is asymptotic to both the zero and the 100 percent values, the horizontal scale on probability paper cannot reach either zero or 100 percent, but must start with a small number, usually 0.01, and extend to a magnitude near 100 percent, such as 99.99, as is illustrated in Figure 99.

The characteristic shape of the cumulative graph, or ogive, of the normal distribution is an elongated **S**. When the axes of the graph are reversed to correspond with the probability paper axes, the graph appears as in Figure 99. It is noticeable that the central part of the curve—from about the 25 percent point to the 75 percent point of the distribution—is almost a straight line. A

[8] Probability paper is produced commercially and can be obtained from stationers and drafting supply houses.

[9] Francis Galton, "A Geometric Determination of the Median Value of a System of Normal Variants, from Two of Its Centiles," *Nature*, Vol. 61 (November 30, 1899), pp. 102-4; Allen Hazen, "Storage to be Provided in Impounding Reservoir for Municipal Water Supply," *Transactions American Society of Civil Engineers*, Vol. 77 (December, 1914), pp. 1539-1669. In an earlier discussion the same year (p. 627), Mr. Hazen refers to the probability paper which he devised as follows: "A new kind of cross-section paper is made, in which the spacing of the lines in one direction is computed from tables of the probability curve, so that figures representing the summation of that curve plotted on it fall in a straight line."

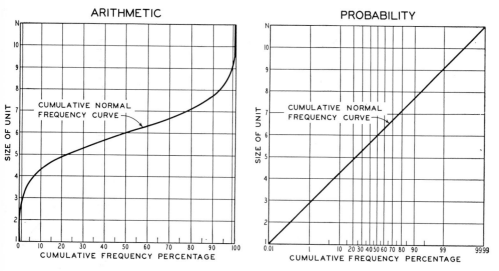

Figure 99. Comparison of Cumulative Frequency Distribution Plotted on Arithmetic Grid and on Probability Grid.

grid that will straighten this central part has to be stretched only slightly from the equal arithmetic ruling, but in the sharply curved extremes a considerable amount of stretching or expansion of the grid is required. The probability grid is characterized by extremely wide spacing at the upper and lower ends of the scale, quickly decreasing spacing in the regions between 1 and 20 percent and between 80 and 99 percent, and almost equal spacing in the central part of the scale. (See Figures 99 and 100.)

Because of the construction of the grid, then, the graph of the cumulative heights of ordinates of any perfectly normal distribution will appear as a straight line when plotted on probability paper. In demonstrating the normalcy of a distribution, it is much easier to detect and demonstrate deviations from a straight line than from any of the more complicated curves, such as the ogive. Figure 100 shows a comparison between the graph of the cumulative frequencies of an approximately normal distribution and the straight line which represents the normal distribution having the same mean and standard deviation. It is easy to see that the distribution is almost perfectly normal except in the usually erratic extreme cases which violate the otherwise straight-line pattern on the probability paper.

The scale for the independent axis may be ruled either arithmetically or logarithmically. If the ogive is expressed as a straight line on arithmetic probability paper, the original frequency distribution can be considered symmetrical upon an arithmetic projection; similarly, if an ogive is represented by a straight line on logarithmic probability paper, the original frequency distribution can be considered asymmetrical, and can be made symmetrical by plotting on logarithmic projection. This provides a test for proportional asymmetry.

Probability paper also is a useful addition as a technique of statistical analysis, such as demonstrating comparisons between empirical and theoretical distributions and prediction. The rationale of using paper of this kind for prediction purposes is based on the law of probability as expressed by the normal frequency curve. For example, it can be used for predicting the longevity of telephone poles, steam locomotives, freight cars, steel cable, cross ties, electric lamps, and pumps; probable weekly sales of certain items; probable proportions of defective units in testing or inspecting materials; probable attendance at expositions and fairs; probable variation in maturity of crops or stock; and human mortality.[10]

Special grids can be developed readily for the simplification of complicated curves, but it might be pointed out that extensive use of such techniques may result in criticism that the data are being distorted by graphic trickery. Probability paper and a few other special grids of this type have been found useful and may be considered above such criticism.[11] If the usefulness of a special grid can be demonstrated, there is no reason why it should not be adopted; but if clear advantage in its use is not present, the better understood, more conventional grids will make the presentation more acceptable and require less explanation.

[10] See Walter E. Weld, *How to Chart Facts from Figures with Graphs* (Norwood, Mass: Codex Book Co., Inc., 1947), pp. 88-92; Edwin Kurtz, "Replacement Insurance," *Administration*, Vol. 2 (November, 1921), pp. 41-69.

[11] A special grid known as *binomial paper* has become increasingly popular with theoretical statisticians. It has the property of making estimation of many of the answers required in binomial problems a matter of direct inspection of the graph on binomial paper.

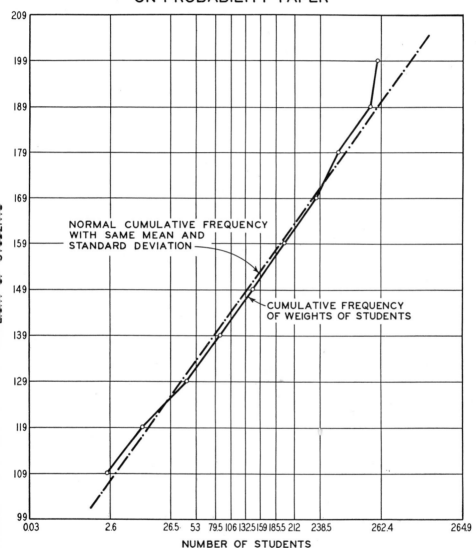

CUMULATIVE FREQUENCY OF WEIGHTS OF 265 FRESHMEN MALE STUDENTS AT THE UNIVERSITY OF WASHINGTON ON PROBABILITY PAPER

NORMAL CUMULATIVE FREQUENCY WITH SAME MEAN AND STANDARD DEVIATION

CUMULATIVE FREQUENCY OF WEIGHTS OF STUDENTS

NUMBER OF STUDENTS

Figure 100. Illustration of Use of Probability Paper in Comparing Cumulative Frequency of Weights of University Students with Normal Cumulative Frequency. (Data taken from Calvin F. Schmid, "Basic Statistical Concepts and Techniques," in Pauline V. Young, *Scientific Social Surveys and Research*, 1949, Ch. XIII, pp. 286-347.)

The most satisfactory method of laying out a probability paper grid is by using a strip of commercial probability paper as a scale and proceeding as explained in detail in Chapter 5, "Semilogarithmic or Ratio Charts." [12]

Charting Age-Specific Rates and Ratios

Distributions of age-specific rates often look like frequency distributions and as a consequence are sometimes mistaken for them. Like frequency distributions, distributions of age-specific rates may be more or less bell-shaped, U-shaped, J-shaped, or S-shaped; they may be relatively symmetrical or asymmetrical. Statistically, however, there is a basic difference between frequency distributions and distributions of age-specific rates.

Figure 101 graphically presents a series of age-specific rates for male and female misdemeanants in the city of Seattle for 1950 and 1951. The relationship between age and sex and the commission of certain misdemeanors is clearly revealed. Age, the independent variable, is shown on the horizontal axis, and the incidence of arrest, the dependent variable, is plotted on the vertical axis. The rates for each sex are differentiated by two distinct curve patterns. Age-specific rates show much more about the volume of these particular phenomena than simple frequencies, since in series of this kind the frequencies are directly related to the number of people in each specific age group. The differentials in the age and sex behavior patterns for four categories of misdemeanors are indicated clearly.

---

[12] In developing the scale independently, it will be recalled that the range of normal probability is unlimited and the probability scale, expressed in percentage of a total, can never read zero or 100. However, all but 0.006 per cent of the normal probability range is found between plus and minus four standard deviations from the mean, or within a range of eight standard units. The method of computing the probability scale, then, consists of locating the position of the cumulated normal percentage frequency in relation to a corresponding standard deviation unit. Tables of areas of the normal curve and other data are required to derive the values of a probability scale. A detailed step-by-step discussion of the construction of probability paper is perhaps too advanced for a text of this kind. Table III in George C. Whipple, "The Element of Chance in Sanitation," *Journal of the Franklin Institute*, Vol. 182 (July, 1916), pp. 37-59, will be found very useful if one were interested in constructing probability paper. It will be observed that Whipple uses "probable error" rather than "standard error." At the present time, the "standard error" concept has almost entirely supplanted "probable error."

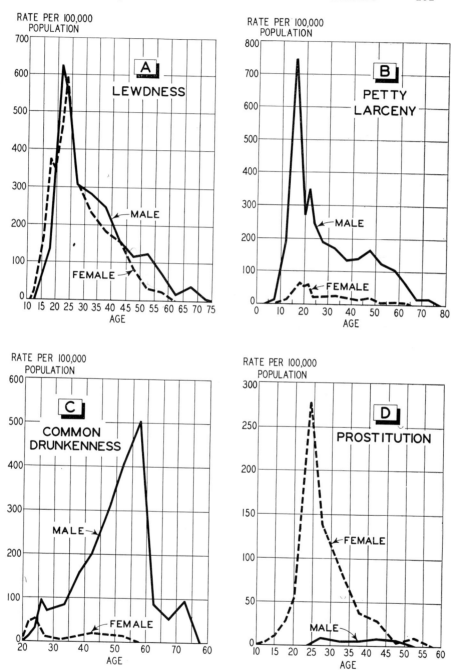

Figure 101. Graphic Portrayal of Several Series of Rates on Arithmetic Grids.
Data represent two-year means.

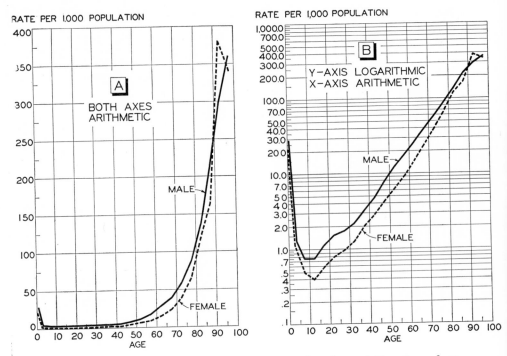

Figure 102. Same Series of Mortality Rates Plotted on Arithmetic and on Semilogarithmic Grids.

One of the most common types of age-specific rates pertains to vital processes, such as fertility, mortality, morbidity, marriage, and divorce. The incidence or "force" of these phenomena varies with sex, age, race, nativity, education, occupation, and other conditions.

Figure 102 portrays two series of age-specific mortality rates for all causes for the triennial period 1949 to 1951 for the state of Washington. In the left panel both the scales are arithmetic, whereas in the right panel the horizontal scale is arithmetic and the vertical scale is logarithmic. Generally, arithmetic scales are used in charting age-specific rates, but sometimes logarithmic ruling may be found more appropriate. Logarithmic ruling may be used for both axes or for either the X or Y axis, depending on the problem or purpose at hand.

NONEFFECTIVE RATES BY AGE GROUP
NAVY AND MARINE CORPS - 1949

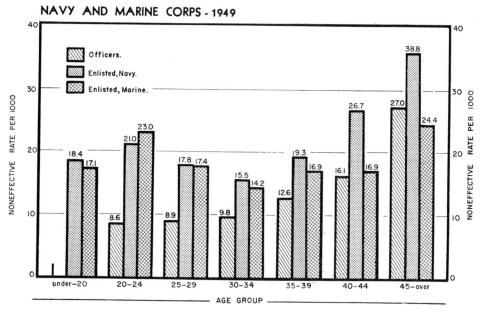

Figure 103. **The Use of Columns to Portray Age-Specific Rates.** Shows noneffective rates by seven age groups for officers, Navy enlisted personnel and Marine corps enlisted personnel, respectively. "Noneffective rate" is one of the standard measures of temporary manpower loss among military personnel; it indicates the average number of individuals on the sick list each day throughout the year in each 1,000 average strength. (From *Statistics of Navy Medicine,* May, 1951, p. 6.)

It will be observed from Figure 103 that columns as well as curves can be used to portray age-specific distributions of rates. Noneffective rates per 1,000 population by seven age groups for 1949 are shown for (1) Navy and Marine Corps officers, (2) Navy enlisted personnel, and (3) Marine Corps enlisted personnel. A crosshatching and stippling scheme is used to differentiate the columns representing these three categories.

CHAPTER 7

Miscellaneous Graphic Forms

This chapter is devoted to a discussion of certain miscellaneous graphic forms which, generally speaking, are neither as basic nor as widely used as those covered in the foregoing chapters. It will be observed that among these miscellaneous forms, certain of them, such as the pie chart and the correlation charts, are more flexible and adaptable than the trilinear or the ranking charts, which have more limited application. Nevertheless, all of the graphs and charts have distinctive advantages for certain types of problems. It is, therefore, essential for specialists in the field to be thoroughly familiar with as many graphic forms as possible, so that when the occasion arises the most appropriate design can be selected.

Pie Chart

Although the pie or sector chart ranks very high in popular appeal, it is held in rather low esteem by many specialists in graphic presentation. Since the pie chart possesses more weaknesses perhaps than most graphic forms, it is especially important to observe proper discretion in its construction and application.

The pie chart is used to portray component relations. The various sectors of a circle represent component parts of an aggregate or total.

Figure 104 shows three commonly used graphic forms for depicting component relations: (1) the pie chart, (2) the one-hundred percent bar graph, and (3) the simple bar chart. These illustrations are all based on the same data, namely, the class status of veterans enrolled at the University of Washington during the fall quarter of 1951. It will be observed that each of the three forms possesses certain advantageous features. It is extremely difficult to state in an absolute sense which of the three

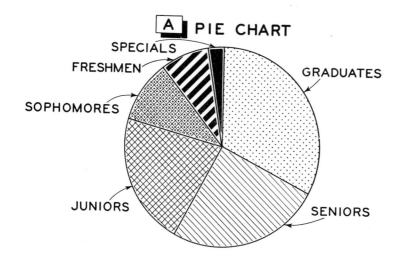

A PIE CHART

SPECIALS
FRESHMEN
SOPHOMORES
GRADUATES
JUNIORS
SENIORS

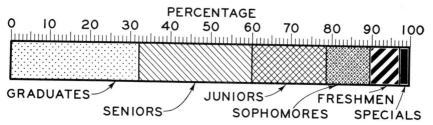

B ONE-HUNDRED PERCENT BAR CHART

PERCENTAGE

0   10   20   30   40   50   60   70   80   90   100

GRADUATES
SENIORS
JUNIORS
SOPHOMORES
FRESHMEN
SPECIALS

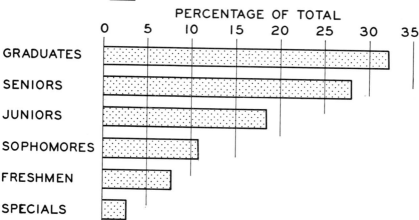

C SIMPLE BAR CHART

PERCENTAGE OF TOTAL

0   5   10   15   20   25   30   35

GRADUATES

SENIORS

JUNIORS

SOPHOMORES

FRESHMEN

SPECIALS

Figure 104. Comparison of Different Chart Forms Portraying Components of a
One-Hundred Percent Total. *A,* Pie Chart; *B,* One-Hundred Percent Bar Chart;
C, Simple Bar Chart. Data show class status of veterans (exclusive of Law,
Dentistry and Medicine) enrolled at the University of Washington, Autumn
Quarter, 1951.

forms is the "best," since the audience for whom a chart is designed and the purpose at hand are relative factors which must be taken into consideration. Moreover, there are no detailed, accurate, systematic, and valid tests for evaluating the various types of graphs and charts. Such comparative evaluations of graphic forms that do exist are largely impressionistic and a priori. It must not be overlooked, of course, that a few attempts have been made to determine objectively the relative merits and applicability of the pie, bar, and other simple graphic forms. The results of these investigations are suggestive but not conclusive.[1]

As a general rule it is recommended that the bar chart be used for simple comparison, particularly if there are more than four or five categories.

In constructing a pie chart the first step is to prepare the data so that the various component values can be transposed into corresponding degrees on the circle. Suppose there are four components in a series representing the following values: (1) 60 percent, (2) 20 percent, (3) 15 percent, and (4) 5 percent. Since 1 percent is equal to 3.6 degrees $(360/100 = 3.6)$, then the corresponding values of the four components in the illustration are $(60.0)(3.6) = 216°$; $(20)(3.6) = 72°$; $(15)(3.6) = 54°$; and $(5)(3.6) = 18°$.

The second step is to plot a circle of appropriate size with a bow pencil or compass.

Third, points on the circle representing the size of each sector are measured with a protractor. Protractors calibrated in percentages rather than degrees are, of course, much more efficient for chart work. With a percentage protractor it is possible to plot percentage values directly, thus obviating the intermediate step

[1] See, for example, W. C. Eells, "The Relative Merits of Circles and Bars for Representing Component Parts," *Journal of the American Statistical Association,* Vol. 21 (June, 1926), pp. 119-32; R. von Huhn, "A Discussion of Eells' Experiment," *ibid.,* Vol. 22 (March, 1927), pp. 31-36; F. E. Croxton and R. E. Stryker, "Bar Charts versus Circle Diagrams," *ibid.,* Vol. 22 (December, 1927), pp. 473-82; F. E. Croxton and H. Stein, "Graphic Comparisons by Bars, Squares, Circles, and Cubes," *ibid.,* Vol. 27 (March, 1932), pp. 54-60; Ruth G. Strickland, *A Study of the Possibilities of Graphs as a Means of Instruction in the First Four Grades of the Elementary School* (New York: Teachers College, Columbia University, 1938), *passim.*

of transposing percentages to degrees. Printed chart sheets with circles divided into one hundred parts (percentages) are available commercially.

In laying out the sectors for a pie chart it is good practice to follow some logical arrangement pattern or sequence. For example, it is a common procedure to arrange the sectors according to size, with the largest at the top and the others in sequence running clockwise. An essential feature of the pie chart is the careful identification of each sector with some kind of explanatory or descriptive label. If there is sufficient room, the labels can be placed inside the sectors; otherwise, the labels should be placed in contiguous positions outside the circle, usually with an arrow pointing to the appropriate sector. Sometimes the several sectors of a pie chart are identified by means of a key or legend directly below or on the side of the pie. But this method is more cumbersome than the other two described. Also, it is customary to indicate the percentages or other values represented by each sector directly below the identifying label. In order to differentiate clearly the sectors, it is a recommended practice to hatch them according to a density sequence from dark to light or vice versa. For display charts color is appropriate. The pie chart may be made more attractive by superimposing pictorial symbols or by laying out the chart in three-dimensional form. These techniques are discussed in Chapters 9 and 10.

Perhaps by pointing out certain weaknesses and dangers inherent in the basic design and application of the pie chart, more obvious mistakes can be avoided. First, it is generally inadvisable to attempt to portray a series of more than four or five categories by means of pie charts. If, for example, there are six, eight, or more categories, it may be very confusing to differentiate the relative values portrayed, especially if several small sectors are of approximately the same size. Second, the pie chart may lose its effectiveness if an attempt is made to compare the component values of several circles, as might be found in a temporal or geographical series. In such case the one-hundred percent bar or column chart is more appropriate. Third, although the proportionate values portrayed in a pie chart are measured as distances along arcs about the circle, actually there is a tendency

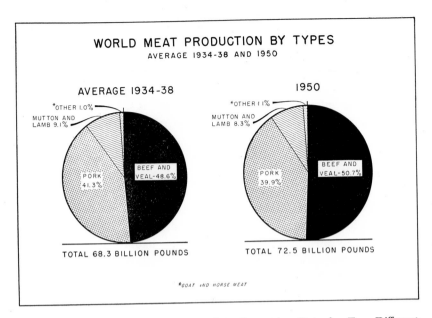

Figure 105. Pie or Sector Charts Used in Comparing Data for Two Different Periods. (From U. S. Office of Foreign Agricultural Relations, *Foreign Agricultural Outlook Charts*, 1952, p. 65.)

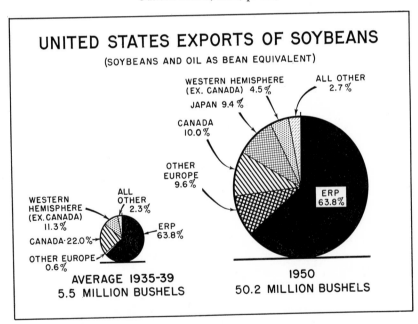

Figure 106. Comparison of Two Series of Data for Different Periods by Means of a Pie or Sector Chart. Note that the respective areas of the circles have been drawn in proportion to the annual volume of exports for the two periods. (From U. S. Office of Foreign Agricultural Relations, *Foreign Agricultural Outlook Charts*, 1952, p. 53.)

to estimate values in terms of areas of sectors or by the size of subtended angles at the center of the circle.

Figures 105, 106, and 107 are examples of three different applications of the pie chart. Figure 105 shows a comparison of world meat production classified in four major categories for two different periods. The pie on the left portrays the annual average for the five-year period 1934 to 1938, and the one on the right is for the year 1950. It will be observed that they are slightly different in area, since one represents a total of 68.3 billion

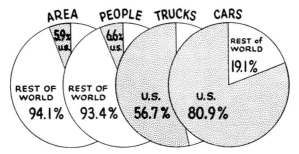

Figure 107. Four Pie Charts in Juxtaposition for Comparing Four Different Categories. It will be noted that emphasis is placed on the relatively high proportion of passenger cars and trucks in comparison to the area and population of the United States. (From Automobile Manufacturers Assn., *Automobile Facts and Figures*, 27th Ed., 1946 and 1947, p. 30.)

pounds and the other a total of 72.5 billion pounds. It will be recalled that the area of a circle varies as the square root of its diameter. Such features as the arrangement of the sectors, cross-hatching, identification labels for sectors, figures indicating the values of the respective categories, subtitles, and explanatory notes should be carefully observed. Figure 106 in many respects is similar to Figure 105, but the disparity in totals as well as in the number of sectors is very apparent. Figure 107 is an effective application of the pie chart in emphasizing the marked contrasts between the United States and the rest of the world with respect to area, population, trucks, and passenger cars.

Trilinear Chart

The trilinear chart is used to portray simultaneously three variables expressed in the form of elements or components of a total. It is characteristically a one-hundred percent chart, since the sum of the three values indicated is equal to 100 percent.

The trilinear chart is drawn in the form of an equilateral triangle, each side of which is calibrated in equal percentage divisions ranging from zero to 100. The rulings are projected across the chart parallel to the sides in the manner of coordinates. For example, the lines indicating the scale divisions for the horizontal axis are drawn parallel to it and, similarly, the scale lines for the two other axes are parallel to their respective sides.

The trilinear chart is based on the geometric principle that in an equilateral triangle the sum of the three perpendiculars drawn from any point within the triangle to the sides is a constant, and is equal to the altitude of the triangle. Therefore, as in the trilinear chart, the altitude represents 100 percent; and, accordingly, the perpendiculars from a given point within the triangle will represent the percentages of the three variables composing the whole.

The essential characteristics of a trilinear chart are portrayed in Figure 108. The scale lines and scale figures for each of the three axes are clearly indicated. For example, the base line for component A is shown on the left, with the various scale lines drawn parallel to it. The base line and other scale lines for component B are drawn correspondingly on the right side. The horizontal axis and the scale lines drawn parallel to it are referents for component C. The point X indicates a value for each variable: for component A, 20 percent; for component B, 30 percent; and for component C, 50 percent.

Trilinear charts are useful in portraying such data as the following: (1) properties of chemical compounds—mixtures and alloys composed of three elements or characteristics; (2) caloric values for different kinds of foods in terms of fats, proteins, and carbohydrates; and (3) operating, production, or other costs expressed by a threefold breakdown.

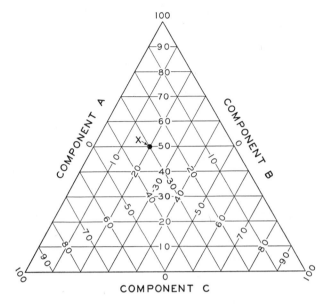

Figure 108. Trilinear Chart.

Although trilinear charts do not have a time scale, it is possible to plot the values of three or four series for different time periods on the same triangle, if the points are properly labeled. In order to avoid confusion, it is important not to plot too many values on the same chart.

Scatter Diagram and Other Correlation Charts

The scatter diagram (scattergram) and other types of correlation charts portray in graphic form the degree and type of relationship or covariation between two series of data. In statistical terminology the relationship between two or more variables is described as correlation.[2] The relationship or correlation between two variables may be either positive or negative. When one variable increases (or decreases) and the other changes by constant or nearly constant amounts in the same direction, the

[2] For a brief, elementary discussion of correlation, see Calvin F. Schmid, "Basic Statistical Concepts and Techniques," in Pauline V. Young, *Scientific Social Surveys and Research* (New York: Prentice-Hall, Inc., 1949), chap. xiii, pp. 286-347.

relation of the two series is positive or direct; but, if the changes in the two variables are in opposite directions, the correlation between the two series is negative or inverse. For example, the height and weight of human beings are positively correlated, since taller people on the average weigh more than shorter people.

Figure 109 shows that the correlation between land values and pedestrian traffic and vehicular traffic in the central business district of a large city is positive. This fact is indicated by the patterning of the dots (more noticeable in the scatter diagram on the left), which is generally from the lower left corner to the upper right corner. On the other hand, if the dots tended to scatter diagonally in the opposite direction, the correlation would be negative. When there is a relatively low degree of correlation, the dots are widely scattered over the entire chart, with little or no tendency to align themselves diagonally either from left to right or from right to left. The precise degrees of relationship between land value and pedestrian traffic and land values and vehicular traffic are indicated by coefficients of correlation: $r = +.840$ between land values and pedestrian traffic and $r = +.469$ between land values and vehicular traffic. The product-moment or Pearsonian coefficient of correlation (r) is a pure number and ranges in value from positive one $(+1.0)$ down through zero (0.0) to negative one (-1.0).

In constructing a scatter diagram the first step is to select suitable class intervals for the respective variables, so that each variable will have approximately eight to fifteen divisions. This procedure is similar to that for making a frequency distribution. Actually, the scatter diagram is a two-way or bivariate frequency distribution.

Second, the axes representing the variables are laid out at right angles to each other. Generally, it is immaterial which variable is considered independent (horizontal or X axis) and which is dependent (vertical or Y axis). Also, in choosing the size and number of class intervals for each variable, it is important that the space required be approximately the same for both series. A scatter diagram in the form of a square is much more satisfactory than one in the form of a rectangle with markedly unequal sides.

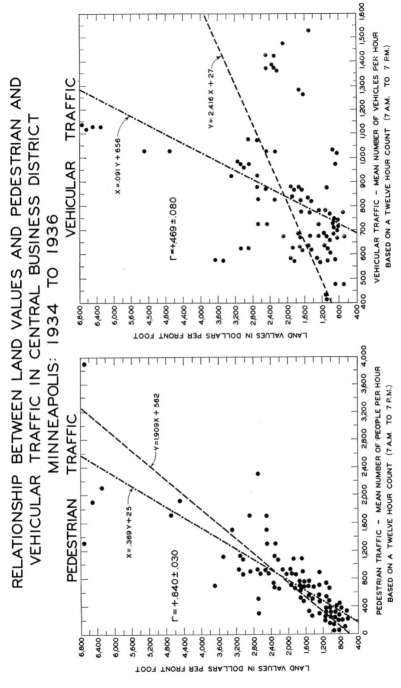

Figure 109. Correlation Charts or Scatter Diagrams. (From Calvin F. Schmid, "Land Values As An Ecological Index," *Research Studies of the State College of Washington*, Vol. IX, March, 1941, pp. 16-36.)

173

Third, the spacing of the divisions on each axis for the class intervals should be large enough to accommodate the necessary lettering and tally marks or dots. Vertical and horizontal lines are drawn through the class-interval division points, thus forming a grid.

Fourth, the class intervals for the X variable should read from left to right and, unlike the conventional frequency distribution, the intervals of the Y variable should read from bottom to top.

Fifth, each entry that is recorded by a dot or tally mark in the proper cell should always represent two numerical values, one measured on the X axis and the other on the Y axis.

Figure 110 includes fifteen scatter diagrams showing the relationship between various population and housing indices according to census tracts for twelve large American cities. It will be observed that some of the scatter diagrams indicate positive correlations and others show negative correlations. The coefficients of correlation and the regression lines measure the type and amount of correlation in each of the scatter diagrams. A few of the scatter diagrams manifest curvilinear rather than rectilinear correlation. The constancy of the ratio of change of the two variables determines whether the correlation is rectilinear or curvilinear. If the amount of change in the two variables bears a constant ratio, the correlation is rectilinear; if it does not, the relationship is curvilinear.

Sometimes a scattergram plotted on a double logarithmic grid can be much more effective than one plotted on natural scales. The purpose of Figure 111 is to portray graphically the relationship between a series of population estimates for 238 incorporated towns and cities of the state of Washington for April 1, 1948, with figures derived in the subsequent decennial census taken as of April 1, 1950. If natural scales had been used in Figure 111, it would have been virtually impossible to include without extreme distortion the wide range of values from less than 50 people for Hatton to 467,000 for Seattle. All but a few of the dots representing the larger cities would have been concentrated in an indistinguishable, unintelligible mass in the lower left-hand part of the grid.

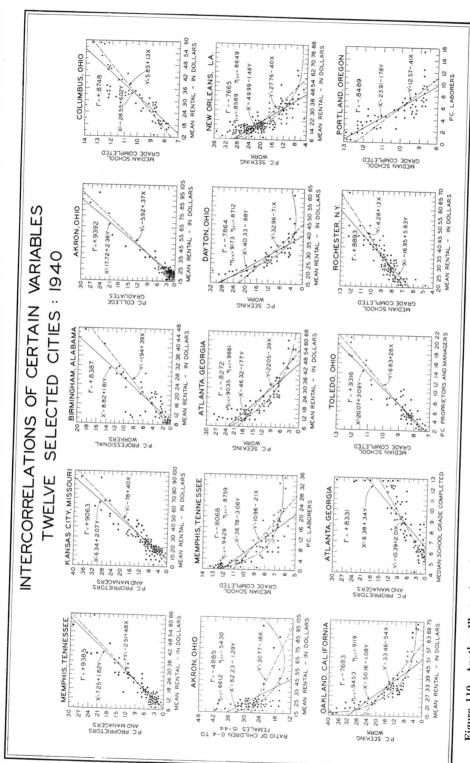

Figure 110. Another Illustration of Correlation Charts. Note especially curvilinear relationship of several pairs of variables. (From Calvin F. Schmid, "Generalizations Concerning the Ecology of the American City," *American Sociological Review*, Vol. XV, No. 2, April, 1950, pp. 264-81.)

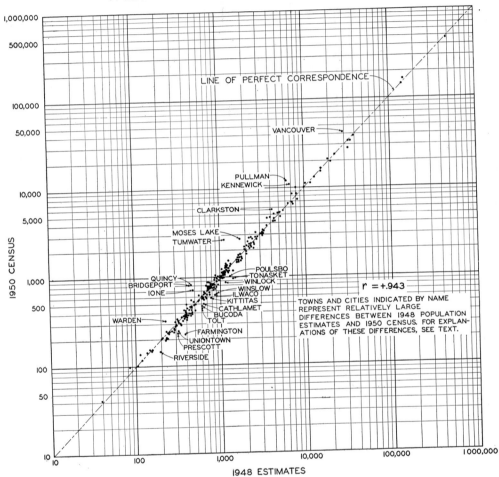

Figure 111. **A Scatter Diagram Drawn on Double Logarithmic Ruling.** Note the wide range of values shown on both the vertical and horizontal axes.

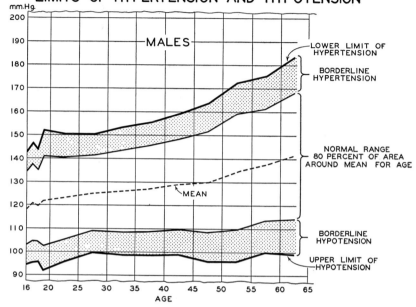

RANGE OF NORMAL SYSTOLIC PRESSURE AND
LIMITS OF HYPERTENSION AND HYPOTENSION

Figure 112. Another Technique for Showing Relationship Between Two Variables. (Redrawn from Arthur M. Master, Louis I. Dublin, and Herbert H. Marks, "The Normal Blood Pressure Range and Its Clinical Implications," *The American Statistician,* Vol. 5, June-July, 1951, pp. 6-7.)

An example of another type of correlation chart is shown in Figure 112. This chart shows the normal range of systolic pressure as well as degrees of hypotension and hypertension according to age for a sample of the male population. It will be observed that there is a normal positive correlation between systolic pressure and age.

Figure 113 shows the relationship between effective rates of individual income tax and net income (single person, no dependents) according to the Acts of 1944, 1945, 1948, and the one proposed for 1951. The income tax rate is indicated on the vertical axis and net income on the horizontal axis. It also will be observed that the vertical scale is ruled arithmetically and the horizontal scale is ruled logarithmically. It is only by means of the logarithmic scale that such a wide range of values, from $500 to $500,000, in a chart of this kind can be appropriately plotted.

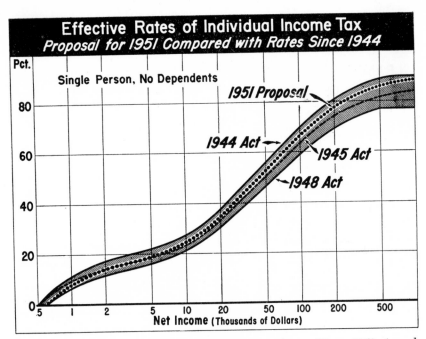

Figure 113. Another Example of a Relationship Chart. (From *1950 Annual Report of the Secretary of the Treasury*, p. 237.)

RANGE OF FLOOR AREAS FOR NEW HOUSES OF DIFFERENT VALUES

(SQUARE FEET IN 50% AND 90% OF HOUSES IN EACH FHA VALUATION GROUP)

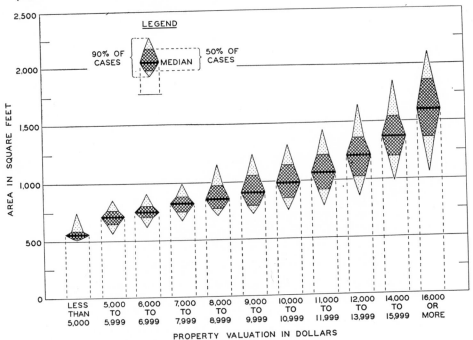

Figure 114. Illustration of Another Type of Correlation Chart. (Redrawn from *Third Annual Report Housing and Home Finance Agency*, 1949, p. 226.)

Perhaps it would have been an improvement if the logarithmic divisions on the scale had been more clearly indicated.

Figure 114, portraying the relation between floor areas of new houses and their valuation, represents another type of correlation chart. As would be expected, the correlation between these two variables is positive; that is, as the floor areas of houses increase, values manifest a definite tendency to rise. For example, houses with a median floor area of approximately 550 square feet are valued at less than $5,000, whereas houses with a median floor area of approximately 1,600 square feet are in the highest valuation category of $16,000 or more. The chart also shows the relative dispersion of floor areas for the several valuation categories. It will be observed that the dispersion in square footage tends to increase as the valuation increases.

Fan Chart

The purpose of the fan chart is to portray rates of change for two different periods either by percentages or index numbers. As many as ten or fifteen items may be shown on a chart of this kind, depending on the range and scatter of the values. If there are relatively large increases and decreases, the curves spread out from the base point in fanlike fashion. The base point is always zero if the figures are expressed in percentages, and usually 100 if expressed as index numbers.

Figure 115 shows the essential features of the fan chart. It will be observed that the changes in enrollment by college for the University of Washington from 1940 to 1952 are expressed in percentages. All the values are plotted from the 1940 zero base point. The specific rates of increase or decrease can be interpreted from the vertical axis. The chief advantage of this chart is its simplicity. Also, herein lies its most serious limitation. To measure rates of change merely by selecting two different dates may be unrepresentative and misleading. The selection of the base period as well as the later period frequently may be very arbitrary and atypical. Moreover, no intermediate values are taken into consideration. Again, the presentation of two percentages in graphic form without knowing the basic data from

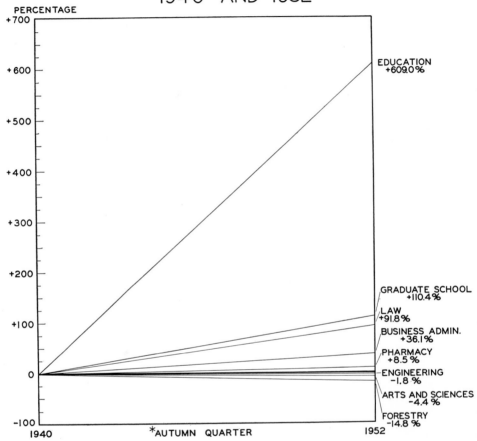

PERCENTAGE CHANGE IN ENROLLMENT BY COLLEGE, UNIVERSITY OF WASHINGTON 1940 AND 1952*

Figure 115. Illustration of Fan Chart.

which they were derived also may lead to erroneous interpretation. For example, the increase of 609 per cent recorded for the College of Education seems phenomenal and may leave the impression that the enrollment figures are far in excess of most of the other divisions of the University. Actually, the original 1940 base was only 100 students, as compared to an enrollment of 709 in 1952. With such a relatively small base as 100 to begin with, any sizable increment would register a large percentage increase. In comparison, the College of Arts and Sciences had enrollments of more than 5,000 students in both 1940 and 1952. Because of the inadequacies of the fan chart, the semilogarithmic chart generally will be found more satisfactory for portraying rates of change.

Organization and Flow Charts

Unlike the other forms of graphic presentation discussed in this book, the typical organization chart as well as a large proportion of flow charts is not used to portray or interpret statistical data. Nevertheless, these charts possess definite utility for certain kinds of research and administrative problems. With well-designed organization and flow charts it is possible to present a large number of facts and relationships simply, clearly, and accurately without resorting to extensive and sometimes involved verbal description. Characteristically, the organization chart is used to present structural forms and logical relationships, whereas flow charts emphasize process and movement.

An organization chart portrays every essential part of an organization in its proper relation to all other parts. More specifically, it shows the relation of one official or department or function to another; titles and sometimes names of officials, and names of departments and their functions; and sources, lines, and types of authority.

There are no standardized rules or practices that can be prescribed for the design and construction of organization charts. The major prerequisite for making a chart of this kind is a thorough understanding of the organization itself. The next step is to prepare several freehand, preliminary sketches of the chart in order to ascertain which design is most satisfactory in terms of accuracy, clarity, and detail. The various names, titles, and descriptive labels are generally enclosed in squares, circles, or other shapes which are connected by various kinds of lines.

Flow charts portray, for example, the various steps in a series of operations, or the specific processes and sequences involved in the planning, production, and distribution of some product, or

RANK ORDER FOR HUSBANDS

RANK ORDER FOR WIVES

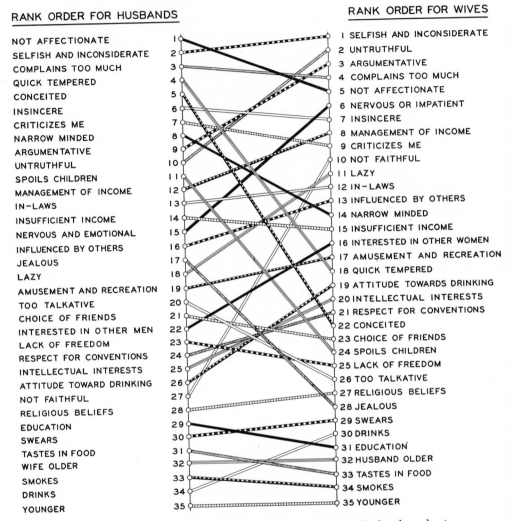

Figure 116. A Ranking Chart. Shows differences between husbands and wives in ranking the seriousness of thirty-five grievances. (By permission from *Psychological Factors in Marital Happiness*, by Louis M. Terman, McGraw-Hill Book Company, Inc., 1938, p. 105. Chart redrawn.)

the flow of income and expenditures as indicated by specific sources of funds and the manner in which they are disbursed.[3]

Several illustrations of organization and flow charts will be found in Chapter 9 (Figures 159, 160, 161, and 162). These charts were included in Chapter 9 rather than the present chapter because of the emphasis on pictorial techniques in the former.

Ranking or Rating Charts

In ranking or rating charts, emphasis is placed on the position of certain items or categories, usually on the basis of magnitude or frequency. For example, states, cities, and other political units are often ranked for several different periods according to population size. In this type of chart, emphasis is placed on rank-order position, rather than on the values themselves. An illustration of a ranking chart will be found in Figure 116. Thirty-five marital grievances are arranged in rank order by husbands and wives, respectively. It will be observed, for example, that the most common complaint of a husband is that his wife is "not affectionate." In the listing of complaints by wives this category ranks in fifth place. The connecting lines indicate the comparative ranking of the various categories for husbands and wives.

---

[3] Another type of chart similar to the flow chart is the "progress" chart. Progress charts are typically schedule or production control charts used in planning and coordinating certain administrative, procurement, production, and distribution processes. Since these charts are so very specialized, with particular emphasis on operational control and coordination, they are not discussed in this book. Examples of some of the better-known forms of progress charts will be found in Wallace Clark, *The Gantt Chart* (London: Sir Isaac Pitman and Sons, Ltd., 1948); William Henry Smith, *Graphic Statistics in Management* (New York: McGraw-Hill Book Co., 1924); William B. Rice, *Control Charts in Factory Management* (New York: John Wiley & Sons, Inc., 1947); Department of the Army, *Defense Production: A Technique for Graphic Production Coordination* (Washington, D. C.: Department of the Army, 1952).

In this connection it also should be pointed out that students of "sociometry" and "group dynamics" have developed the "sociogram" and other geometric techniques to portray various forms and patterns of social relationships. In some respects these techniques are similar to the organization and flow charts. For a more detailed discussion of charts of this kind, see J. L. Moreno, *Who Shall Survive?* (Beacon, N. Y.: Beacon House, Inc., 1953); K. Lewin, *Field Theory in Social Science* (New York: Harper & Bros., 1951); Frank Harary and Robert Z. Norman, *Graph Theory* (Ann Arbor, Mich.: University of Michigan Institute for Social Research, 1953).

CHAPTER 8

Statistical Maps

The most effective technique for portraying spatial relationships is the map. Geographic data are sometimes arranged alphabetically or magnitudinally in tables and graphs, but the spatial character of the data when presented in this manner is largely obscured. The map provides the necessary medium for presenting areal relationships of spatial data clearly, meaningfully, and adequately.

Although the point of view and emphasis in this book are on the application of graphic techniques in presenting statistical data, it should not be overlooked that charts are also valuable for analytical purposes. This is particularly true of maps. Maps are often indispensable in locating problems, testing hypotheses, analyzing data, and discovering hidden facts and relationships.

There are many varieties of maps used in portraying statistical data. They can be grouped under the following basic types: (1) crosshatched or shaded maps; (2) spot or point-symbol maps; (3) isoline maps; (4) maps with one or more types of graphs superimposed, such as the bar, column, line, flow, or pictorial forms; and (5) a combination of two or more of the preceding types.

Base Maps

Delineation of the base map is one of the first steps in the preparation of the various types of maps enumerated in the foregoing paragraph. The base map may be designed as a simple, outline map with a minimum of detail, or it may be laid out in relatively complex form with land-use patterns, topographical features, and other information. In either case the base map should be appropriate to the purpose at hand. In constructing a base map consideration should be given to the following points:

1. The choice of the scale depends on such factors as the nature and amount of detail to be superimposed on the map, the purpose of the map, and the amount of reduction of the finished map.
2. The map projection should be such as not to create any marked distortions and in other respects be suitable for graphic presentation.
3. The amount of detail on the base map should be consistent with the purpose as well as the type and design of the finished map.[1]

Figure 117 illustrates two relatively simple outline types of base maps for the state of Washington. Both show the boundaries and names of the thirty-nine counties. The map at the top was designed for crosshatching purposes. The county boundaries are drawn in relatively heavy, full lines. The lettering of the names of the counties is relatively prominent and centered in each county division. The lower map is suitable for spots or point symbols, flow diagrams, and other graphic forms such as bars, columns, and curves. The county boundaries are drawn in light dot-and-dash lines, and the lettering is small and inconspicuous. Both base maps have space at the top for titles and space on the left side for legends and explanatory notes.

A more detailed base map is shown in Figure 118. This map provides an important background or framework for primary data which are superimposed upon it. In constructing this map a careful selection was made of the features of the physical and man-made environment which are of fundamental importance in conditioning the spatial distribution of social phenomena. The facts are indicated by means of stippling, crosshatching, lettering, and other techniques. Characteristics of the physical environment which are often included on maps of this kind are rivers, lakes, hills, and other topographical features. Some of the factors of the cultural environment are railroads, railway yards, canals, main thoroughfares, industrial areas, vacant property, parks, and cemeteries. In actual practice, it may be necessary to forego a detailed presentation of all of these characteristics,

[1] United Nations, Department of Social Affairs, *Modern Cartography: Base Maps for World Needs* (Lake Success, N. Y.: United Nations Publication, 1949), pp. 78-86.

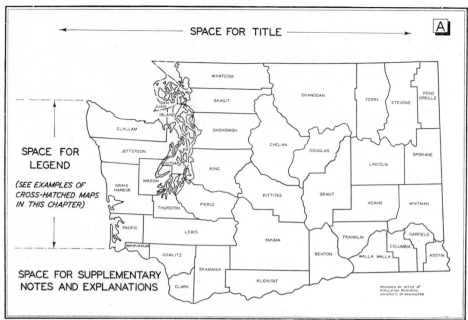

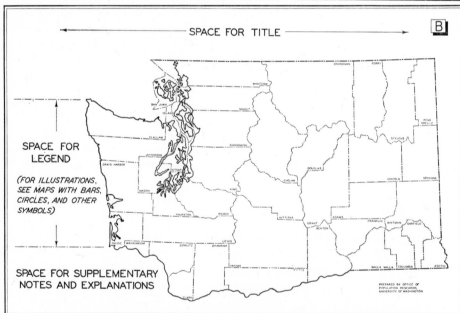

Figure 117. Examples of Simple Outline Base Maps. *A,* This map was designed for crosshatching. Note relatively heavy lines representing county boundaries and also central position of county names. *B,* This base map was made for superimposing various kinds of symbols such as circles, spheres, and bars. The county boundaries and names are much less conspicuous than in the other type of base map.

especially if the map is to be published in reduced form. A map cluttered up with too many inconsequential details can be confusing and misleading. The base map represented by Figure 118 was designed for superimposing point symbols, flow diagrams, and other graphic forms. Another type of map without stippling and shading but showing the basic land-use pattern by dashed lines was prepared for crosshatching.

The size of the original base map in Figure 118 is about 20 by 30 inches. Since a large number of these maps, along with a similar one for crosshatching, will be required for a series of studies on population, crime, and other subjects, several hundred copies were photo-offset printed on high-grade vellum paper. By duplicating these two base maps in this manner, thousands of dollars in labor and materials will be saved. The approximate cost per printed map was considerably less than one dollar. To trace a base map of this kind by hand in accordance with the prevailing rates of pay would cost about $75.

Crosshatched or Shaded Maps

Characteristically, the crosshatched or shaded map is used to portray rates and ratios that are based on clearly delimited areal units such as regions, nations, states, counties, or census tracts. In the case of spot maps, emphasis is placed on absolute numbers or sizes, whereas in crosshatched maps emphasis is on relative frequencies and proportions. In crosshatched maps value ranges or rates and percentages are represented by a graded series of crosshatchings.

A few more or less typical examples of data which are appropriate for crosshatched maps are as follows: marriage rates, divorce rates, birth rates, morbidity rates, mortality rates, and crime rates; percentage of the total population classified according to age, sex, race, or nativity; percentage of population consisting of carpenters, college graduates, unemployed, and so forth; mean or median rent and mean or median value of dwelling units; median grade completed for population twenty-five years of age and over; population density; per capita income, sales, taxes, and so on; percentage of votes for particular candidates or issues; per capita consumption of coffee, beer, sugar, butter, or ciga-

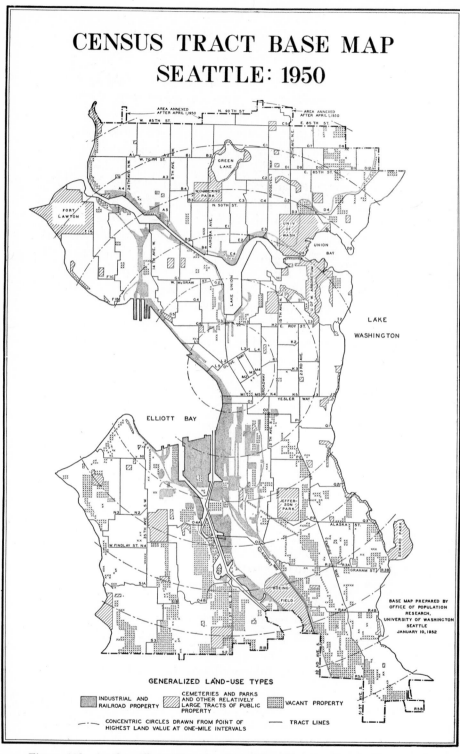

Figure 118. Another Illustration of a Base Map Showing Census Tracts and
Generalized Land-Use Features of a Large City.

rettes; amount of wheat, corn, potatoes, or tobacco produced per acre; percentage of land in farms or forests; and rates of increase and decrease of population, of income, of sales, or of manufacturing or agricultural production.

Occasionally, crosshatched maps are constructed to portray simple chronological series or groupings of qualities or attributes that are basically nonstatistical. Since this book is devoted to graphic forms used in presenting statistical data, the qualitative type of crosshatch map will be given only cursory treatment here.

The fundamental principle to be observed in the crosshatching technique is to arrange the density of lines in such a way as to give an optical effect from light to dark or dark to light with respect to intensity of tone or pattern. Each type of crosshatching indicates a value interval in a series of rates or percentages. Generally the smallest value is indicated by light stippling or crosshatching. Each successive interval is indicated by an increasingly heavier type of hatching, the highest interval usually being represented by black.

Construction of Crosshatched Maps. The first step in the construction of a crosshatched map is to arrange the rates, percentages, averages, or other data into an array. If the number of cases is relatively large, say about a hundred or more, it would be difficult to arrange the data into an array. A frequency distribution with relatively small, equal class intervals should be compiled. After a very careful study of the array or frequency distribution, the data should be grouped into from six to eight class intervals, each interval being represented by an appropriate hatching pattern. As previously indicated, the lightest hatching or stippling normally corresponds to the smallest magnitude, with increasing densities showing successively higher values. Generally there should not be more than eight class intervals, since more than eight hatchings are confusing and difficult to differentiate.

Experience shows that spatial series do not necessarily conform to symmetrical bell-shaped curves. Many series are skewed markedly or are U-shaped or J-shaped in varying degrees. Intervals of equal size are desirable, but the character of many distributions is such as to make this impossible. For some purposes the class intervals may be expressed in terms of standard deviations, quartiles, quintiles, deciles, or some other measure of a frequency distribution. Also, in population density maps, for example, class intervals may be indicated in the form of an arithmetic or geometric progression. If in a geometric progression a series of density intervals begins with 0 to 49, the second would be 50 to 149; the third, 150 to 349; the fourth, 350 to 749; the fifth, 750 to 1,549; and so on.

Use of Colors and Tints. Color is frequently used in the construction of maps and for certain purposes has distinct advantages. Color can make charts attractive and appealing, but color presents serious limitations as a substitute in the typical crosshatched map. First, there is no optical progression of colors that can identify variations in magnitude as precisely, logically, or with the same visually graded impression as crosshatching. A color gradation that manifests degrees of intensity is as follows: white, light yellow, golden yellow, orange, pink, light brown, dark brown, dark green, purple, and black.[2] Even where only one color is used it is very difficult to develop a practical color density or intensity sequence. Generally, it is preferable to show intensity gradations for one color than to use a multicolor density scheme. Second, the cost of printing color is prohibitive for most purposes. Moreover, in photostatic or other types of black and white reproduction, colors in original charts are meaningless or actually a detriment, since certain colors or color intensities do not reproduce clearly. Color can be used successfully to show areal distributions of attributive or chronological series. Maps of this type can be shown either in distinct colors or in tints. Political, geological, and soil maps are examples of nonquantitative distribution maps. In political maps, for example, where each country or other governmental unit is distinct, no color gradation is required. Geological maps frequently conform to a conventionalized color scheme very close to a chromatic scale of yellow, green, blue, violet, and red, supplemented with hues and patterns when necessary.

[2] National Resources Committee, *Suggested Symbols for Planning Maps and Charts* (Washington, D. C.: Government Printing Office, April, 1937), p. A-4.

Shortcomings of the Crosshatched Map. Although the crosshatched map is a very valuable graphic technique, there are three shortcomings which should be recognized. First, an entire areal unit representing a single class interval is crosshatched uniformly regardless of the great differences which may exist within the unit itself. For example, one small corner of an area may be densely populated while other parts may be relatively sparse or entirely uninhabited, but the entire area is expressed as an average with uniform shading. Second, actually the transition in value from one spatial unit to another is usually gradual and not abrupt. Since data for crosshatched maps are based on discrete areal divisions, an impression of definitive and abrupt change may be conveyed by maps of this kind. Third, the amount of crosshatching is determined solely on the basis of geographic area and not by the number of cases each district contains. In terms of visual impression, it is a natural tendency to judge the larger geographic areas as being more important, but actually, in comparison to the number of cases, the smaller areas may be far larger and more significant from a quantitative point of view. Where some factor other than area is of determinative significance, the divisions may be drawn in proportion to the value of the factor rather than according to normal geographic size, thereby eliminating this objection.

Crosshatching Techniques. There are two techniques which can be used in applying crosshatching to a map: (1) ruling pen and ink or (2) commercially prepared crosshatching patterns such as Zip-A-Tone or Visitype. Figure 119 illustrates a series of pen and ink hatchings which the author has used in dozens of maps and other types of charts. It will be observed that the hatchings follow a visual gradation from light to dark, each block representing a particular pattern. The spacing, weight, and other characteristics of hatching schemes should be adapted to the size and other significant features of the chart. If the chart is to be reproduced, consideration should be given to the type of reproduction as well as the amount of reduction. Crosshatching made with pen and ink is more flexible than commercially prepared crosshatching screens, since such factors as size of drawing, line thickness, spacing, and type of reproduction can be fully

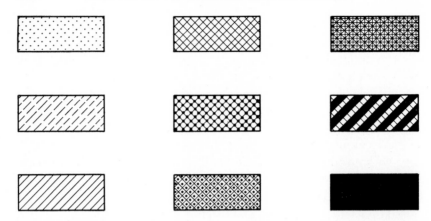

Figure 119. Hatching Scheme Made with Pen and Ink. Note use of these hatchings on several maps in this chapter.

evaluated and allowed for in the design and execution of the chart. In order to achieve equal spacing of lines for crosshatched patterns, distances can be measured with a scale or with a strip of printed graph or cross-ruled paper held in place with thumbtacks, drafting tape, or rubber cement. A section-liner also may be found effective.

Figure 120 is a reproduction of a sample of the commercially prepared Zip-A-Tone. The manufactured hatching screens are press-printed on thin acetate. The underside is coated with paraffin for adhesive purposes. After the screen is cut out to the size and shape of an area, it is carefully applied to the chart with a burnishing bone.[3]

Printed screens possess two main advantages: (1) No skill in tracing or drawing is required to use them. (2) For certain purposes, they may save time and expense. The disadvantages of printed screens include: (1) Lack of flexibility—the weight and spacing of lines of the various hatching patterns are not always adaptable to large-scale maps. (2) They are more costly and time consuming for some types of work. (3) They do not adhere

[3] The idea of printing hatching patterns on paper and applying them to maps is an old one. More than fifty years ago William Z. Ripley described this technique which he used in the preparation of the maps for his well-known work, *Races of Europe* (D. Appleton & Co., 1915). See William Z. Ripley, "Notes on Map Making and Graphic Representation," *Quarterly Publication of the American Statistical Association,* Vol. 6 (1898-99), pp. 313-27.

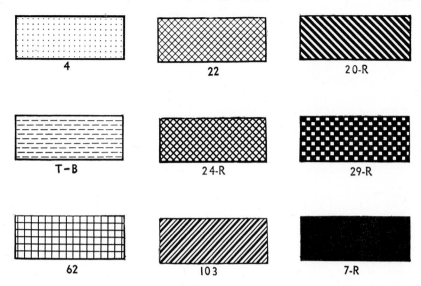

Figure 120. **Sample Zip-A-Tone Hatchings.** Numbers identify type of hatching for ordering and filing purposes.

satisfactorily to flexible material such as vellum or tracing cloth, especially when rolled. They also tend to peel off stiff surfaces after a certain period of time, depending on room temperature, handling, and other factors. (4) Unless the tracing is protected by a layer of transparent acetate, it is difficult to make inexpensive contact prints, such as blue- and black-line prints with printed screens. The heat from the machine lights is usually great enough to melt the paraffin adhesive and cause the screen material to loosen.

Figures 121, 122, and 123 illustrate the crosshatching technique. Incidentally, the hatching of these maps was drawn on tracing cloth and then was made with pen and ink. Figure 121 shows the percentage of the population classified as Negro in each census tract in the city of Indianapolis in 1940. The proportion of Negroes for the 107 census tracts ranges from less than 1 percent to over 95 percent. The pattern of spatial segregation of Negroes in Indianapolis is typical of the large American city.[4] In constructing this map the first step was to indicate the

[4] Julius Jahn, Calvin F. Schmid, Clarence Schrag, "The Measurement of Ecological Segregation," *American Sociological Review,* Vol. 12 (June, 1947), pp. 293-303.

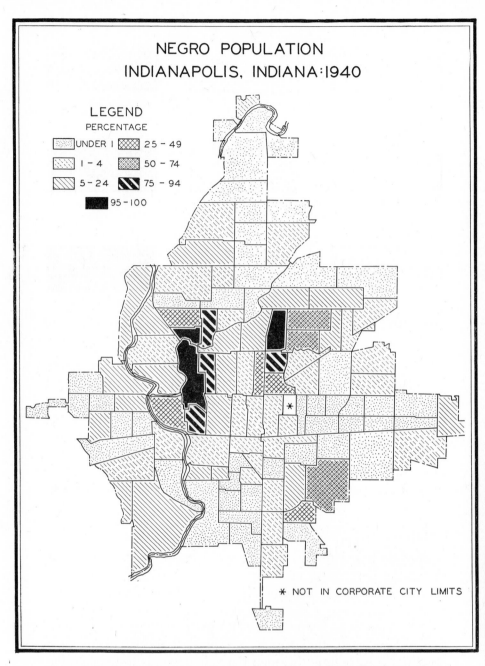

Figure 121. Crosshatched Map Showing Proportion of Total Population Classified as Negro According to Census Tracts for the City of Indianapolis. (Prepared from original data in *Population and Housing: Statistics for Census Tracts*, Sixteenth Census of the United States, 1940.)

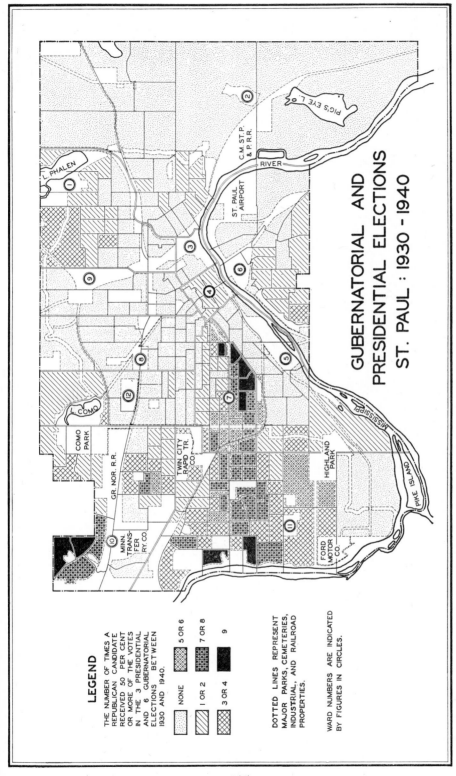

Figure 122. Another Application of the Crosshatching Technique Showing Frequencies of Occurrence.

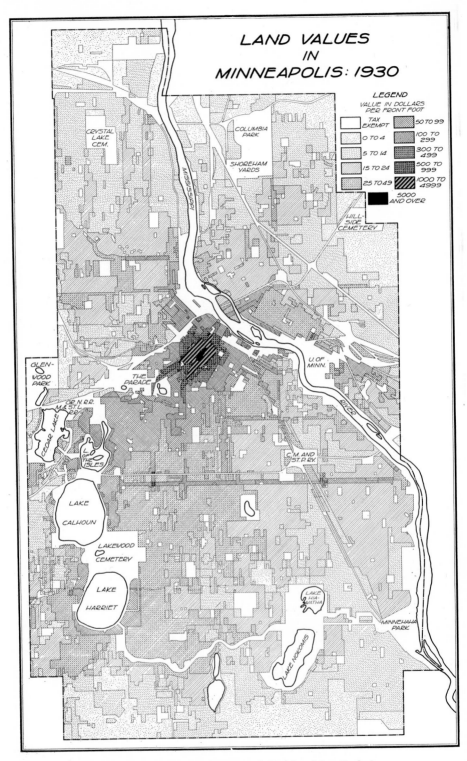

Figure 123. Another Application of Crosshatching Technique.

percentage of the population classified as Negro in each census tract. The second step was to prepare an array of the percentages. For the third step, the percentages were grouped into class intervals to bring out the essential characteristics of the distribution. It will be observed that it was necessary to use intervals of unequal size. Fourth, a hatching scheme graded in density of pattern was constructed for the seven class intervals. The heavy concentration of Negroes in two sections, the gradient character of the patterning extending in different directions from the two major focal points, and the relatively large portion of the city with virtually no Negro residents are clearly presented by this map.

Another somewhat different application of the crosshatching technique is presented in Figure 122. The basic statistics pertain to voting data by precincts in the city of St. Paul for the three presidential and six gubernatorial elections between 1930 and 1940. The problem was to summarize clearly and graphically the comparative strength of the Republican Party in various parts of the city. After the original voting data were tabulated, percentages were computed for each of the nine elections. A frequency distribution was constructed showing the number of times the respective Republican candidates received 50 percent or more of the votes for each of the precincts indicated on the map. The resulting frequencies were written on the work map and a simple sixfold hatching scheme was developed. The consistently Republican and Democratic strongholds, as well as the intermediate areas, are clearly revealed by this map.

Figure 123 was selected to illustrate how the crosshatching technique can be used effectively to portray highly detailed and complex data. The basic data represent the front-footage assessed valuation of every tract of land in the corporate city of Minneapolis. In attempting to map data of this kind, one is confronted with two complex problems: (1) the areas for which the data are given are exceedingly small and numerous, and (2) the range of values is very wide. After careful study was made of the basic data, eleven class intervals were selected, and the front-

(*Figure 123.*) Note especially fine gradation of density for ten different categories. From Calvin F. Schmid, "Land Values as an Ecological Index," *Research Studies of the State College of Washington*, Vol. IX, March, 1941, pp. 16-36.)

footage value of every lot and every larger tract of land in the city was transferred from original records to a work map in accordance with a color scheme corresponding to the eleven class intervals. The smallness of the areas, as well as the large number of class intervals, made it particularly difficult to work out a system of graded hatching patterns and to draw these patterns on the map. The problem of reduction for printing also had to be taken into consideration. A careful examination of the map will reveal further details of planning and construction and also the relative effectiveness of the map in portraying graphically the essential patterning of land values in a large American city.

Figure 124 illustrates the application of the crosshatching technique in portraying nonquantitative data on maps. It will be observed that the various parcels of land annexed to the city of Chicago are differentiated by a series of hatching patterns. Each pattern represents the annexations recorded during certain intercensal periods, beginning in 1850. Sometimes it may be found expedient to arrange the hatching density in a gradation to conform to a chronological sequence; for example, the lightest pattern might indicate the earliest period, with increasingly darker patterns for successive periods.

Spot or Point-Symbol Maps

Emphasis in spot or point-symbol maps is placed on frequencies or absolute amounts rather than on rates or proportions. Although there may be a certain amount of overlapping, spot maps can be differentiated into five types on the basis of the symbols used. Symbols may stress: (1) size, (2) number, (3) density, (4) shading, or (5) form.

Spot Maps with Areal and Cubic Symbols. In the first type of map the size of each symbol is proportional to the frequency or magnitude of the phenomena represented. Symbols may be either two- or three-dimensional and are normally in the form of circles or spheres rather than rectangles, cubes, or irregular forms. If circles are utilized, the respective areas are in proportion to the value represented. Similarly, in the case of spheres the respective volumes are drawn in accordance with the frequency or mag-

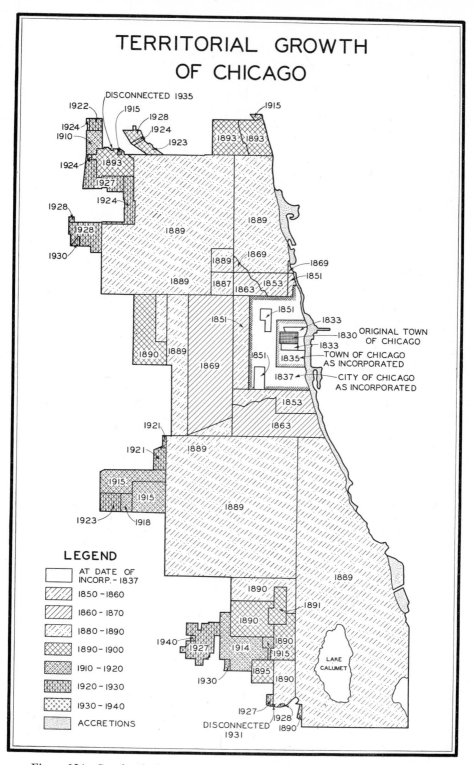

Figure 124. Crosshatched Map Portraying Historical Data. (Map prepared from data furnished by Chicago City Plan Commission.)

199

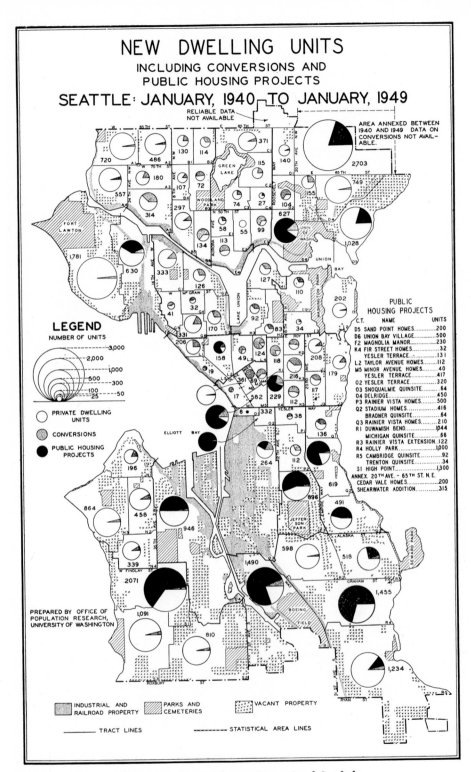

Figure 125. Map with Two-Dimensional Symbols.

200

nitude portrayed. Figure 125 illustrates the application of two-dimensional symbols in portraying the spatial distribution of housing construction in the city of Seattle during the nine-year period from January, 1940, to January, 1949. The original data were derived from files of the building inspector and each dwelling unit was allocated according to census tract. The areas of the

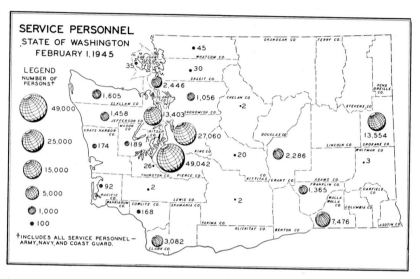

Figure 126. Map with Three-Dimensional Symbols.

circles were drawn in proportion to the number of dwelling units. It will be observed that the number of dwelling units for each tract is clearly indicated on the map. In order to differentiate private housing, public housing, and conversions, the circles were divided into sectors. The sector representing private housing is indicated in white; public housing, in black; and conversions, in stippling. A legend in the form of a series of eccentric circles of different sizes with their corresponding values is also indicated on the map.

Spherical symbols are portrayed on Figure 126. The data indicate the distribution of military personnel in the state of Washington as of February 1, 1945. The main justification for using three-dimensional symbols on maps is a very practical one. Where

(*Figure 125.*) Area of each circle is proportional to number of dwelling units in its census tract. Note threefold classification of dwelling units. (Map prepared from data compiled from records of the Seattle Building Inspector.)

the range of values is very wide and the space on the map limited in size, it becomes necessary to use a type of symbol that can be properly fitted on the map. Also, where the number of symbols is large, the problem of available space becomes accentuated. For example, if two-dimensional symbols had been selected for Figure 126 and the smallest value were represented by a point of microscopic size, the symbols representing the larger figures, such as 49,042 for Pierce County and 27,060 for King County, could not have been contained within these respective county boundaries. Similarly, with one-dimensional symbols (bars) it would have been impossible to compare on any map of reasonable size such values as 2 (Yakima and Chelan Counties) or even 20 (Kittitas County) with 49,042 (Pierce County). In detailed population density maps, which include both large and small cities as well as more widely distributed agglomerations of population, three-dimensional symbols may be found very appropriate.[5]

Procedure in Drawing Areal and Cubic Symbols. Correct drafting of circles as symbols for comparison of sizes is not difficult if it is kept in mind that it is the *area* of the circle that represents the size being compared. The area of a circle is equal to its radius squared times the constant pi; that is, $A = \pi r^2$. Since the diameter, the dimension of the circle which is most useful in laying out a chart, may be expressed as twice the radius, the area of any circle may be expressed as $\pi(\frac{1}{2}d)^2$, or $(\pi/4)d^2$. Expressing the constant $\pi/4$ as a unit of measurement, the area of the circle is found to be a function of the square of the diameter, or the area increases directly as the square of the diameter. That is, increasing the diameter of a circle to three times its previous length will increase the area of the circle to nine times its previous value. In laying out circles as symbols for comparison of sizes, then, the diameters of the circle symbols should be proportional to the square root of the sizes to which they correspond.

For example, in order to construct a series of comparable circles for the values 16, 25, 49, 81, and 144, the first step is to extract their respective square roots. Their square roots (4, 5, 7, 9, and 12) will determine the diameters of the circles. It is im-

[5] Sten de Geer, "A Map of the Distribution of Population in Sweden," *Geographical Review*, Vol. 12 (1922), pp. 72-83.

portant to draw circles compatible with the general layout and dimensions of the chart. The initial step in this procedure is to determine the actual sizes of the largest and smallest circles in the series.

The smallest square root in the series will be used as a divisor for all of the others. If the most desirable size of diameter, in inches, for the smallest circle is .3, then each derived quotient in the series is multiplied by .3. In the above illustration the quotients so derived are as follows: $5/4 = 1.25$; $7/4 = 1.75$; $9/4 = 2.25$; $12/4 = 3.00$. If the diameter of the smallest circle is .3, the diameters for the remaining circles are $(1.25)(.3) = .375$; $(1.75)(.3) = .525$; $(2.25)(.3) = .675$; and $(3.00)(.3) = .9$.

Similar considerations are encountered when the volume of spheres is used as a device for comparison of sizes. The spherical symbol is outlined as a circle, the great circle of the sphere, and then shaded, or marked in some way to indicate the three-dimensional aspect of the symbol. Since it is the volume which is to be proportional to the sizes being compared, the relationship between the volume of a sphere and the diameter of its great circle must be considered. The volume of a sphere is found by the formula $V = 4/3\pi r^3$, or the constant four-thirds of the number pi times the cube of the radius. Since the radius is one-half the diameter, this formula may be written $V = 4/3\pi(\frac{1}{2}d)^3$, or $V = \frac{1}{6}\pi d^3$. As in the case of using circles for comparison by areas, the constant $\pi/6$ can be expressed as a unit of measurement, and the volume of the sphere is found to be a function of the cube of its diameter. Increasing the diameter of the great circle of the sphere to three times its original length will increase the volume of the sphere to 27 times its original value. To compare the sizes 8, 64, and 1,000, circular symbols with diameters of 2, 4, and 10 units, when shaded or marked to indicate their spherical nature, will be correctly proportioned to represent the comparison by volume of spheres.

Examples of linear, areal, and cubic comparisons of the populations of six counties in the state of Washington in 1950 are shown in Table VII.

An examination of the table clearly reveals the specific steps for deriving comparable circles and spheres. For circles, the first step is to extract the square root of each figure in the series

TABLE VII

Linear, Areal, and Cubic Comparisons: Illustration of Techniques for Drawing Comparable Sizes of Circles and of Spheres
(Data represent population of six counties
in the state of Washington in 1950)

County	Popu-lation	Circles			Spheres		
		$\sqrt{\text{Col. 2}}$	Col. 3 $\div$ $\sqrt{3{,}245}$	(Col. 4) mult. by (factor) *	$\sqrt[3]{\text{Col. 2}}$	Col. 6 $\div$ $\sqrt[3]{3{,}245}$	(Col. 7) mult. by (factor) *
(1)	(2)	(3)	(4)	(5) (inches)	(6)	(7)	(8) (inches)
Clark	85,307	292.08	5.13	2.57	44.00	3.13	1.57
Grays Harbor ...	53,644	231.61	4.07	2.04	37.72	2.68	1.34
Kittitas	22,235	149.11	2.62	1.31	28.10	2.00	1.00
Klickitat	12,049	109.77	1.93	1.00	22.80	1.62	.83
Ferry	4,097	63.32	1.11	.56	16.00	1.14	.57
San Juan	3,245	56.96	1.00	.50	14.05	1.00	.50

* "Factor" can be any desired size of diameter or radius of circle or of sphere representing the smallest value. In this table the "factor" selected was .5 inch.

(Column 3). Second, each square root is divided by the square root of the smallest figure (Column 4). Third, a desirable diameter is selected for the smallest circle which is used as a factor for all of the values in the series. For illustrative purposes .5 inch was chosen. In developing three-dimensional symbols the same procedure is followed, except, of course, cube roots of the values in the series are computed. It will be observed that, although the respective diameters of the circle and sphere were made identical for San Juan County, the corresponding diameters for Clark County are considerably different in size. This fact further illustrates the significance of areal and volume symbols.

One of several methods can be used in extracting square roots and cube roots. Tables of square roots and cube roots are available. Perhaps the best known is *Barlow's Tables*. The logarithmic relationships of numbers also can be utilized in deriving square and cube roots. For example, one-half the log of a number is the log of the square root of the number, and one-third the log of a number is the log of the cube root of the number. Another method of extracting roots is by use of the binomial expansion. One of the most common techniques for deriving square roots is the mechanical method of successive divisions taught to pupils in junior high school.

Spot Maps Which Emphasize Frequency of Symbols. In the second type of spot map the basic criterion is not size but number or frequency of spots or point symbols. The spots are uniform in size, each representing a specific value. The design and arrangement of spots make them readily countable. With a well-constructed map of this kind it is possible to ascertain at a glance whether one geographic area contains more or fewer dots than another, and if one desires to make exact comparison between two or more areas it is very easy to count the dots and compare the results. Usually the dots are distributed within statistical or administrative divisions such as counties, precincts, or census tracts. For example, the author has prepared maps of this kind indicating the number of votes for a Communist candidate by precincts, the number of substandard housing units by enumeration districts, and the number of robberies and other crimes by census tracts. As a general rule, the smallest geographic area on the map will determine the size of the dot and the number of units of frequencies to be represented by each dot. Figure 127 is an illustration of this type of map. The exact location of each house of prostitution is indicated and the general pattern is related to the natural areas and to the census tracts of the central segment of the city.

Spot Maps Emphasizing Density of Symbols. The third type of map is also a multiple-dot variety, but instead of emphasizing countable frequencies, comparative density and distribution are emphasized. Actually, of course, the map stressing numbers or frequency of spots may also at the same time indicate density of distribution, but not as exactly or characteristically as one designed with that purpose in mind. The spots used in density maps are invariably small black dots.

The size of the dots should be made commensurate with the over-all size of the base map as well as with the number and distribution of dots. Also, if the map is to be reproduced, the

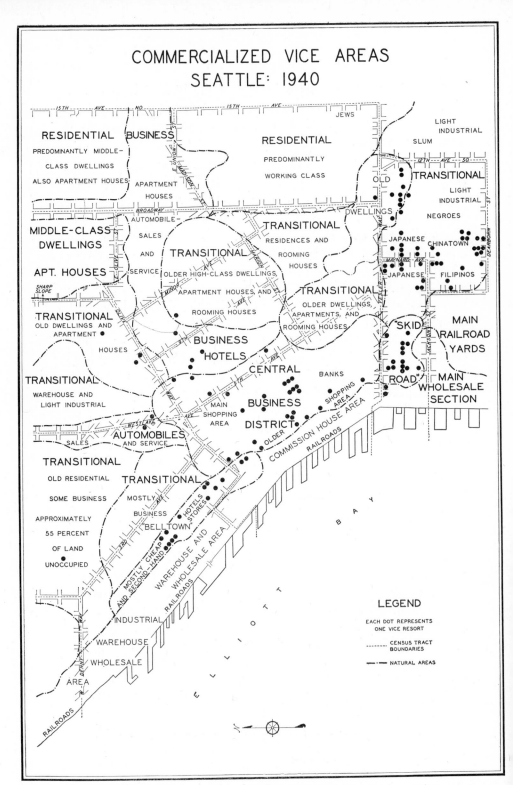

Figure 127. A Spot Map Showing Distribution of Vice Resorts in Relation to Natural Areas in the Central Segment of a Large City.

amount of reduction should be carefully considered. In planning a map of this kind the dot ratio must be carefully worked out. One dot may be equivalent to 1, 5, 10, 25, 50, 75, 100, 200, 500, 1,000, or some other number of items. If the ratio shown is too small, the number of dots may be so large that they cannot be included on the map. On the other hand, if the ratio is too large, the dots may be so few that a clear pattern of density cannot be developed.

Several different techniques can be used in making dots of this kind. The bow pen and drop pen are used most frequently. For relatively small dots a Wrico, LeRoy, Payzant, or similar type of lettering pen will be found quick and efficient. Sometimes it may be found convenient to use small disk-shaped gummed paper or cloth.

Figure 128 portrays the distribution of the Negro population of Seattle according to a density-dot system. The purpose of a map of this kind is to indicate over-all spatial patterning. A mere glance at the map reveals pronounced clusterings of Negroes in certain areas as well as a complete absence in other areas. In comparison with Figure 121, which uses the crosshatching technique, the pattern of segregation for racial minorities is depicted in a very different manner. As has been pointed out before, alternate graphic techniques may be used to portray the same phenomena. In such instances it may be irrelevant to assume that one technique is necessarily superior to another, because the respective purposes of the charts may be entirely different. Crosshatched maps, for example, emphasize rates or proportions for specified areas; whereas density-dot maps show specific location and concentration of frequencies.

Spot Maps with Shaded Symbols. In the fourth type of spot map the criterion is shading. The size of the symbols is uniform but the amount of shading is indicative of the magnitude or value represented. The most common shading technique is based on the quarter-section system. For example, the smallest value interval may be an open circle; the next highest interval is represented by a circle with a portion, usually one-fourth, shaded; progressively higher values are indicated by larger shaded sectors, with solid black indicating the highest.

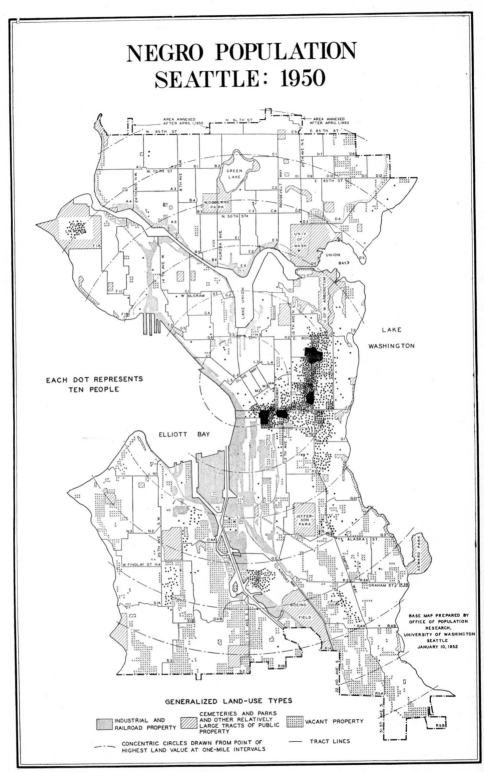

NEGRO POPULATION
SEATTLE: 1950

EACH DOT REPRESENTS
TEN PEOPLE

ELLIOTT BAY

LAKE
WASHINGTON

GENERALIZED LAND-USE TYPES

INDUSTRIAL AND
RAILROAD PROPERTY

CEMETERIES AND PARKS
AND OTHER RELATIVELY
LARGE TRACTS OF PUBLIC
PROPERTY

VACANT PROPERTY

CONCENTRIC CIRCLES DRAWN FROM POINT OF
HIGHEST LAND VALUE AT ONE-MILE INTERVALS

TRACT LINES

BASE MAP PREPARED BY
OFFICE OF POPULATION
RESEARCH,
UNIVERSITY OF WASHINGTON
SEATTLE
JANUARY 10, 1952

Figure 128. An Example of a Spot Map Emphasizing Density of Symbols.

Spot Maps with Symbols Representing Qualities or Attributes.
Unlike the four types of spot maps already discussed, the criterion
for the symbol map is a qualitative one. The form of the symbol
represents certain qualities or attributes. For example, if the
dichotomy male and female are to be portrayed on a map, one
type of symbol would represent male and another type, female.
Likewise, if a number of different kinds of institutions such as
churches, schools, hospitals, or factories are to be depicted, each
type of institution would be represented by a different symbol.[6]

As part of four different ecological studies of suicide, multiple-
attribute spot maps of this type were used with much success.
Figure 129 is an example of one of these maps.[7] It will be observed from the legend that the basic criteria of classification are
the sex and residence of the suicide. Males are indicated by
circles, females by triangles; the plain circle and triangle show
that the place of self-destruction was the same as the residence
of the suicide. The crosses in the circles and triangles indicate
residents of Seattle who committed suicide in some place other
than their domicile; the symbols with the solid center designate
nonresident suicides, and the symbols that are entirely black
indicate that the identity of the suicides is unknown.

Figure 130 is another adaptation of this type of map. It shows
the location and integration of health services in the state of
Oklahoma. Base, regional, and district hospitals are shown by
triangles, and rural or community hospitals by dots. Heavy
circles indicate existing health department headquarters, and
light circles show proposed health department headquarters.
Dark lines connecting the various symbols represent the integration of health services for the various health areas throughout the
state.

[6] The following publications contain many valuable suggestions concerning map
symbols, hatchings, color schemes, land-use patterns, as well as certain standard
practices: National Resources Committee, *Suggested Symbols for Plans, Maps, and
Charts* (April, 1937); United States Geological Survey, "Standard Symbols" (21 by
33 inch sheet); United States Forest Service, *Forest Service Map Standards;* National Park Service, *Guides and Symbols;* Department of the Army, *Topographic
Symbols* (1952).

[7] Calvin F. Schmid, *Social Trends in Seattle* (1944), pp. 203-15.

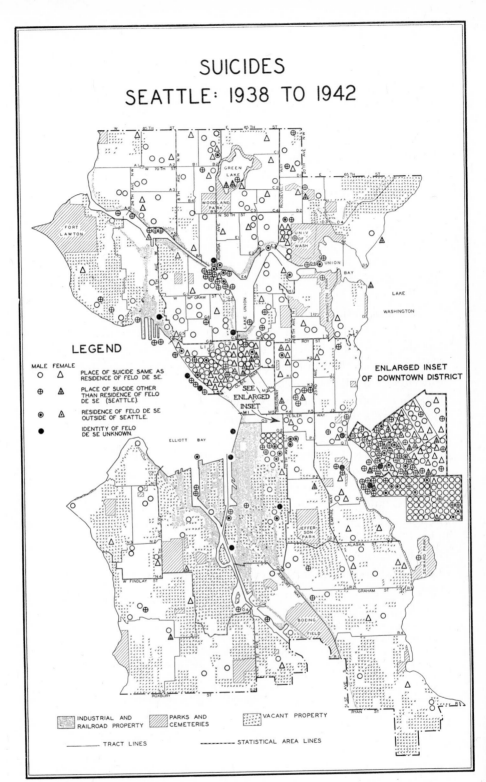

Figure 129. Spot Map in Which the Form of the Symbol Is the Basic Criterion.
(From Calvin F. Schmid, *Social Trends in Seattle*, 1944, p. 204.)

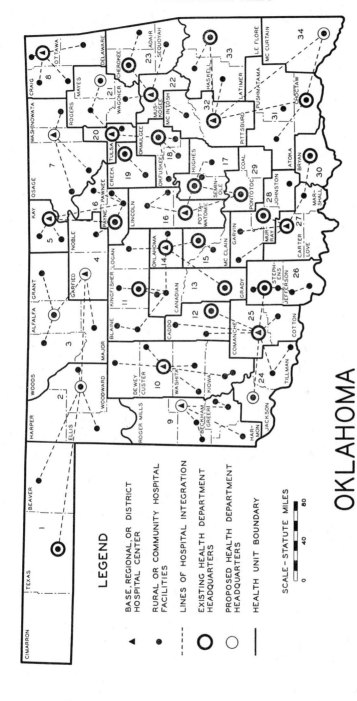

Figure 130. **Application of Spot Map Technique for Mapping Local Health Service Areas.** Shows location and interrelations of various health services. (Redrawn from Joseph W. Mountin and Clifford H. Greve, *Public Health Areas and Hospital Facilities,* U. S. Public Health Service, p. 86.)

Isoline Maps

Isoline (from *isos,* meaning "equal") is a generic term which describes a type of map widely used by geographers to show the distribution of meteorological, physiographic, economic, demographic, and other data.[8] The basic data used in the preparation of isoline maps may be samples of absolute measurement for particular points or ratios for certain areas. In both instances, points having identical values are joined together by continuous flowing lines.

Some of the more familiar examples of isoline maps include those pertaining to a series of points of equal temperature, which are called "isotherms"; of equal rainfall, "isohyets"; of equal barometric pressure, "isobars"; of equal elevation, "isohypses" (or more commonly, "contour lines"); of equal magnetic variations, "isogenes"; of equal time, "isochrones."

There are two fundamental types of isoline maps: (1) the isometric map, in which the lines are drawn through points of equal value or intensity, and (2) the isopleth map, in which the lines connect equal rates or ratios for specific areas. In the isometric map a sample of measurements is taken at different points on a map, and those of equal values or magnitude are connected by continuous lines.[9] In contrast the values used in the isopleth maps are rates or ratios computed on the basis of areal units, such as census tracts, townships, precincts, or counties. In this type of map the value for an area is reduced to a point. A topographic map is an example of the isometric type, and a population density map with lines showing equal densities is an example of the isopleth type.

---

[8] The beginner may find the terminology of maps of this type very confusing, since there is little agreement upon usage among cartographers. Instead of "isoline" some cartographers prefer "isogram" (equal-line), "isopleth" (equal-measure), or "isorithm" (equal-number). The terms "isometric" and "isontic" also have been used.

[9] The term "isometric" as used to describe a specific type of isoline map has an entirely different connotation from that used to describe a form of projection. See Chapter 10, "Projection Techniques in Graphic Presentation," for a discussion of isometric projection.

The isopleth map is particularly valuable for graphic presentation in the social sciences. In the construction of isopleth maps, however, there are four basic considerations which must be kept in mind. First, the areal units for which the data have been collected bear a close and significant relationship to the reliability, comparability, significance, and general appearance of the isopleth map. If the base areas are relatively large, meaningful variations are masked and the isopleths are extremely general. On the other hand, if the areas are relatively small, chance and possibly meaningless variations in the data will be recorded as myriads of tiny "islands" or "peaks" on the isopleth map. Most important, however, is the loss of measurability which occurs when adjacent base areas on a map are different in size. If one control point is based on a relatively large area and an adjacent control point on a relatively small area, the interpolation of values between them is subject to errors of interpretation which cannot be controlled statistically. If it is impossible or impracticable to use base areas of the same shape and size, extreme caution should be followed in interpreting the resulting isopleths. Usually data are available only for blocks, enumeration districts, census tracts, and political subdivisions. Since the census or political subdivisions are not identical in size and shape, the above considerations are particularly important. If the same data are available for more than one type of base area, selection should be determined mainly by the relationship and significance of the data to the size of the base area.

Second, the "control point" must be accurately located according to some specific assumption for each areal unit for which a rate or ratio has been derived. If the unit is symmetrical in shape and the distribution of the phenomenon is relatively uniform, the geographical center naturally would be chosen as the control point or "spot height." In actual practice, census tracts, precincts, counties, and other areas for which statistics are compiled are seldom symmetrical, and the patterns of distribution of most economic, social, and other phenomena are uneven. The problem is to determine the most typical or representative point in the area. This point in any type of area, with even or uneven distribution, is the center of gravity or pivot point where the distribution would balance if it were supported by a rigid and weightless plane.[10]

The third consideration [11] is the laying out of the "isopleths" which are drawn with reference to the values indicated by the control points in each statistical area. The procedure is largely one of interpolation and inference with reference to the various control points. Many mathematical interpolation methods could be used; but complicated interpolations cannot usually be justified by the data and technique of isopleth mapping, and linear interpolation should be used in most instances. On this question, the following quotation from Wright is pertinent.

Thus an isopleth representing a density of 20 to the square mile is made to connect figures "20" on the base and to pass halfway between a "15" and a "25," two-thirds of the way from an "18" to a "21," etc. The method is convenient and not misleading if the density figures are numerous and closely spaced, but it should always be remembered that an isopleth, although drawn in a similar manner, is not at all comparable to a contour line. One may determine the altitude of a point, but one cannot define the density of population at a point, since density can be measured with respect to areas (or volumes) only. Between the 20- and 40-foot contour lines the elevation is everywhere between 20 and 40 feet, but it is not true that the density of population within an area marked off by the 20- and 40-per-square-mile isopleths is necessarily between 20 and 40 to the square mile.[12]

The fourth consideration is the choice of intervals for the isopleths. The isopleth interval may be based on either a geometric or arithmetic progression or some division or multiple of

[10] A discussion of techniques for locating control points for isopleth maps will be found in the following papers: J. Ross Mackay, "Some Problems and Techniques in Isopleth Mapping," *Economic Geography*, Vol. 27 (January, 1951), pp. 1-9; Ernest W. Mowrer, "The Isometric Map as a Technique of Social Research," *The American Journal of Sociology*, Vol. 44 (July, 1938), pp. 86-96; Fr. Uhorczak, "Metoda Izarytmiczna W. Mapach Statystycznych," *Polski Przeglad Kartograficzny*, Tom IV (Grudzien, 1929), pp. 95-124.

[11] The third and fourth points are also relevant to the construction of the isometric type map.

[12] John K. Wright *et al.*, "Notes on Statistical Mapping, with Special Reference to the Mapping of Population Phenomena." Published by American Geographical Society and Population Association of America (1938), p. 13. See W. D. Jones, "Ratios and Isopleth Maps in Regional Investigation of Agricultural Land Occupancy," *Annals Association of American Geographers*, Vol. 20 (1930), pp. 177-95. A method of drawing isopleths according to mathematical principles is explained in *Basic Problems, Techniques and Theory of Isopleth Mapping*, by Calvin F. Schmid and Earle H. MacCannell (in press).

5 or 10, such as 0, 5, 10, 25, 50, 100, 500, or 1,000. The size of
the interval should be adapted to each map, particularly in
relation to the type of distribution, reliability, and other characteristics of the data. If the intervals are too large, the result may
be an overgeneralized and meaningless map. On the other
hand, if the isopleths are plotted in accordance with small class
intervals or when a map has widely separated control points, an
unwarranted impression of precision is conveyed. The value of
each isoline is indicated on the map with the appropriate number, the significance of which is included in a supplementary
legend.[13]

An illustration of the isometric type of isoline map is shown
in Figure 131. This chart is a simplified contour map of Seattle.
It will be observed that the contour lines are drawn at 50-foot
intervals ranging from zero to 50 to over 500. The spaces
between the isolines are crosshatched in accordance with the
principles outlined in the section on crosshatched maps. There
is a total of eleven different class intervals. The shading between
the isolines focuses attention on the spaces between the contour
lines, and it helps to make the map more readily intelligible and
graphic.

Figure 132 is an isopleth map showing the educational status
of the population of Chicago as indicated by the distribution of
the median number of school grades completed by persons
twenty-five years old and older. The various steps used in constructing this map are illustrated in Figure 133. This figure is
an enlarged portion of the work map used in developing the
isolines for Figure 132. The areal bases for the original data are
census tracts, which are shown by stippled boundary lines and
tract numbers. "Control points," indicated by circles, are located
at the geographic center of each tract. The value for each control point represents the median grade completed for persons
twenty-five years old and older within the tract. Each control
point is connected by a straight line—an interpolation axis—with
each adjacent control point. Adjacent control points are taken

[13] J. Ross Mackay, op. cit.; J. W. Alexander and G. A. Zahorchak, "Population-
Density Maps of the United States: Techniques and Patterns," Geographical Review, Vol. 33 (1943), pp. 458-60.

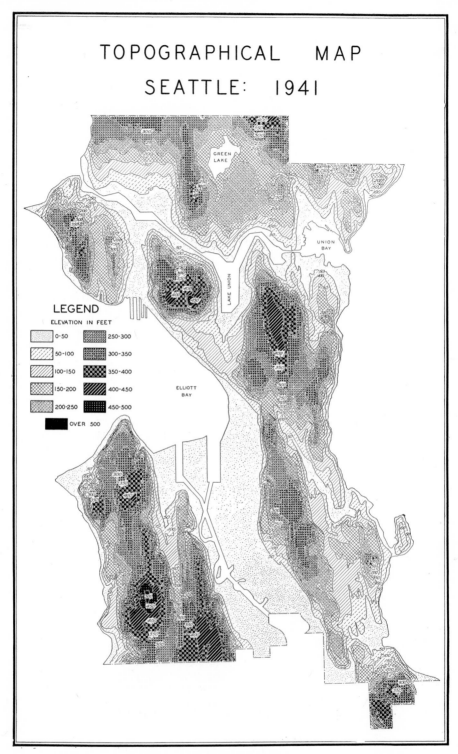

Figure 131. A Contour Map on Which Is Superimposed a Simplified Crosshatching Scheme for the Purpose of Differentiating Elevations. (From Calvin F. Schmid, *Social Trends in Seattle*, 1944, p. 52.)

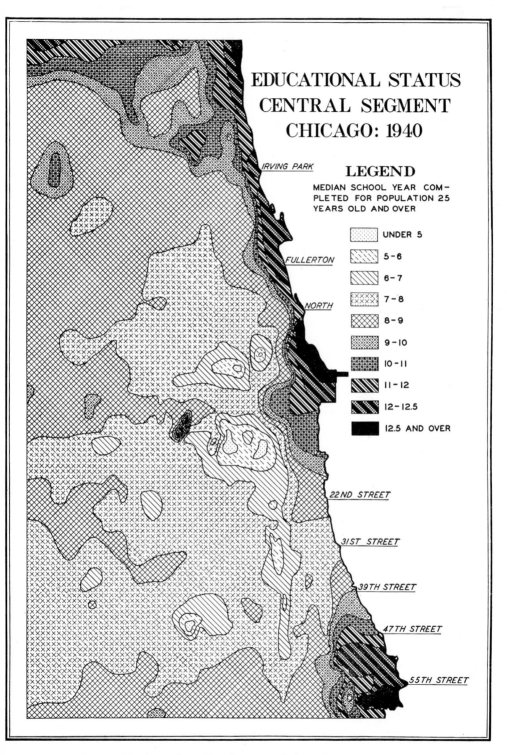

EDUCATIONAL STATUS
CENTRAL SEGMENT
CHICAGO: 1940

LEGEND

MEDIAN SCHOOL YEAR COM-
PLETED FOR POPULATION 25
YEARS OLD AND OVER

UNDER 5
5-6
6-7
7-8
8-9
9-10
10-11
11-12
12-12.5
12.5 AND OVER

IRVING PARK

FULLERTON

NORTH

22ND STREET

31ST STREET

39TH STREET

47TH STREET

55TH STREET

Figure 132. An Isoline Map Constructed from Census Tract Data.

217

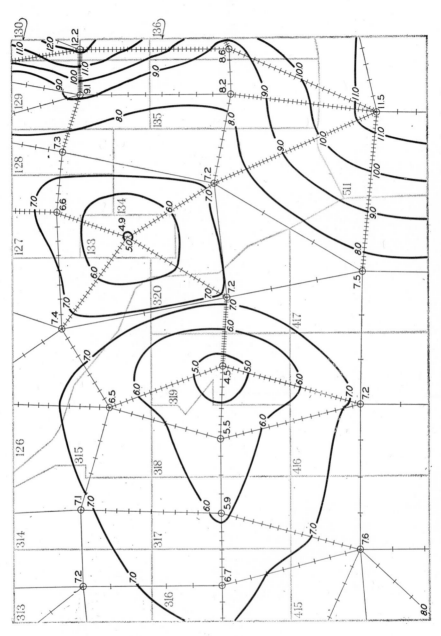

Figure 133. Procedure in Constructing Isolines from Areal Data. See text for further details.

to mean the control points of tracts which have common boundaries. No interpolation axes are drawn between control points of tracts that touch only at corners. Equal linear divisions along interpolation axes have been laid out between each pair of control points. When suitable intervals have been determined—in this case, one school year—smoothed curves are drawn through points of equal value on each interpolation axis.

Maps with Graphic Forms Superimposed

Frequently, various graphic forms such as bars, columns, curves, and pictorial symbols are superimposed on base maps. Where geographic location is of primary importance, a combination of one or more simplified graphs on a map may be very effective. Figure 134 presents the distribution of cattle throughout the world for three different periods by means of seven column charts superimposed on an outline map. The legend in

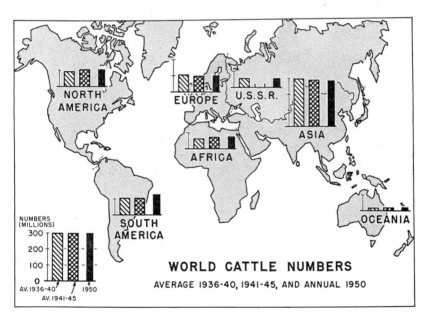

Figure 134. A Simple but Effective Application of the Column Chart and Map.
(From U. S. Office of Foreign Agricultural Relations, *Foreign Agricultural Outlook Charts,* 1951, p. 47.)

the lower left-hand corner of the chart includes a scale, along with an identification of the three columns by means of cross-hatching. In order to provide a more definite and graphic background, the map is stippled, and the various parts of the world for which data are presented are labeled properly.

Figure 135 shows the number of inmigrants and outmigrants as well as net migration by states between 1935 and 1940 by a

IN- AND OUT-MIGRANTS, UNITED STATES:1935 TO 1940

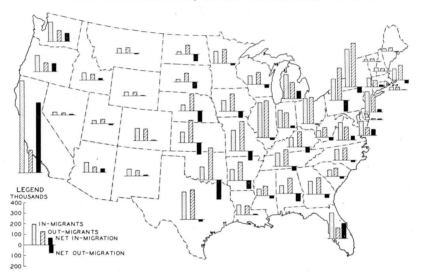

Figure 135. Effective Use of Column Chart in Combination with Map. (From U. S. Bureau of the Census, *Internal Migration: 1935 to 1940*, 1943, p. iv.)

series of column charts drawn on a map of the United States. The first column on the left, which is stippled, shows the number of inmigrants, and the second column, which is crosshatched, indicates the number of outmigrants. The difference between inmigrants and outmigrants is indicated by the black column. If there is an excess of inmigrants, the column is drawn above the base line; if the opposite is true, the column extends below the base line. The legend on the map shows a scale as well as other explanatory information.

(*Figure 136.*) Type, direction, and density of lines portray development of intra-city public transportation in Seattle from 1890 to 1941. (From Calvin F. Schmid, *Social Trends in Seattle*, 1944, p. 65.)

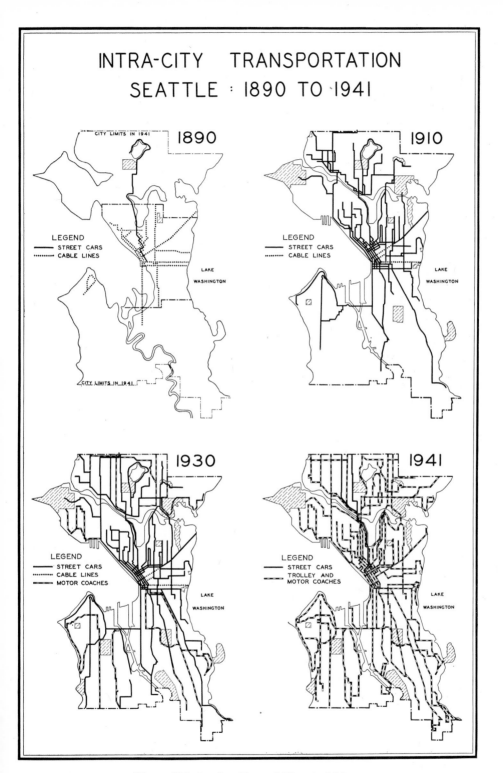

Figure 136. Another Type of Historical Map.

221

In addition to the use of columns, bars, line charts, and other graphs on maps, various symbols and other devices are used to portray movement. Population migration, traffic flow, spread of disease, and diffusion of culture traits or complexes are a few examples of phenomena that can be depicted on maps. Frequently, in flow charts of this kind, the volume of migration is proportional to the thickness of lines of each stream. An example of such a chart, showing population migration within the state of Washington, will be found in Chapter 10 (Figure 201). Similarly, the breadth or height of lines on the typical traffic flow map is determined by the reported number of vehicles at different points on streets and highways (see Figure 202).

The data for Figure 136 also possess dynamic significance, but the emphasis is on historical change rather than on spatial movement. The chronological development of intercity public transportation in Seattle from 1890 to 1941 is shown by a series of four maps on which is superimposed a network of lines indicating the type and routes of public transportation for each of the four years shown on the chart.

CHAPTER 9

Pictorial Charts

Pictorial graphs are used mainly because of their popular appeal. To the technically trained person they add very little or nothing to what might be conveyed by a well-designed conventional graphic form. To the layman or child who has only a slight understanding, perhaps even dislike, for statistical charts, pictorial techniques may be extremely effective.

Because of their simplicity, as well as their dramatic and interest-creating qualities, pictorial charts are far superior to conventional graphic forms as a medium of popular communication. In addition, there seems to be some evidence that facts portrayed in pictorial charts are remembered longer than facts presented in tables or in nonpictorial graphs.

More than for any other type of graphic form, the design and construction of pictorial charts demand both an artistic sense and a thorough understanding of the principles and rationale of charting statistical data. Furthermore, there are more serious pitfalls involved in preparing pictorial charts than there are in most other types of charts. It is important to recognize at the outset that certain types of pictorial forms and techniques violate the basic standards of acceptable form and practice, and these, of course, should be carefully avoided.

In general, there are four basic types of charts in which pictorial symbols are used. The distinguishing criteria for these four types of pictorial charts are purpose and emphasis. It is, of course, correct to say that the fundamental purpose of all types of pictorial symbols is to enhance the popular appeal of a chart, as well as its effectiveness, by means of artistic expression. In some pictorial charts, however, the symbols or pictures may represent units of measurement, whereas in other types they may function merely as embellishment.

223

The four types of pictorial charts are: (1) charts in which the size of the pictorial symbols is made in proportion to the values portrayed; (2) pictorial unit graphs in which each symbol represents a definite and uniform value; (3) cartoon and sketch charts in which the basic graphic form, such as a curve or bar, is portrayed as a picture; and (4) charts with pictorial embellishments ranging from a single pictorial filler to elaborate and detailed pictorial backgrounds.

Pictorial Symbols of Proportionate Size

The least satisfactory type of pictorial chart, but unfortunately one of the most common, is characterized by two or more symbols drawn in proportion to the values represented. For example, in order to compare the sizes of navies of two countries by this method, two symbols of warships drawn in proportion to the respective total tonnage of each navy are placed in juxtaposition. Seemingly a chart of this kind possesses the virtues of simplicity, graphic appeal, and easy comparison. However, such is not the case. It is extremely difficult, if not sometimes impossible, to make intelligible comparisons based on varying sizes of complicated symbols, such as human beings, ships, automobiles, houses, domestic animals, and the like. As indicated in Chapter 4, the basis of comparing geometric forms may be either area or volume.

Figures 137 and 138 illustrate the shortcomings and difficulties inherent in comparing pictorial symbols drawn ostensibly in proportion to the values represented. For example, if one wishes to indicate by means of pictorial symbols of this kind that the magnitude of one category is twice that of another, one symbol can be made twice the height or length of the other. This is precisely what would be done if a bar or column chart were used. The basis of comparison in this instance would be linear or one-dimensional. Suppose this logic were followed in comparing the size of two symbols representing human beings or, in fact, any phenomenon generally conceived as possessing "normal" proportions. The results are portrayed by the symbols A and B in Figure 137. Symbol B is twice the height and twice the area of symbol A, and

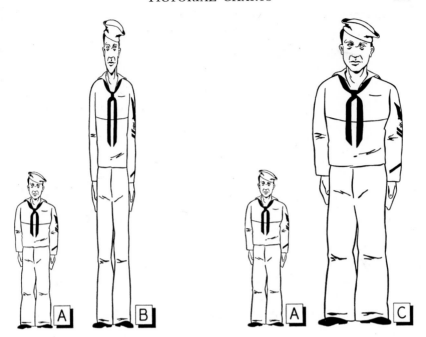

Figure 137. Comparison of Sizes of Pictorial Symbols. *A*, Original symbol. *B*, Original symbol doubled in height only. *C*, Original symbol doubled in both height and width. It will be observed that this symbol is four times as large in area and eight times as large in volume as the original symbol.

Figure 138. Comparison of Sizes of Pictorial Symbols. *A*, Original symbol. *D*, Symbol made twice the area of original symbol. *E*, Symbol is twice the volume of original symbol.

the one-dimensional basis of comparison is logically acceptable. However, symbol *B* does violence to one's artistic sensibilities because of its grotesque elongation. Therefore, in order to satisfy an artistic sense of proportion or normality, symbol *C* was made twice as high and twice as wide as *A*. The consequences are quite apparent, since the size of symbol *C* has been increased four times in area and eight times in volume.[1]

Under the circumstances, in order to avoid distortion or misrepresentation, it might be assumed that the proper solution of a problem of this kind is to reconstruct the symbols on the basis of a more consistent and comparable criterion, such as area or volume. In Figure 138, symbol *D* represents twice the area of symbol *A*, and symbol *E* is twice the size of symbol *A* on the basis of volume. From the points of view of logic and mathematical accuracy, both sets of symbols in this figure are acceptable. From the standpoint of the visual impression, such comparisons are quite incomprehensible. Even to the expert, it would be impossible to judge the size relationships of *A* and *D* or *A* and *E*.

Generally, it can be said that three classes of people construct pictorial charts of this kind: (1) the novice or dilettante who is not aware of the shortcomings of such charts; (2) propagandists who may consider charts of this kind the most effective techniques for disseminating and implanting certain ideas; and (3) the person who possesses an appreciation of the weaknesses of such charts but is convinced, perhaps against his better judgment, that the qualities of simplicity and graphic appeal may outweigh other considerations in popular presentation.

It will be observed from Figure 139 that the sizes of the symbols portraying contributors are drawn in proportion to the number represented. In 1936 there were 415,000 contributors, as compared to 987,000 in 1946. Accordingly, the height of the 1946 symbol is more than twice that of the 1936 symbol. On the basis of area, however, the 1946 symbol is four times that of 1936, and on the basis of volume, eight times that of 1936. The monetary symbols depicted as stacks of coins are one-dimensional and are laid out in approximately correct form.

---

[1] See Chapter 4, "Bar and Column Charts," for a more detailed discussion of the logic and implications of linear, areal, and cubic comparisons.

10-YEAR GROWTH IN FUND SUPPORT

(EXCLUDING WAR YEARS — 43, 44, 45)

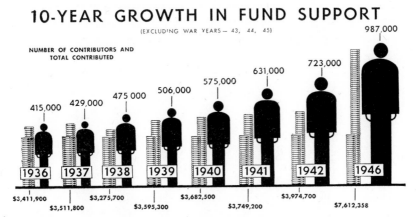

Figure 139. **Another Illustration of a Pictorial Column Chart.** Note distortion of symbols representing contributors. (From *Annual Report,* 1946, Community Fund of Chicago, Inc., p. 10.)

In Figures 140 and 141 similar data are presented in both pictorial and column form. The data represent the average number of police department employees per 1,000 inhabitants for all American cities grouped according to population size. The size of the columns in Figure 141 varies in one dimension, but the pictorial symbols in Figure 140 vary either in two dimensions (area) or three dimensions (volume), depending on interpretation.

Pictorial Symbols Primarily Representing Counting Units

The rationale of the second type of pictorial chart has a much more logical and, from the point of view of graphic presentation, more acceptable basis than the preceding type. Values do not vary according to the size of the symbol. In this type of pictorial chart, each symbol is of uniform size and of specified value. They are primarily counting units. If, for example, a chart of this kind were used to portray income and expenditures of an industrial corporation over a period of years, the basic monetary symbol could be designed to represent $100,000. Accordingly, in constructing the chart, two symbols would indicate $200,000; three symbols, $300,000; four symbols, $400,000; and so on.

The logical relationship between a pictorial chart of this kind and a simple bar or column chart is clear and direct. It will be

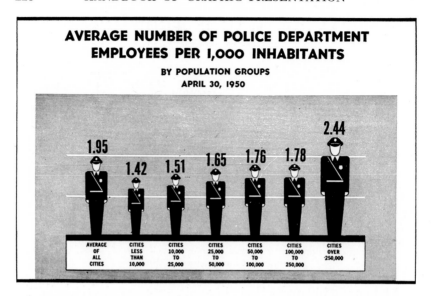

Figure 140. **A Misleading Pictorial Chart.** (From Federal Bureau of Investigation, *Uniform Crime Reports*, Semiannual Bulletin, Vol. XXI, 1950, p. 18.)

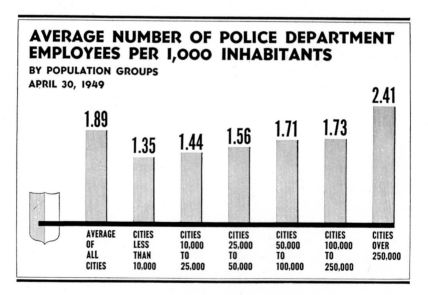

Figure 141. **Data Similar to Those Presented in Figure 140 Shown by a Simple Column Chart.** (From Federal Bureau of Investigation, *Uniform Crime Reports*, Semiannual Bulletin, Vol. XX, 1949, p. 22.)

recalled from Chapter 4 that in the conventional bar and column chart, values are measured by calibrations on a scale. In the bar and column chart, a more or less arbitrarily chosen distance is used to indicate a definite value. For example, if one-fourth inch on the scale is equivalent to 100 people, then one-half inch would indicate 200 people; three-fourths of an inch, 300 people; one inch, 400 people; and so forth. It can be deduced readily that on the pictographic chart each symbol in a fundamental sense

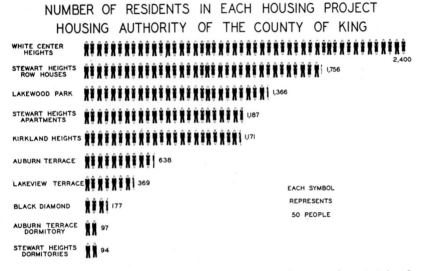

NUMBER OF RESIDENTS IN EACH HOUSING PROJECT
HOUSING AUTHORITY OF THE COUNTY OF KING

Figure 142. An Illustration of a Pictorial Unit Chart. (From Calvin F. Schmid, *Public Housing in King County, Washington: A Progress Report, 1939-1945*, p. 42.)

is analogous to a mensurational unit on the scale of a bar or column chart.

Figure 142 illustrates the essential features of a pictorial unit chart. The symbols representing males and females are, of course, self-explanatory. Each symbol represents 50 people. Accordingly, for example, the row depicting White Center Heights Housing Project, with 2,400 residents, has 48 symbols. Stewart Heights Dormitories, with 94 residents, has slightly less than two symbols. In designing this particular chart, fractions of symbols commensurate with the values represented were used. It is not an uncommon practice, however, to use only whole symbols. In this instance, if a fractional value to be portrayed is 50 percent or more, a whole symbol is added, but if the fractional value is less than 50 per cent, nothing is added.

Historical Background of Pictorial Unit Chart. Perhaps more than any other single person, Dr. Otto Neurath has been responsible for the creation and development of the modern pictographic technique for portraying statistical and other types of data. Dr. Neurath's endeavors date back to about 1923, when he first developed a series of pictorial charts for a housing exhibit in the city of Vienna under the auspices of the Austrian Housing and Garden Plot Association. In 1924, this exhibition was transferred into the famous *Gesellschafts und Wirtschaftsmuseum in Wien.* It was here that he conceived the idea of creating a consistent "visual language" by means of pictographs. In 1930, Neurath's basic work, *Gesellschaft und Wirtschaft,* was published.[2]

It should be pointed out that Neurath was not actually the first person to use the pictorial unit type of chart. In 1914, Willard C. Brinton, in his *Graphic Methods for Presenting Facts* (pp. 39-40), presented illustrations of the pictorial unit chart. In illustrating the rationale of this type of chart, he selected an example showing the increase in passengers carried on American railroads from 1899 to 1911, and he pointed out that "it was not a larger passenger, but more passengers, that the railroads carried." In his *Graphic Presentation,* published in 1939, Brinton reproduces three pictorial unit charts originally published in 1916 and 1917 (pp. 123-24). When Neurath developed his system, he was not aware of Brinton's work. The history of the pictorial unit chart is a good example of what the anthropologists call "parallel invention." Brinton, however, did not pursue the development of the pictorial graph technique beyond his initial exposition.

Besides creating an elaborate pictorial technique of portraying statistical and other data, Neurath directed his energies toward the development of an auxiliary international picture language. The basic symbols of his system were called "isotypes" (I-nterna-

[2] Acknowledgment is made to Dr. Mary L. Neurath for a comprehensive bibliography of Dr. Otto Neurath's work, as well as for special data and offprints of pictorial charts. Perhaps the best example of Dr. Neurath's work in English is *Modern Man in the Making* (New York: Alfred A. Knopf, Inc., 1939).

tional S-ystem O-f TY-pographic P-icture E-ducation). From 1934, when he left Vienna, until his death, Neurath devoted much time to the development of his system and to the philosophy of international picture language.[3]

In addition to Dr. Neurath himself, several of his former associates, particularly Dr. Rudolph Modley, have exerted a strong influence in the popularization and diffusion of the pictorial unit chart in the United States. Dr. Modley's book *How To Use Pictorial Statistics* (1937) has proved to be a very useful manual in this field. Portions of this book have been reproduced, with certain revisions and additions, in another volume, prepared in collaboration with Dyno Lowenstein *et al.*, entitled *Pictographs and Graphs* (1952). Also, these men and their associates in Pictorial Statistics, Inc. (1934) (renamed Pictographic Corporation in 1940), through the preparation of hundreds of pictorial unit charts on a commercial basis for governmental agencies, newspapers, magazines, and books, literally brought this type of chart into virtually every American home.

Basic Principles in Designing a Pictorial Unit Chart. In the construction of a pictorial unit chart, certain basic rules and principles should be observed:

1. The symbols should be self-explanatory. If the chart is concerned with ships, the symbol should be an outline of a ship.
2. All the symbols on the chart should represent a definite unit of value. Each symbol usually represents a convenient sum of individuals.
3. The chart should be made as simple and clear as possible. The number of facts presented should be kept to a minimum.
4. Pictographs should give only an over-all picture; they should not show minute details.
5. Only comparisons should be charted. Isolated facts in themselves cannot be presented effectively by this method.
6. There are many facts that by their very nature cannot be shown pictorially. This is true of large bodies of data that require more refined and elaborate techniques of analysis.[4]

[3] Otto Neurath, *International Picture Language* (London: K. Paul Trench, Trubner & Co., Ltd., 1936), *passim*.

[4] Rudolph Modley, *How To Use Pictorial Statistics* (New York: Harper & Bros., 1937), pp. 12-17; Rudolph Modley, Dyno Lowenstein *et al.*, *Pictographs and Graphs* (New York: Harper & Bros., 1952), pp. 24-28.

LABORERS

FARMERS

FARMERS

MEN

Figure 143. Illustration of Pictorial Symbols. (From files of U. S. Bureau of Agricultural Economics.)

In designing effective pictorial unit charts, the importance of clear, artistic, meaningful symbols cannot be overemphasized. In general, symbols should meet the following standards:

1. A symbol should be drawn in accordance with the principles of good design established by the fine and applied arts.
2. A symbol should be usable in either large or small size; it should be effective on a billboard as well as in a two-column newspaper chart.
3. A symbol must represent a general concept (such as ship, man, child) and not an individual of the species (not the *Queen Mary*, George Washington, or Prince Charles).

SERVICE MEN AND WOMEN

WOMEN

CHILDREN

FAMILY GROUPS

Figure 144. Illustration of Pictorial Symbols. (From files of U. S. Bureau of Agricultural Economics.)

4. A symbol must be clearly distinguishable from every other symbol.
5. A symbol should be interesting.
6. A symbol is essentially a counting unit, and must be clear as such.
7. A symbol must be usable in outline as well as in silhouette.[5]

Figures 143 and 144 are examples of pictorial chart symbols taken from the files of the United States Bureau of Agricultural Economics. The chart-maker has the choice of making his own

[5] Modley, Lowenstein, *et al.*, *op. cit.*, p. 47.

symbols or of purchasing them commercially. If a large number of charts is planned or if the symbols used are distinctive or unique, it is more economical to design and print them than it is to purchase them. Designing and printing can be done very simply, quickly, and inexpensively.

In making a set of symbols, even of different sizes, it actually is necessary to draw only a single symbol. From this single

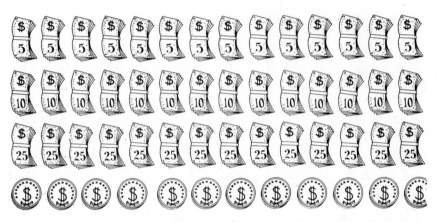

Figure 145. Symbols for Pictorial Unit Chart. See text for details of design and reproduction.

original sketch, a large number of photostatic positive copies of desired size can be made. Generally, for flexibility of design, it is recommended that two or three different sizes of symbols be printed. The symbols thus reproduced can be cut out and aligned in rows with rubber cement on 8½ by 11 inch white mounting board. The completed copy is then printed by photo-offset process in black ink on good quality, smooth finish white paper. According to present prices, 1,000 copies can be printed for $10 to $15. In constructing a pictorial unit chart, rows of symbols can be cut out and mounted with rubber cement on relatively heavy cardboard. Figure 145 shows samples of monetary symbols prepared by the author in accordance with the processes outlined above.[6]

[6] Pictorial symbols are sold by Pictograph Corporation, New York City, and Chart-Pak, Incorporated, Stamford, Conn.

OUTPUT PER MAN-HOUR:

Key to future welfare

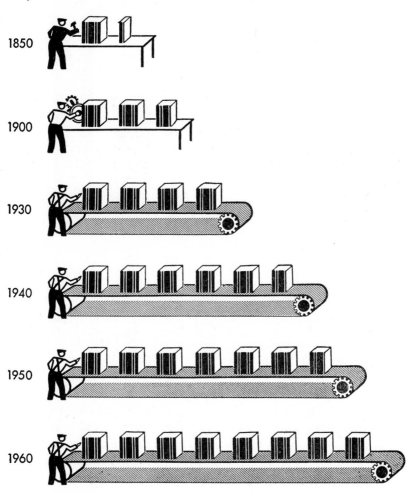

Each symbol represents 20 cents worth of output at 1947 prices

Figure 146. Horizontal Bar Chart in Pictorial Form Portraying Time Series.
(From Thomas R. Carskadon and Rudolf Modley, *U.S.A.: Measure of a Nation,*
1949, p. 99.)

If Gold Again Is Revalued

If the price of Gold were raised from $35 an ounce to $55, it would increase the value of nation's gold stock . . . .

from **$24.6** BILLION

to **$38.6** BILLION

A PROFIT OF
$14
BILLION

COULD BE REALIZED FOR
USE IN AID TO FOREIGN
NATIONS AND FOR
OTHER PURPOSES

Figure 147. Another Example of a Pictorial Chart with a Definite Popular Appeal.
The two columns on the right are based on linear comparisons. The moneybag
symbol on the left, however, does not represent any logical basis for comparison.
(From *U. S. News and World Report,* August 19, 1949, p. 15.)

Figures 146 through 151 illustrate several variations of pictorial unit charts, as well as certain standards and characteristics which must be observed in their design. Figure 146 is basically a simple bar chart in which a pictorial symbol represents the measuring unit. The chart shows the increased output per man hour from 1850 to 1960 as expressed in monetary value. Each symbol represents twenty cents' worth of output at 1947 prices. It will be observed that the symbols are divided to show fractions of the basic unit. The symbol of the workmen makes more visual and comprehensible the significance of the concept "man hour" in relation to the number of unit values produced.

Figure 147 is a simple column chart showing a comparison of two magnitudes and indicating how a revaluation of gold from $35 to $55 an ounce would affect the dollar value of the nation's gold stock. Each pecuniary symbol represents about 1.4 billion dollars. Generally, it is a much more acceptable practice to select values of whole units rather than fractions. Also, it is important that the size of the unit, as well as the spacing of the symbols, be chosen to provide a well-balanced and well-proportioned chart.

Another example of a column type of pictorial chart is shown in Figure 148. Actually, of course, the two series of columns are so arranged as to comprise an effective flow chart showing the sources of the Borden sales dollar and how it is allocated. Accordingly, each division of the respective columns represents one cent. The other pictorial symbols are used as explanatory fillers for the various categories of income and expenditures and to add interest to the chart.

Figure 149 is a one-hundred percent bar chart drawn in pictorial form. It shows the proportion of persons charged with certain crimes who were found guilty and the proportion discharged for one reason or another. The data cover 181 large American cities for the calendar year 1947. The comparisons among the four bars emphasize the similar proportions (rather than marked contrasts) for the two disposition categories. The range of persons found guilty is from 78.0 to 82.4 percent. Normally, the bars should be arranged in rank order according to the largest proportion. Accordingly, the bar representing auto theft should be second, rather than fourth. It is possible that the bar for auto theft was placed next to larceny because, according to criminal law, as well as the definitions in the Uniform Crime Reporting System, auto theft is a form of larceny. As a matter of practice, a quantitative rank order criterion is generally more logical and consistent.

Figure 150 portrays changes in the occupational structure of the population of the United States from 1870 to 1940. The basic graphic form is a sliding one-hundred percent bar chart. (It will be observed that this chart has the same characteristics as Figure 151.) There are four occupational categories shown on the chart: (1) agriculture and forestry, (2) mining and manufacturing, (3) trade and transportation, and (4) clerical and other services. Each type of occupational grouping is indicated by an appropriate symbol. The decreased proportion of farmers

THE BORDEN SALES DOLLAR

WHERE IT CAME FROM...

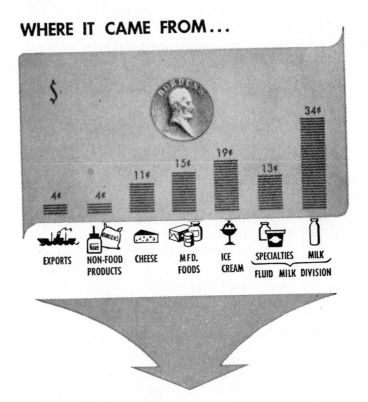

WHERE IT WENT...

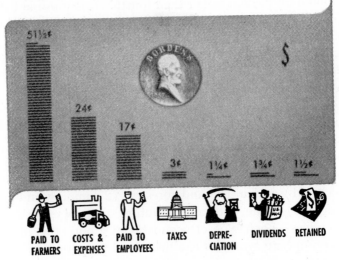

Figure 148. Another Illustration of a Flow Chart in Pictorial Form. (From The Borden Co. Annual Report, 1947, p. 11.)

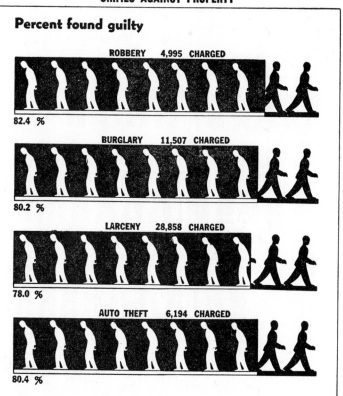

Figure 149. A One-Hundred Percent Bar Chart in Pictorial Form. (From Federal Bureau of Investigation, *Uniform Crime Reports,* Semiannual Bulletin, Vol. XIX, 1948, p. 59.)

OUR JOBS CHANGE

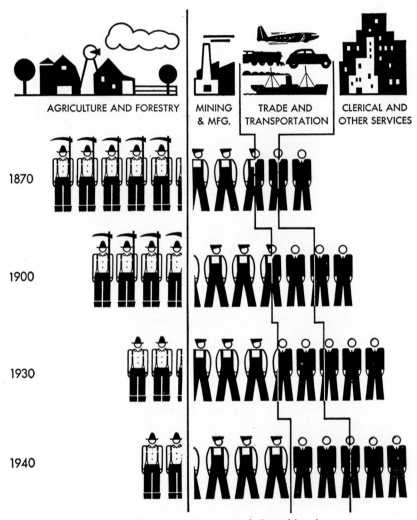

Each symbol represents 10 per cent of all gainful workers

Figure 150. Another Illustration of a One-Hundred Percent Sliding-Bar Chart in Pictorial Form Showing Time Series. (From Thomas R. Carskadon and Rudolf Modley, *U.S.A.: Measure of a Nation*, 1949, p. 11.)

and the increased proportions of the three other categories are the main facts revealed by this chart.

Figure 151 is another form of the sliding bar chart. The chart compares the rural-urban composition of the population of the United States, England and Wales, Germany, and France in 1880

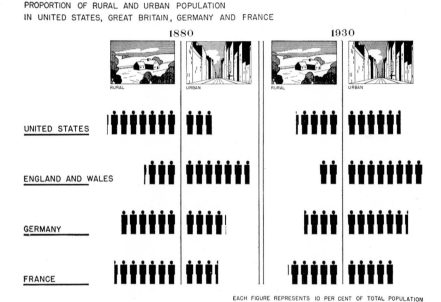

Figure 151. Double One-Hundred Percent Sliding-Bar Chart in Pictorial Form. (From National Resources Committee, *Our Cities: Their Role in the National Economy*, 1937, p. 25.)

and 1930, respectively. The bars on the left are for 1880 and those on the right for 1930. For each series of bars there is a line separating rural and urban proportions. The design of the chart could be improved by arranging the countries in terms of some form of rank order, such as the proportion of the population classified as rural in 1880. This arrangement would still place the United States at the top, but France would be second; Germany, third; and England and Wales, fourth. Also, the lettering of the title should be appreciably larger.

Pictorial Charts in the Form of Sketches or Cartoons

The third type of pictorial chart discussed in this chapter comprises various basic graphic forms designed as completed pictures, sketches, or cartoons. Usually charts of this kind are relatively simple, although occasionally they may be very elabo-

Figure 152. A Pictorial Chart in the Form of One-Hundred Percent Band Chart. It emphasizes the farmer's share of the consumer's food dollar from 1913 to 1951. (From U. S. Bureau of Agricultural Economics, *1952 Agricultural Outlook Charts*, p. 34.)

rate. Figure 152 is an example of this type of chart. It is a one-hundred percent band or stratum chart drawn as a dollar bill. The pictorial fillers at the bottom are an attractive but not essential part of the graph itself. The vertical and horizontal axes of the band chart, with scale points and scale figures, are clearly indicated. The dividing line representing the respective proportions of "marketing charges" and "farmer's share" is indicated as a tear in the dollar bill.

HOW WE USED THE $45,182,063 RECEIVED FROM OUR CUSTOMERS

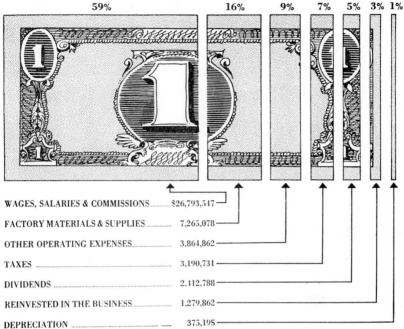

| 59% | 16% | 9% | 7% | 5% | 3% | 1% |

WAGES, SALARIES & COMMISSIONS............$26,793,517

FACTORY MATERIALS & SUPPLIES...............   7,265,078

OTHER OPERATING EXPENSES......................   3,864,862

TAXES   3,190,731

DIVIDENDS   2,112,788

REINVESTED IN THE BUSINESS..................   1,279,862

DEPRECIATION   375,195

Figure 153. A One-Hundred Percent Bar Chart in Pictorial Form. (From Royal
Typewriter Co., Inc., Annual Report, 1949, p. 4.)

Figure 153 is also drawn as a dollar bill, but the basic graphic
form which it represents is a one-hundred percent component-
bar chart. The various components, as well as the relative and
absolute proportions of the total which they represent, are clearly
indicated by explanatory legends and corresponding amounts in
both dollars and percentages.

Figure 154 is similar to Figure 153 in that it is a one-
one-hundred percent component type of chart. The divisions in
Figure 154 are arranged vertically rather than horizontally, thus
classifying it as a column chart. There are two weaknesses in the
chart which should be pointed out: (1) The actual one-hundred
percent column comprises only that portion of the can below the
rim around the shoulder of the can, whereas the portion above
the rim, which is approximately one-third of the total height of

the can, is supposed to be excluded with reference to the total or component values. Visually this may be very confusing. (2) A better balanced chart might have been achieved if the largest components were placed at the bottom rather than at the top. Pictorial charts of this type have their place in graphic presentation, but extreme care must be taken to avoid optical illusions and other types of distortions.

Figure 154. A Simple One-Hundred Percent Column Chart Presented in Pictorial Form. One feature of this chart which may tend to be misleading is the fact that only the part of the can below the handles actually represents the one-hundred percent total. (From H. W. Gilbertson, *Educational Exhibits*, U. S. Department of Agriculture, Misc. Publ. No. 634, p. 24.)

Figure 155 is a dramatic illustration of a pictorially designed column chart. The columns drawn in pseudo-perspective projection with shading and jagged edges were designed, of course, to represent stone. The cloud around the upper portion of the tallest column, as well as the pictorial fillers representing Uncle Sam, add to the appeal as well as the effectiveness of the design. The horizontal scale figures and the values of each column are clearly indicated. This figure is an excellent example of the third type of pictorial chart discussed in this chapter.

Gross Federal, State, and Local Debt

END OF SELECTED FISCAL YEARS 1902-1949

BILLIONS

$273.6

$92.1

$39.1

$33.2

$3.4 $5.7

1902   1912   1922   1932   1942   1949

Figure 155. Pictorial Column Chart Drawn in Pseudo-Perspective Projection.
(From The Tax Foundation, *Facts and Figures on Government Finance, 1950-
1951*, p. 178.)

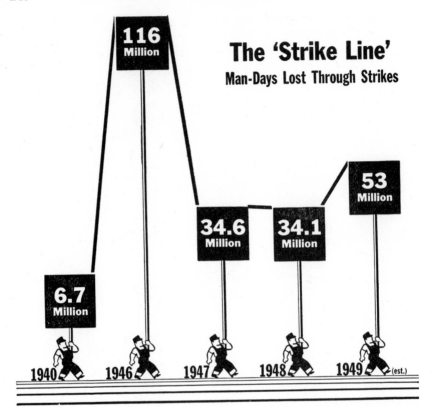

Figure 156. The Use of Pictures to Popularize Statistical Data. Basically the chart has features of both the column chart and the arithmetic line chart. (From *U. S. News and World Report*, February 10, 1950, cover page.)

In the next chapter, there are several examples of charts of this type. They are drawn either in axonometric, oblique, or perspective projection. Logically, these charts could have been discussed in the present chapter, but because of the special emphasis on projection techniques rather than on pictorial symbols, they were included in Chapter 10. In constructing charts such as Figure 155, it is essential to possess a thorough understanding of basic projection techniques, as well as a knowledge of chart design and artistic ability.

A pictorial chart with characteristics of both the arithmetic line graph and the column chart is presented in Figure 156. The chart portrays the number of man days lost through strikes from 1940 to 1949. Although the chart might be considered reasonably effective, it does not conform to the highest standards of graphic presentation. First, the values on the vertical scale are apparently gauged from the top of the left hand of the workman to the bottom edge of the sign. In other words, the base line is an imaginary line drawn horizontally across the top of the left hand of each symbol. Second, the approximate squares representing signs, as well as the worker symbols, are of uniform height, respectively, which give a distorted impression of relative yearly values. For example, the distance from the bottom of the pictorial symbol to the top of the sign for the 1940 figure is over one-fourth the height of the corresponding height for 1946. Actually, of course, 6.7 million is less than one-seventeenth of 116 million. Third, if this figure is considered basically a line chart, then the six-year break between 1940 and 1946 gives an erroneous impression. Moreover, the curve should not connect the top of the signs, since, as was pointed out above, the vertical values are not represented at those levels. Fourth, if the design of this figure is thought of as a column chart, then correct comparisons would be based on the length of the poles attached to the signs.

In the light of these remarks, it is obvious that the lay reader could be profoundly confused if asked for a critical evaluation of the chart and the data which it purports to portray. Needless to say, charts of this kind should be avoided.

Charts with Pictorial Embellishments

The fourth type of pictorial chart discussed in this chapter represents more or less conventional graphic forms embellished with various kinds of pictures or symbols ranging from simple fillers to comparatively elaborate and detailed photographic or artistic backgrounds.

It will be recalled that a few of the charts presented in the preceding chapters were embellished with relatively simple pictorial fillers. Additional illustrations of this kind will be found in Figures 157, 158, and 159. The interpretation and significance

Prices received by farmers for commodities – 1914-22 – 1939-47

Figure 157. An Arithmetic Line Chart with Simple Pictorial Sketches Superimposed. Techniques of this kind can add much human interest to statistical charts. (From H. W. Gilbertson, *Educational Exhibits,* U. S. Department of Agriculture, Misc. Publ. No. 634, p. 25.)

of these charts are apparent. They are designed to arouse interest and provide visual association and emphasis to certain facts presented in the chart. The humorous chart, such as is indicated by the fillers in Figure 157, if properly done, may reinforce the appeal and influence the technique of this kind. The series of flow charts (Figures 160, 161, 162, and 163) also demonstrate the dramatic impact of pictorial symbols in creating popular interest and clarifying facts and relationships.

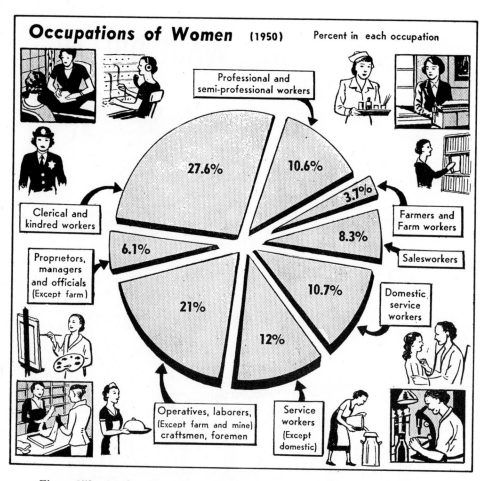

Occupations of Women (1950)   Percent in each occupation

Professional and semi-professional workers

27.6%

10.6%

3.7%

Clerical and kindred workers

Farmers and Farm workers

6.1%

8.3%

Proprietors, managers and officials (Except farm)

Salesworkers

21%

10.7%

Domestic service workers

12%

Operatives, laborers, (Except farm and mine) craftsmen, foremen

Service workers (Except domestic)

Figure 158. Another Illustration of the Pie Chart with Pictorial Fillers Symboliz-ing the Various Occupational Categories. Also, note the separation of sectors which helps to emphasize quantitative differences among groupings as well as to facilitate comparisons. (Part of a *Chicago Sun-Times* "Graphichart" prepared by Tom P. Barrett.)

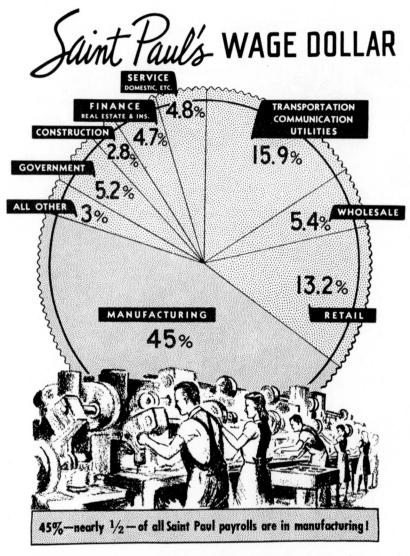

Figure 159. A Pie Chart in Which the Sector Representing Manufacturing Is Emphasized by a Pictorial Illustration. (From Saint Paul Assn. of Commerce, *An Invitation to Industry,* p. 6.)

SCRAP CYCLE IN STEELMAKING

Showing Some of the Principal Scrap Sources

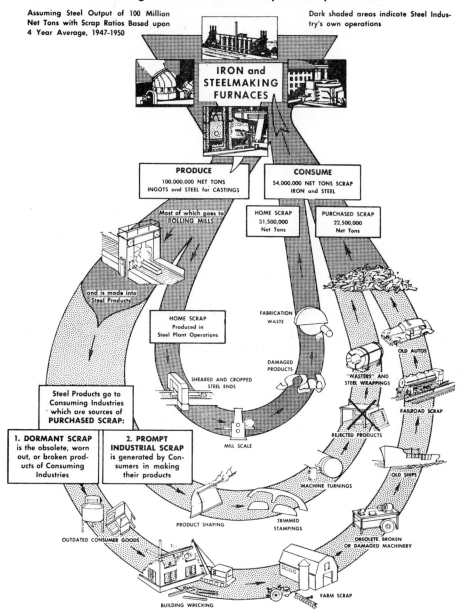

Figure 160. An Illustration of a Flow Chart Embellished with Pictorial Sketches.
(Prepared by American Iron and Steel Institute)

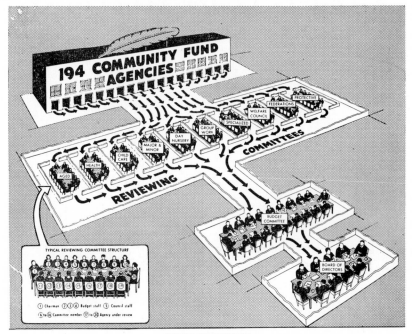

, PATTERN FOR BUDGETING
Citizen participation: a guarantee of equitable distribution of welfare funds

Figure 161. A Pictorial Projection Flow Chart. (From *Our Common Welfare,*
May, 1949, p. 11.)

The flow charts in Figures 160, 161, 162, and 163 are also excellent illustrations of how pictorial symbols and sketches can be an extremely valuable addition to charts of this kind. Figure 161 is drawn in perspective. The application of perspective and other projection techniques to graphic presentation is discussed in the following chapter.

Figures 160, 161, and 162 emphasize various stages and processes typical of the flow chart. Figure 160 illustrates the main sources of scrap metal in steel manufacturing. Figures 161 and 162 portray the successive steps in the development of budgets and allocation of funds to Community Fund agencies in the city of Chicago. Figure 163 shows the various steps recommended for improving the Chicago Police Department. It will be noted that the various elements of this chart do not follow a definite sequence of steps such as is indicated in Figures 160, 161, and 162.

Figure 162. An Example of a Pictorial Flow Chart. (From Community Fund of Chicago, Inc., *The Facts for 1947*, p. 3.)

What Should Be Done to Get Better Police in Chicago

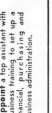

Enforce rule that policemen must pass a marksmanship test six times a year. Make firing ranges fit for use.

Get maximum efficiency from every employee. After that increase the force if necessary.

Give police modern steel shields, better bullet-proof vests and an armored car to help save their lives.

Eliminate intense rivalry between district police and bureau men to get better co-ordination.

Increase police salaries and shorten waiting time for promotion. (*Some patrolmen wait as long as 11 years for promotion.*)

Consolidate police districts by reducing the present 39 districts to 15. (*Cleveland cut 22 districts to 6.*)

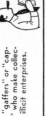

The recommendations listed here, made by the Chicago Crime Commission, civic leaders and authorities on police administration, were outlined in a series, "What's Wrong With Our Police?" published last week in The SUN-TIMES.

Take police out from under political domination and control so that policemen can do their duty without fear of a ward heeler's retaliation.

Restore system of supervising captains or divisional inspectors to keep district captains on their toes.

Appoint a top assistant with business training to set up a financial, purchasing and business administration.

Eliminate "gaffers" or "captain's men" who make collections from illicit enterprises.

Use two-fisted discipline by police commissioner to get better results from subordinates who ignore rules.

Replace policemen at school crossings with women, and replace police clerical workers with civilians.

Maintain a school of instruction with refresher courses for all grades and ranks. (*Only school now in operation is for sergeants*).

Move police commissioner's office from the City Hall to Police Headquarters for better control of department.

Figure 163. **A Special Application of the Flow Chart.** Well designed with strong popular appeal. Each division of the chart represents a separate step in a recommended program for improving the Chicago Police Department. (Part of a *Chicago Sun-Times* "Graphichart" prepared by Tom P. Barrett.)

254

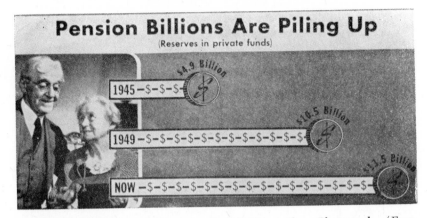

Figure 164. Pictorial Unit Chart in Combination with a Photograph. (From *United States News and World Report,* September 28, 1951, p. 50.)

Figures 164, 165, 166, and 167 illustrate how conventional graphic forms can be superimposed on more or less elaborate pictorial backgrounds. No specific rules can be laid down in the design of charts of this kind. Figure 164 is a simple pictorial unit chart on an appropriate photographic background. The backgrounds for the charts in Figure 165 are comparatively simple pen and ink sketches. On the other hand, the pictorial backgrounds for Figures 166 and 167 are elaborate and detailed wash drawings. Additional labor costs involved in the preparation of charts of this kind may be an important consideration, regardless of the graphic advantages which these charts might possess.

U.S. Meat Supply Large ; More Expected in 1951

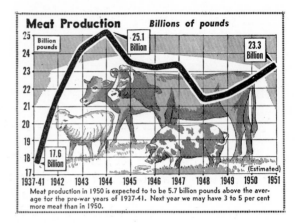

Figure 165. **Illustrations of Rectilinear Coordinate Graphs Superimposed on Pictorial Backgrounds.** Note that the ordinal scale values for *A*, Meat Production, range from 17 to 25 billion pounds; the corresponding values for *B*, Meat Consumption, are 130 to 155 pounds. (Part of a *Chicago Sun-Times* "Graphichart" prepared by Tom P. Barrett.)

Figure 166. Column Chart with Background Symbolizing Data Portrayed. For creating popular appeal or for emphasizing certain factors, a chart superimposed on a photomosaic, photomontage, or similar print may be found very effective. In the original publication the columns were shown in shaded pale blue color. Also, note the two symbols in the upper left-hand corner representing rural and urban populations which graphically emphasize the urbanization process. In this connection see the discussion in this chapter on areal and cubic symbols. (From U. S. Public Health Service, *Water Pollution in the United States*, 1951, p. 12.)

GROWTH OF INDUSTRY

INDEX OF RISING INDUSTRIAL PRODUCTION IN THE
UNITED STATES (1935-39 average equals 100)

Figure 167. Another Illustration of a Chart Superimposed on Detailed Artistic Background. The curve in the original publication was printed in pale blue ink. (From U. S. Public Health Service, *Water Pollution in the United States*, 1951, p. 13.)

CHAPTER 10

Projection Techniques in Graphic Presentation

The purpose of this chapter is to discuss the techniques, as well as the advantages and limitations, of presenting certain basic types of statistical charts in three-dimensional pictorial form. In recent years it has become common practice to portray rectilinear coordinate graphs, pie charts, bar and column charts, maps, and other types of graphs and charts in axonometric, oblique, or perspective projection. In fact, at the present time the popularity of this form of presentation seems to have surpassed, whether permanently or temporarily, the pictorial unit chart so extensively used during the decades of the 1930's and 1940's.[1] Projection charts, with their depth and other picturelike qualities, unquestionably possess definite popular appeal. It will be found, however, that a large proportion of three-dimensional charts are distorted and misleading because the designer has little or no understanding either of the basic principles of graphic presentation or of projection techniques.[2]

The specialist in graphic techniques should constantly strive to improve the design of charts by presenting them in more pleasing and intelligible form. Oblique, axonometric, and perspective projection have proved especially valuable in attaining these objectives. However, in attempting to develop new graphic

---

[1] See Chapter 9, "Pictorial Charts," for a detailed discussion of the pictorial unit chart.

[2] To date virtually nothing has been published on the application of the principle of the various forms of three-dimensional pictorial projection to graphic presentation. There are two useful but brief articles dealing with special problems of three-dimensional presentation, both written by the same author, Kenneth W. Haemer. These articles are: "The Perils of Perspective," *The American Statistician*, Vol. 1 (December, 1947), p. 19; and "The Pseudo Third Dimension," *ibid.*, Vol. 5 (October, 1951), p. 28.

forms and techniques, standards of precision, good practice, or authenticity of impression should never be sacrificed.

The design of three-dimensional pictorial graphic forms should be based on accepted conventionalized principles of (1) axonometric, (2) oblique, and (3) perspective projection. Sometimes artists may delineate reasonably satisfactory charts purely on an

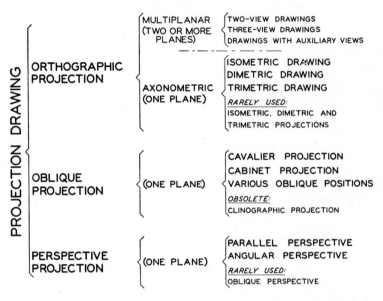

Figure 168. A Simplified Classification of Projection Techniques. The types of projections most frequently used in graphic presentation are indicated in bold lettering. (Classification based on Thomas E. French, *A Manual of Engineering Drawing*, 1941, p. 87.)

impressionistic basis, but inherent in this practice is the danger of distortion and inaccuracy.

The term "projection" as used in this discussion pertains to certain widely used techniques in engineering, architecture, and art for describing the shape and size of objects. The various forms of projection and their relationships to one another are summarized in schematic form in Figure 168. It will be observed that the major interest of the graphic specialist is in certain forms of one-plane pictorial projection techniques, rather than the customary orthographic projection where at least two or three planes are used to describe three dimensions of an object, such as the front, side, and top views of architectural or engineering drawings.

The differences among the various types of uniplanar pictorial projection are determined in one of two ways: (a) in the relation of the object to the plane of projection or picture plane, or (b) in the angular relation of the lines (projectors) along which points of the object are projected to the plane of projection.[3] Detailed consideration will be given to the implications of these criteria, particularly the manner in which they influence projection form and the resultant type of picture. Figure 169 illustrates how a cube looks when drawn in various types of axonometric, oblique, and perspective projection.

Axonometric Projection

To begin with, for the sake of simplicity and clarity, a few basic terms used in the following presentation should be defined: (1) "Planes of projection" are planes or surfaces on which the various views of the object or picture are projected (drawn), and it is the revolving of these planes that determines the location or arrangement of the view.[4] The plane of projection as used in this discussion is analogous to the screen on which a motion picture is projected. (2) The "projection" of a picture (or drawing) is merely the projection of a myriad of points that form a familiar pattern which is referred to as the "picture" or "view." [5] (3) "Projectors" are imaginary lines or visual rays drawn through every point of the figure intersecting a given plane of projection, thus forming a picture. Projectors may be parallel or they may converge according to some other rule of geometric projection.

Axonometric projection is a form of orthographic projection in which one plane of projection is used. In axonometric projection, an object such as a rectangular solid is turned and then tilted so that with reference to the picture plane three faces in a single view are observed; the projectors are perpendicular to the pic-

[3] H. D. Orth, R. R. Worsencroft, and H. B. Doke, *Basic Engineering Drawing* (New York: The Ronald Press Co., 1946), p. 265.

[4] William Wirt Turner, Carson P. Buck, and Hugh P. Ackert, *Basic Engineering Drawing* (New York: The Ronald Press Co., 1950), pp. 76-88.

[5] *Ibid.*

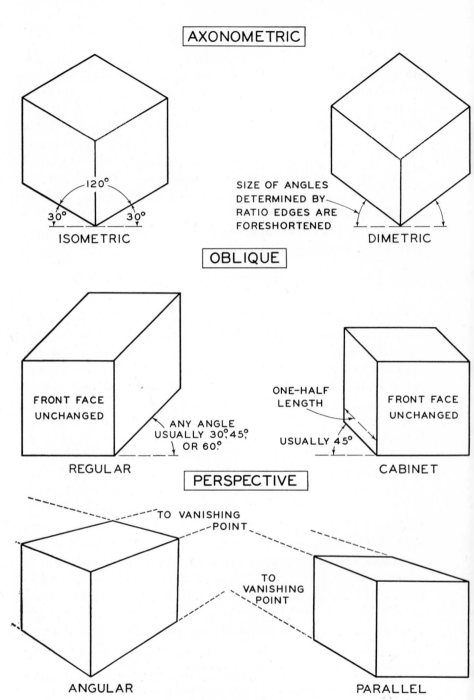

Figure 169. Simplified Illustrations of Types of One-Plane Pictorial Projection
Used in Graphic Presentation.

262

ture plane (Figure 170).[6] Actually, of course, an object may be placed in any number of positions relative to the picture plane, making it possible to construct an infinite number of views with

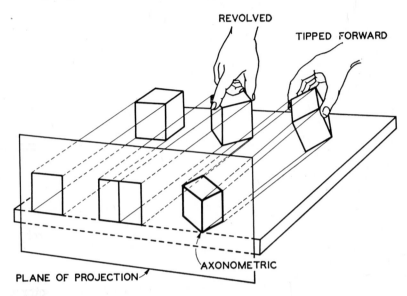

Figure 170. Axonometric Projection.

respect to general proportions, length of edges, and sizes of angles. A few of these possible positions have been classified into the following major divisions of axonometric projection: (1) isometric, (2) dimetric, and (3) trimetric. Again it should be emphasized that the position of the object relative to the plane of projection determines whether the projection is one of these three specific types.

Isometric Projection. The most common, as well as the simplest, form of axonometric projection is isometric (equal-measure) projection. In isometric projection, for example, the three edges of a cube forming the corner nearest the plane of projection are so placed as to make equal angles with the plane of projection. The angles formed by these edges are represented by 120° angles

[6] Figures 170, 175, and 176 have been redrawn from Warren J. Luzadder, *Fundamentals of Engineering Drawing* (New York: Prentice-Hall, Inc., 1950; copyright 1943, 1946), pp. 94, 95, 446.

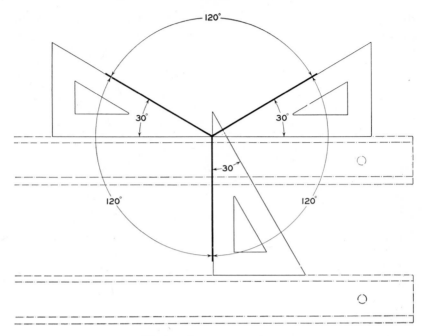

Figure 171. Isometric Axes.

in isometric projection. (See Figures 171 and 172.) Therefore, when one edge is vertical on the picture plane, the other two are represented by lines at 30° to the horizontal, to right and left, respectively. In order to place a cube in isometric projection it is necessary for the cube to be so aligned that the projector of the front corner extends through the rear corner.[7]

The three faces of the cube in isometric position are foreshortened equally, which means, of course, that all of the edges of the cube are of equal length on the projection. Isometric lines (any line parallel to an edge of the cube) are foreshortened approximately 82/100 (.8165) of their length (Figure 173). In order to make an isometric projection theoretically correct, Figure 173 clearly shows how an isometric scale can be constructed by a simple graphic method from a regular scale. Also, the difference between a "true isometric projection" and an "isometric

[7] Orth, Worsencroft, and Doke, *op. cit.*, pp. 266-70; Charles H. Schumann, *Technical Drafting* (New York: Harper & Bros., 1940), pp. 314-23.

drawing" will be found in this same illustration. The isometric drawing is larger than the isometric projection. The proportions, however, are the same, and accordingly have no effect on pictorial projection. In actual practice, objects are seldom drawn in true isometric projection because the use of an isometric scale is both inconvenient and impractical.

Construction of Isometric Drawings. The simplest procedure in laying out charts in isometric drawing is to use commercially

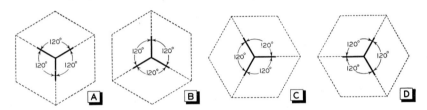

Figure 172. Various Positions of Isometric Axes.

printed isometric paper which is available at engineering and architectural supply stores. Also, a 30° by 60° triangle or isometric protractor can be used. For laying out circles in isometric projection, the simplest method is to use one of the commercially prepared templates, which come in different sizes. If a template is not available, the four-centered approximation technique can be followed.[8]

Figure 174 shows the manner in which two histograms may be constructed for comparative purposes on isometric paper. The data indicate the incidence of rheumatic fever according to income and relief status for new and for totally disabled cases.

The width and position of the columns can be determined readily from the ruled lines on the paper. The height of each column is based on a scale selected to give a well-proportioned chart. The shading and stippling of the columns, the designation of the class intervals, the labeling of values represented by each column, and the description of the two series of data are also necessary features of the chart.

[8] See, for example, Turner, Buck, and Ackert, *op. cit.*, pp. 299-301.

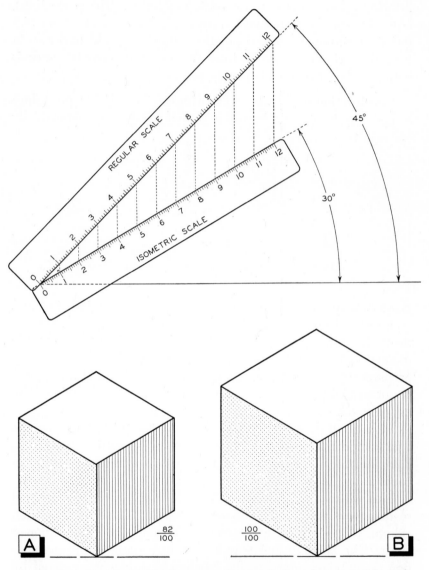

Figure 173. The Relationship Between a Regular Scale and an Isometric Scale.
A, Cube is constructed by means of an Isometric Scale and is known as a true
Isometric "Projection." B, Cube is constructed according to the conventional
method in which all foreshortening is disregarded. It is called an Isometric
"Drawing."

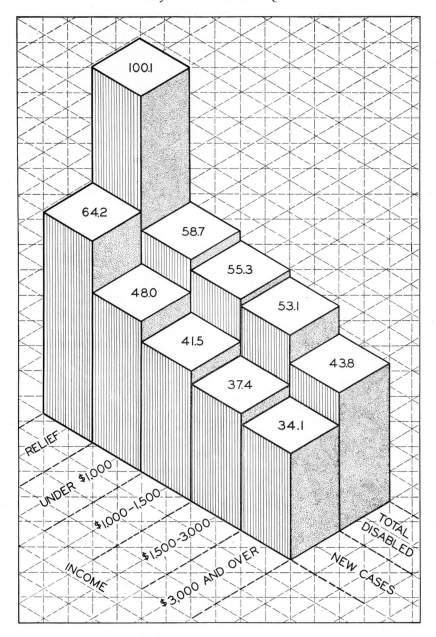

Figure 174. Double Histogram Plotted on Isometric Paper. (Redrawn from Selwyn D. Collins, *The Incidence of Rheumatic Fever as Recorded in General Morbidity Surveys of Families,* Special Supplement No. 198, *Public Health Reports,* 1947, p. 39.)

Dimetric Projection. It will be recalled that in isometric projection all three faces, or surfaces, of an object are equally inclined and that all edges of an object are equally foreshortened. In dimetric projection, only two of the faces, or surfaces, are equally foreshortened. In laying out the axes in dimetric projection, these facts must be kept in mind. For example, a cube is placed in such a position that two of the edges converging at the first corner are foreshortened at the same ratio, and the other is foreshortened at a different ratio. In dimetric projection the object may be revolved into many defined positions and, accordingly, an infinite number of dimetric projections is possible.

Although the dimensions of the original object are frequently not specified in axonometric drawings, the positions resulting in dimetric projection may be detected readily through the relationships of the angles of the axes to the base line. If, as is usually the case, one of the axes is vertical, the drawing is dimetric if the other two axes make equal angles with the base line and are not 30°. (It will be remembered that the special case in which these angles are 30° is the isometric position.) The drawing is also dimetric if one axis is vertical and the angle formed by the axis, which is to be in equal scale with the vertical, is 90° minus two times the other angle. In any other positions the drawing is trimetric.

It will be recalled that a distinction was made between isometric projection and isometric drawing. Similarly, the same general distinction obtains in both dimetric and trimetric projection. Dimetric drawing, for example, has the same shape as a dimetric projection, but the ratio between the object size and the projection is prescribed, whereas this relation does not hold between the object size and the drawing scales.

Trimetric Projection. The axes in trimetric projection are determined by placing the cube in such a position that all three edges converging at the front corner are foreshortened at different ratios. Each of the three axes thus constructed makes a different angle with the plane of projection. Also, this means that the scales of the edges are all different. Trimetric is the most general form of axonometric projection. Whenever an object is not placed in the position with respect to the projection plane which defines an isometric or dimetric projection, the resulting projection is trimetric. It will be observed from the illustrations in this chapter that the most common forms of axonometric drawing can be classified as trimetric. This fact can be attributed to the impressionistic procedure followed by many designers in laying out charts of this kind. Apparently no rigorous, objective standards of projection were followed, and since the trimetric form is most general, it is understandable why charts of this type when designed subjectively are not isometric or dimetric.

Oblique Projection

In the three forms of axonometric projection—isometric, dimetric and trimetric—the projectors are at right angles to the picture planes, but in oblique projection the projectors strike the plane of projection obliquely. In other words, in oblique projection the angle of the projectors is less than 90° (Figure 175).

In oblique projection, three faces of an object are visible, the largest dimension being parallel to the picture plane. Two of the axes are always at right angles to each other, and the third may be at any angle to the horizontal, 30° or 45° being generally used.

Oblique projection "is more flexible and has the following advantages over isometric drawing: (1) circular or irregular outlines on the front face show in their true shape; (2) distortion can be reduced by foreshortening along the receding axis; and (3) a greater choice is permitted in the selection of the positions of the axes." [9]

If the angle of obliquity of projectors to the picture plane is 45°, it is called *cavalier* projection. This is the most widely used type of oblique projection. In order to reduce the apparent distortion and appearance of excessive thickness of oblique projection, the actual length of the receding or lateral axis of the object is often shortened one-half. Oblique projection with modification in this manner is called *cabinet* projection.

In cabinet projection, the receding axis may be any angle, but is usually 30° or 45°. Figure 169 illustrates regular oblique projection, as well as the special cabinet type of oblique projection.

[9] Luzadder, *op. cit.,* p. 435.

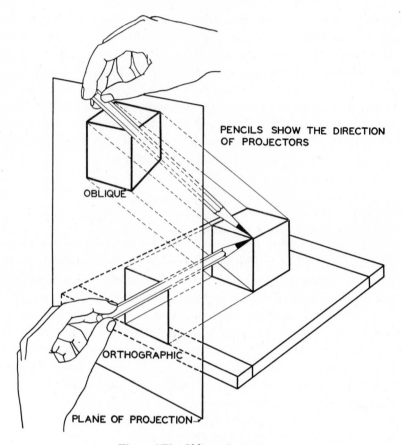

Figure 175. Oblique Projection.

Perspective

Of the several forms of pictorial projection, perspective is perhaps the most realistic. In perspective projection, an object is represented as it is seen by the eye of an observer located at a finite distance from the object which is known as a *station point*. If one were to look at an object through a window and trace an outline of the object on the glass, the basis of the projection on the glass would be perspective. In this illustration, the window-pane represents the picture plane. In axonometric and oblique projections the projectors are parallel, but in perspective the projectors converge to a station point.

There are two types of perspective projection: parallel, or one-point, and angular, or two-point. In parallel or one-point perspective the principal face of the object is placed parallel to the picture plane. There is one set of parallel lines that vanish at a single point.

In angular or two-point perspective, the object is so placed that its vertical faces are at an angle of less than 90° to the picture plane. There are two sets of parallel lines, one for each face,

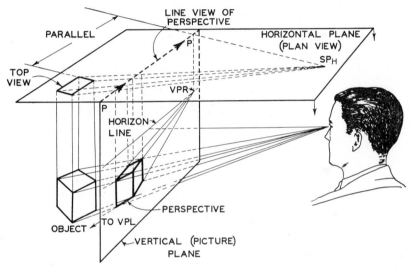

Figure 176. Angular Perspective Projection.

which require two vanishing points. Figure 169 illustrates essential characteristics of the two basic types of perspective.

A more detailed portrayal of angular perspective will be found in Figure 176. In order to be proficient in perspective drawing, the student should familiarize himself with the meaning and application of such concepts as (1) point of sight or station point, (2) picture plane, (3) horizon, (4) horizon plane, (5) vanishing point, (6) vanishing line, (7) ground line, (8) ground plane, and (9) cone of vision.

The actual construction of a simple column chart in angular perspective is illustrated in Figure 177. An examination of this illustration will clearly convey some of the essential implications of perspective techniques in designing and interpreting statistical charts.

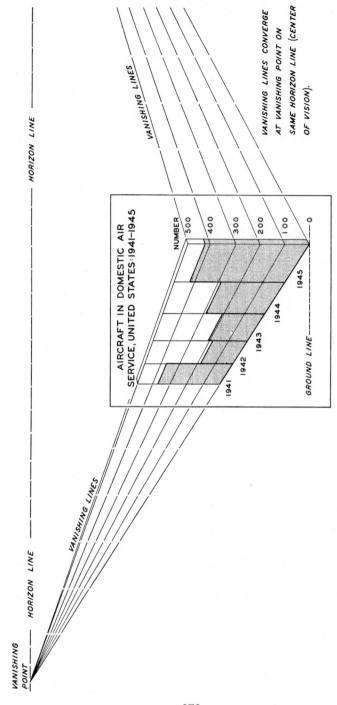

Figure 177. Basic Concepts and Techniques in Perspective Projection. (Data represent number of scheduled domestic aircraft in the United States. From U. S. Bureau of the Census, *Historical Statistics of the United States: 1789-1945*, 1949, p. 224.)

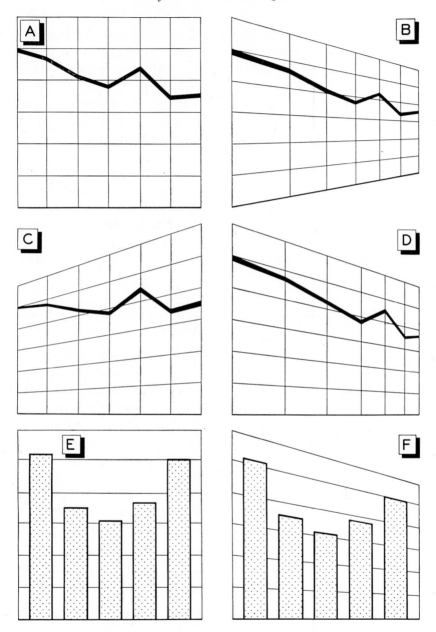

Figure 178. Comparison of Conventional Charts, Forms (A) and (E), with Perspective and Pseudo-Perspective Variations.

The simplest and most efficient procedure in drawing charts in perspective is to make use of such mechanical aids as perspective lined paper, perspective indicator pads (such as Cassel), perspective linead (such as Dietzgen), and a perspective plastic template (such as Bruning's "Perspectric").

Perspective projection as applied to graphic presentation possesses serious limitations. Charts constructed in perspective are generally distorted; they do not portray exact distance, shape, or size. Figure 178 shows an arithmetic line chart and a column chart drawn in conventional form along with variations in perspective and quasi-perspective form. The resultant distortions of the perspective and quasi-perspective projections are obvious, and charts of this particular kind should be avoided.[10] Wherever perspective projection is used, extreme caution should be taken to see that it enhances the value of the chart and does not create distortion or misrepresentation.

Additional Illustrations of Charts Drawn in Various Types of Projection

It will be observed from the illustrations in the following pages that most of the basic graphic forms, such as arithmetic line charts, band and silhouette charts, bar and column graphs, pie charts, frequency polygons and histograms, and maps, have been recast into axonometric drawing, oblique projection, and perspective. In addition, some of the examples do not conform precisely to theoretically correct standards of projection. Nevertheless, they may produce the desired effects. Rather than use merely impressionistic procedures in designing charts in one-plane pictorial projection, it is recommended that the theory and techniques of projection be mastered and followed carefully.

Examples of Charts in Axonometric Projection. Figure 179 is an example of a multiple one-hundred percent bar chart in axonometric drawing (trimetric drawing).[11] There are three compo-

[10] Figure 178 is based on ideas from Kenneth W. Haemer, "The Perils of Perspective," op. cit.

[11] Because of the manner in which several of the following charts have been drawn, it has been difficult to determine the precise form of projection. Accordingly, the designations for such charts represent merely "approximate" descriptions.

nents for each bar showing distribution of the International Harvester Company receipts for 1941, 1947, and 1948 (1) to employees, (2) to stockholders, and (3) to funds for use in business. The divisions of the bars are differentiated properly and explained by figures, legends, shading, and pictorial symbols. A slight optical illusion may be observed in the bar for 1941; this bar seems to be thicker at the right end, but actually this is not the case.

It will be observed from Figure 180 that the type of projection used is similar to that in Figure 179. The chart form, however, is very different. Figure 180 can be described fundamentally as an arithmetic line chart or possibly a rectangular silhouette chart. The data portray variations in net income and cash dividends for the International Harvester Company from 1940 to 1949. The basic features of the chart conform to accepted standards of graphic presentation, and the projection form seems to possess definite popular appeal.

It is both interesting and significant to compare Figure 180 with Figure 181, since they both represent identical graphic forms but different types of axonometric projection. Figure 181 is in isometric drawing, whereas it will be recalled that Figure 180 is in trimetric drawing.

Figure 182 is an effective chart design for comparing two temporal series of data. One series covers net sales and the other net income for the period 1946 to 1950 for the Avco Manufacturing Corporation. The projection used in the chart can be classified as dimetric. Unfortunately, the vertical scales in this chart are not comparable, with the result that the first impression gained is misleading. Just why the designer of this chart used two entirely different scales is extremely difficult to determine.

The one-hundred percent bar chart portrayed in Figure 183 combines both axonometric and oblique projection very satisfactorily. The largest segment, "goods and services," is in isometric drawing; the second largest, "employment," is based on oblique projection; and the remaining segments, trimetric drawing. It is difficult, of course, to ascertain in an example of this kind whether the draftsman based his design on rigorous projection procedures or on merely an impressionistic trial and error sketch.

RECEIPTS LEFT OVER
after Payment of All Bills to Outsiders
(for materials, supplies, taxes and other expenses)

1941 — 81.0% — 11.7% 7.3%

1947 — 84.8% — 8.4% 6.8%

1948 — 85.3% — 7.2% 7.5%

Share to EMPLOYES
Share to STOCKHOLDERS
Share RETAINED for use in the business

Figure 179. A One-Hundred Percent Bar Chart Shown in Trimetric Drawing. (From International Harvester Co. Annual Report, 1948, p. 8.)

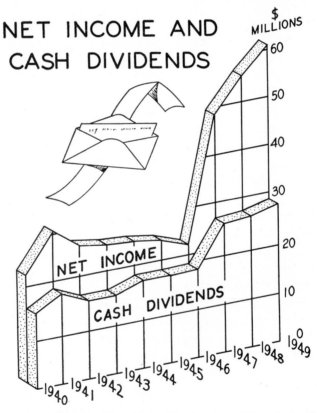

NET INCOME AND CASH DIVIDENDS

$ MILLIONS

NET INCOME

CASH DIVIDENDS

1940 1941 1942 1943 1944 1945 1946 1947 1948 1949

Figure 180. An Arithmetic Line Chart Showing Two Time Series Based on Trimetric Drawing. (Redrawn from International Harvester Co. Annual Report, 1949, p. 7.)

276

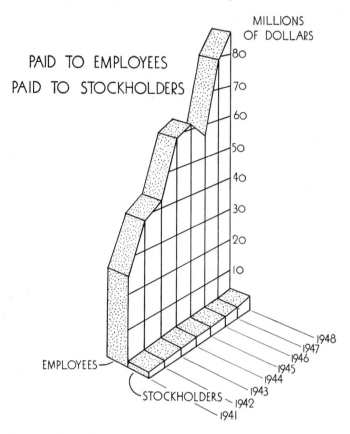

Figure 181. Another Illustration of Arithmetic Line Chart in Approximate Isometric Drawing. (Redrawn from Remington Rand, Inc. Annual Report, 1948, p. 6.)

Figure 184 includes a pictorial chart in which both isometric drawing and oblique projections are utilized. The two top figures are in isometric drawing, and the two lower figures are in oblique projection. Although the conception, as well as the characteristics, of the chart is relatively simple and unique, there does not seem to be any logical basis of comparison between goods sold and income from other sources. Mere artistic beauty or originality is not in itself adequate for an acceptable statistical chart.

As the reader examines the various charts in this chapter, it is suggested that he evaluate them in terms of such criteria as

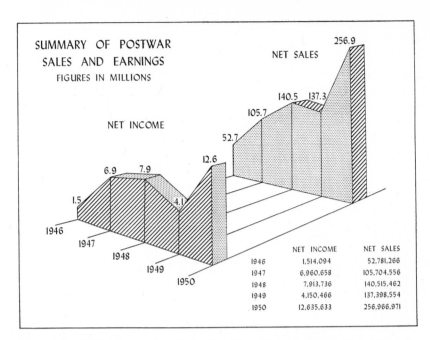

Figure 182. Technique for Comparing Two Time Series in Approximate Dimetric Drawing. The comparison of net sales and net income would be much more effective and reliable if the vertical scales for the two series were identical. (From Avco Manufacturing Corp. Annual Report, 1950, p. 6.)

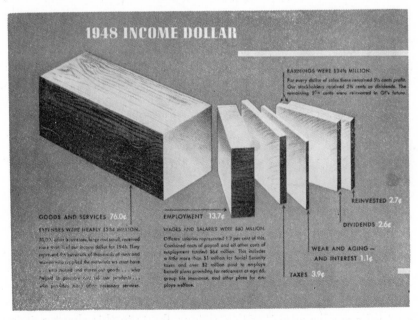

Figure 183. A One-Hundred Percent Bar Chart Shown in Both Axonometric and Oblique Projection. Also, notice pictorial features. (From General Foods Corporation, 1948 Story, p. 4.)

278

simplicity, authenticity, precision, appropriateness, and appeal, especially in comparison with the regular, conventionally drawn chart of the same type.

Correct projection technique and skilled artistry combined with a knowledge of constructing statistical charts can produce an

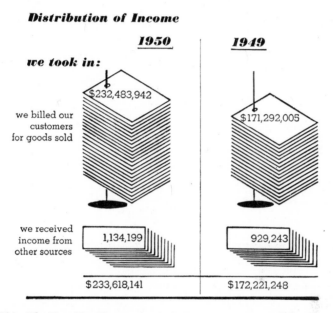

Figure 184. The Two Top Figures Are in Isometric Drawing and the Two Bottom Ones, in Oblique Projection. (From Celanese Corp. of America, 1950 Annual Report, p. 9.)

authentic as well as impressive pie chart. In fact, carefully constructed pictorialized charts of this kind are definitely superior to the conventional flat pie graph. Figures 185 and 186 are examples of well-constructed pie charts drawn by modified isometric projection. It will be recalled from a foregoing discussion in this chapter that a commercially prepared template or a relatively simple drafting technique can be used to construct a circle in isometric projection. The addition of shading, lettering, pictorial fillers, and other features, such as are found on the pie graphs in Figures 185 and 186, are largely problems of artistic ingenuity and skill, which add much to the attractiveness of the finished product.

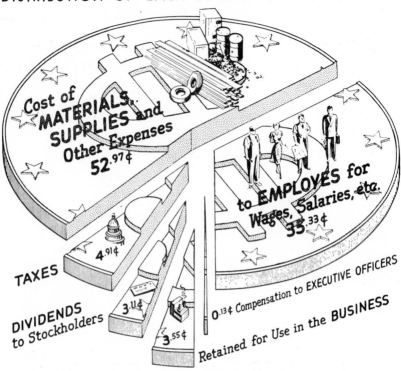

Figure 185. A Pictorial Pie Chart Shown in Isometric Drawing. (From International Harvester Co. Annual Report, 1949, p. 6.)

Figure 186. A Pie Chart Drawn in Isometric Form with Pictorial Fillers. (From the President's Budget Message for 1953.)

Examples of Charts in Oblique Projection. Oblique projection is particularly well adapted to the construction of column charts. The following examples were selected to illustrate the simple, composite, multiple, bilateral, and the more pictorialized variations of the column chart and the frequency histogram.

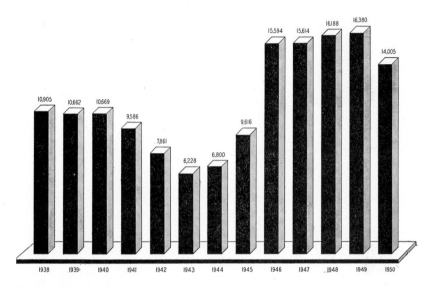

Figure 187. **A Column Chart in Oblique Projection.** (From Calvin F. Schmid, unpublished Report to the President of the University of Washington, *Enrollment Trends in Institutions of Higher Learning in the State of Washington.*)

Figure 187 is a simple column chart showing variations and trends in enrollment at the University of Washington from 1938 to 1950. One of the more important considerations in designing a column chart in oblique form is to determine on what basis the height of the columns is to be measured. Figure 188 graphically illustrates this problem. It will be observed that there are at least five different ways of measuring the height of a column chart drawn in oblique projection.[12] This apparently simple charac-

---

[12] Basic ideas for Figure 188 were taken from Kenneth W. Haemer, "The Pseudo Third Dimension," *op. cit.*

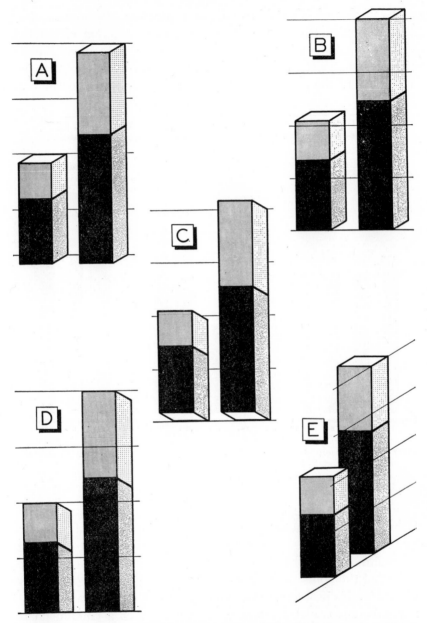

Figure 188. A Common Problem in Pictorial Projection Techniques Is to Determine Precise Distances. As indicated by the above illustrations there are at least five different ways of measuring the height of columns drawn in oblique projection.

teristic can cause much confusion. Furthermore, there does not seem to be any easy solution. The author prefers the arrangement illustrated by B and D in Figure 188. Figure 187 is of this type. In oblique projection, outlines on the front face show their true size and shape. Moreover, the black face of the bars represents fundamentally a conventional column chart, and the sides and top are extraneous features designed to give depth to the chart for sake of pictorialization.

On the other hand, Figures 189 and 190 are very different. Instead of the face of the column, the back edge is chosen as the mensurational referent. Actual scales are shown on both of these charts. Figure 189 is a simple component-column chart that shows total earnings of the Continental Can Company from 1945 to 1949 divided into income taxes, dividends, and reinvestments. The shading and the paper money symbol enhance the pictorial effect of the chart. Figure 190 is a multiple component-column chart without the added shading or pictorial symbols. Both percentage and numerical values are indicated in order to facilitate comparison.

Figure 191 shows a series of column charts in oblique projection in combination with a series of arithmetic line graphs. The arithmetic line graph shows the amounts of investments of insurance companies for certain years from 1923 to 1948 in four types of securities. The columns indicate the fourfold percentage distribution of investments for specified years. It will be observed that the grids are a part of the arithmetic line graphs and have no significance with respect to the series of columns.

Figure 192 is a bilateral- or deviation-column chart drawn in oblique projection. The face of the columns is relatively narrow. Emphasis is placed on the receding side. The data which pertain to deficits and surpluses in the Federal budget from 1931 to 1950 can be interpreted readily. The horizontal shelf or platform that indicates a balanced budget is the main referent line. Columns extending above the referent line indicate surpluses, and those below show deficits. It will be found interesting to compare Figure 192 with Figure 36, an arithmetic line chart, since they both present the same statistics.

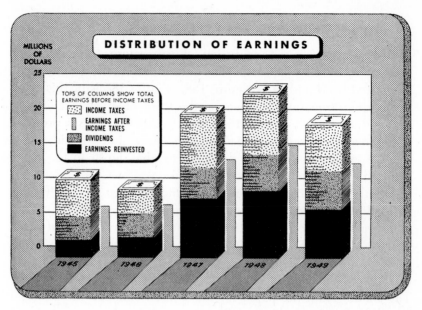

Figure 189. A Pictorial Oblique Projection Column Chart Showing Temporal Series. (From Continental Can Co. Annual Report, 1949, p. 6.)

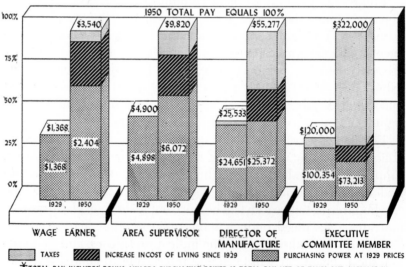

Figure 190. An Illustration of a Grouped Subdivided-Column Chart Drawn in Oblique Projection. It will be observed that the chart compares earnings and cost of living in 1929 and 1950, respectively, for four personnel groups of the Du Pont Company. (Redrawn from E. I. Du Pont de Nemours and Co. Annual Report, 1950, p. 30.)

284

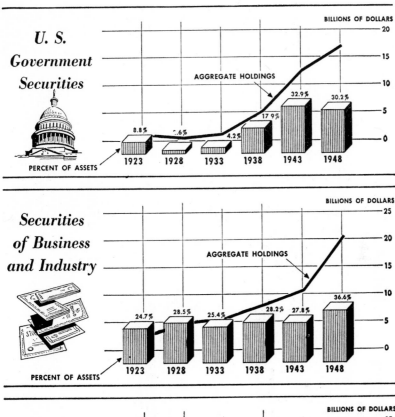

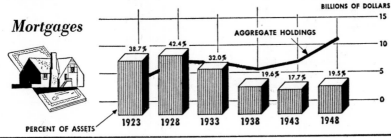

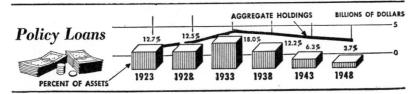

Figure 191. Combination of Column Chart Drawn in Oblique Projection and Arithmetic Line Chart. Also, note pictorial fillers to emphasize significant features of titles. (From Institute of Life Insurance, *Life Insurance Fact Book*, 1949, p. 49.)

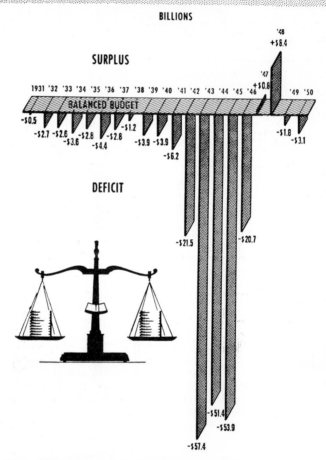

Figure 192. A Deviation-Column Chart Drawn in Oblique Projection. (From The Tax Foundation, *Facts and Figures on Government Finance, 1950-1951,* p. 182.)

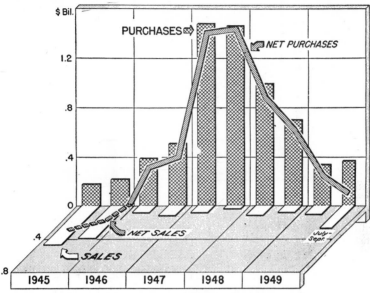

Figure 193. A Combined Column and Line Chart Drawn in Oblique Projection.
(From *1950 Annual Report of the Secretary of the Treasury*, p. 289.)

A combination of a bilateral-column chart and an arithmetic line graph drawn in oblique projection is presented in Figure 193. The most unique features of this chart are the two grids depicted in oblique projection. Although both sets of columns are shown in oblique projection, emphasis is not placed on this fact. Visually the columns possess very little depth except for a slight amount of shading. The vertical columns represent total purchases, and the "horizontal" columns, total sales. Curves superimposed on the two grids indicate sales and net purchases. Charts like this one, as well as others portrayed in this chapter, are basically very simple, and only a rudimentary knowledge of projection principles and techniques is required in order to construct them.

Figures 194 and 195 are examples of frequency histograms in oblique projection. These charts, of course, are similar to the column charts. Figure 194 portrays only one series of data, whereas Figure 195 presents two series for comparative purposes.

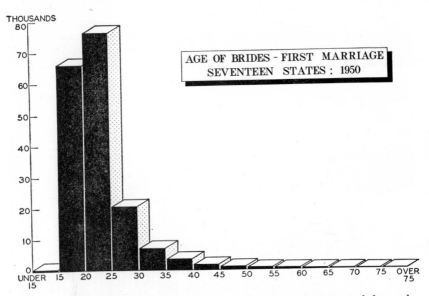

Figure 194. A Histogram in Oblique Projection. (Drawn from original data published by National Office of Vital Statistics, *Special Reports, National Summaries,* "Statistics on Marriage; Specified States, 1950," Vol. 37, December 16, 1952, p. 96.)

PERCENTAGE DISTRIBUTION BY AGE OF JEWISH POPULATION OF ISRAEL AND TOTAL POPULATION OF UNITED STATES

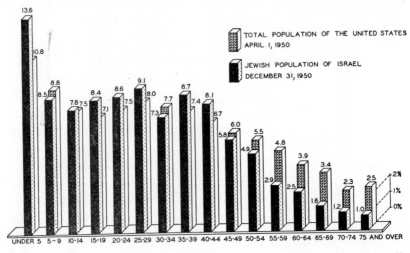

Figure 195. A Double Histogram Drawn in Oblique Projection. Note especially the manner in which the scale has been constructed. It will be observed from Figure 188 that there is no standardized practice in determining base lines for charts of this kind. (Redrawn from Norman Lawrence, *Israel: Jewish Population and Immigration,* 1952, p. 12.)

288

It will be recalled that the horizontal axis of a histogram shows class intervals and the vertical axis either numerical or percentage frequencies. It will be observed that the referent lines for the vertical scales of the two charts are different. In Figure 194, which was designed by the author, all measurements have been made on the face of the column, whereas in Figure 195 the side

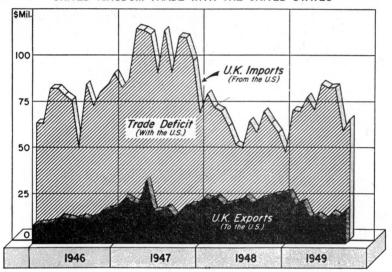

Figure 196. A Band Chart Drawn in Oblique Projection. (From *1950 Annual Report of the Secretary of the Treasury*, p. 300.)

of the column was selected as the basis of measurement. Also, in order to avoid confusion and to make the comparison for each class interval more distinctive, each pair of columns in Figure 195 has been separated by a relatively wide space.

A combination silhouette-band chart drawn in oblique projection is presented in Figure 196. Compared with the same type of charts in axonometric projection (Figures 180 and 181), the oblique form is much simpler. In fact, the basic characteristics and layout of Figure 196 are the same as the conventional type of chart. The third-dimensional feature is largely a simple addition formed by projecting from the face of the plotted values on the

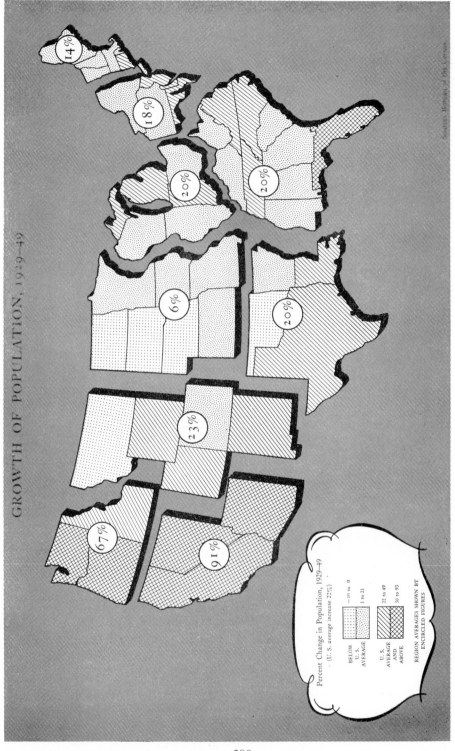

Figure 197. A Crosshatched Map with the Added Feature of Depth Achieved by Means of Shading. (From Victor Roterus and Sterling March, *Economic Development Atlas*, U. S. Department of Commerce, p. 4.)

ENROLLMENTS IN INSTITUTIONS OF HIGHER LEARNING

STATE OF WASHINGTON : FALL TERM, 1950

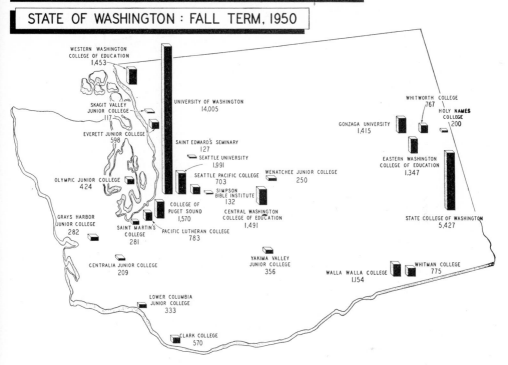

Figure 198. A Map with Columns Drawn in Oblique Projection. (From Calvin F. Schmid, unpublished Report to the President of the University of Washington, *Enrollment Trends in Institutions of Higher Learning in the State of Washington.*)

grid a series of short, 45° lines which are successively joined together. The base of the chart, which includes the abscissal scale divisions and scale figures, is constructed readily by a few short, 45° vertical and horizontal lines.

Pictorialization of maps can be achieved in different ways. One of the simplest is by means of boundary shading. Figures 197 and 198 illustrate this technique. Figure 197 is a cross-hatched map of the United States divided into nine geographical groupings showing rates of population growth from 1919 to 1949. The map projection and crosshatching here are simple and straightforward. The added artistic feature of depth is ef-fected by shading obliquely the boundaries of the geographical divisions. The map in Figure 198 is similarly shaded and, in

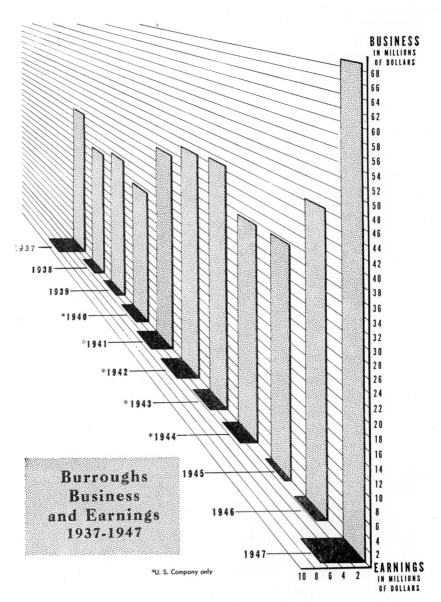

Figure 199. A Combination Bar-Column Chart Drawn in Perspective. Note that columns indicate total amount of business for each year from 1937 to 1947 and bars show corresponding earnings. (From Burroughs Adding Machine Co. Annual Report, 1947, p. 12.)

addition, placed in a tipped position. The most significant features of Figure 198, of course, are the twenty-six columns drawn in oblique projection which represent the 1950 fall term enrollments of institutions of higher learning in the state of Washington.

Examples of Charts in Perspective Projection. Although perspective is the most realistic type of projection, it is the least satisfactory for graphic presentation. Perspective projection tends to distort objects so that it is virtually impossible to portray exact distance, shape, or size; but it should not be implied, however, that perspective projection must never be used in the construction of statistical charts.

Figure 199 illustrates a combination column-bar chart drawn in authentic perspective projection. One axis indicates the amount of business and the other shows the earnings of the Burroughs Adding Machine Company from 1937 to 1947. The grids for both the "vertical" columns and the "horizontal" bars are badly distorted as a consequence of the characteristic recession toward vanishing points. Accordingly, the width and height of the columns and bars are distorted to such a degree that even after a most careful examination the essential implications of the chart are almost impossible to interpret.

A column chart of much simpler design drawn in perspective is shown in Figure 200. The data represent a three-category age distribution of disabling illness rates per 1,000 population. The three age intervals are clearly indicated by figures and pictorial symbols. There are no scale figures for the ordinal axis, although they are not difficult to determine; the values of the three class intervals are shown directly on the columns.

It will be observed that the basic design of Figure 201 is perspective. The construction of a map of this kind according to conventional drafting techniques is extremely complicated and laborious. In preparing this figure, however, the following simple mechanical procedure was used: (1) a county outline map of the state of Washington was drawn in black ink; (2) a photograph was then taken of the map from a focus that would provide a perspective view; (3) the photographic print was enlarged to appropriate size and then traced on cloth; and (4) the flow bands, title, legends, and other features were then added to complete the map.

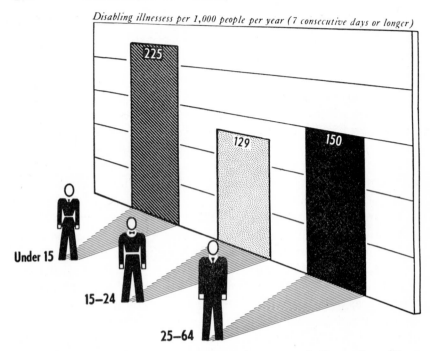

Figure 200. Another Example of a Column Chart Drawn in Perspective. (From Midcentury White House Conference on Children and Youth, *Children and Youth at the Midcentury* (A Chart Book), Chart 38.)

Figure 202 is another example of a flow map drawn in perspective. It shows the volume of traffic on the principal streets of a medium sized city in the state of Washington. The relative height of the bands indicates the number of motor vehicles passing at various points on the main arteries of traffic. Although this type of map possesses unusual popular appeal, it is difficult to portray scale values accurately in many instances.

Figure 203 is an effective organization chart in oblique and quasi-perspective projection. The fifteen bars representing the Federal Security Agency and the various component divisions of the National Institutes of Health are drawn in oblique projection. The general arrangement of the bars, particularly the alignment on the left, emphasizes the perspective features of the chart. It will be observed that the bars and connecting lines are arranged in parallel or one-point perspective.

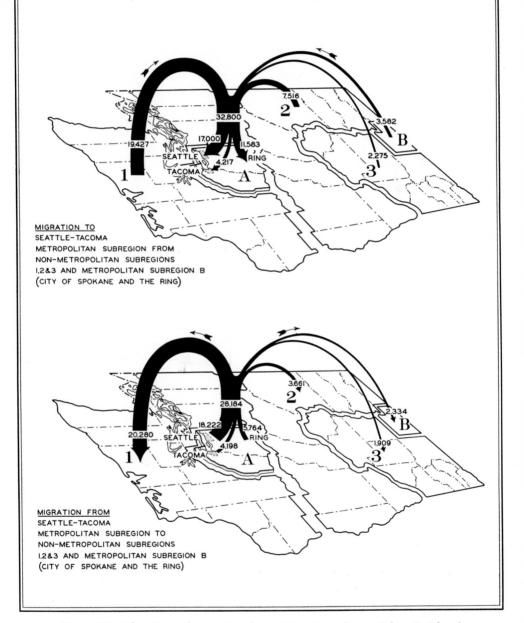

Figure 201. **Flow Maps Showing Population Migration.** (From Calvin F. Schmid and Manzer John Griswold, "Migration Within the State of Washington: 1935-40," *American Sociological Review*, Vol. 17, June, 1952, pp. 312-26.)

TRAFFIC FLOW ON PRINCIPAL STREETS
BELLINGHAM, WASHINGTON: JUNE, 1949

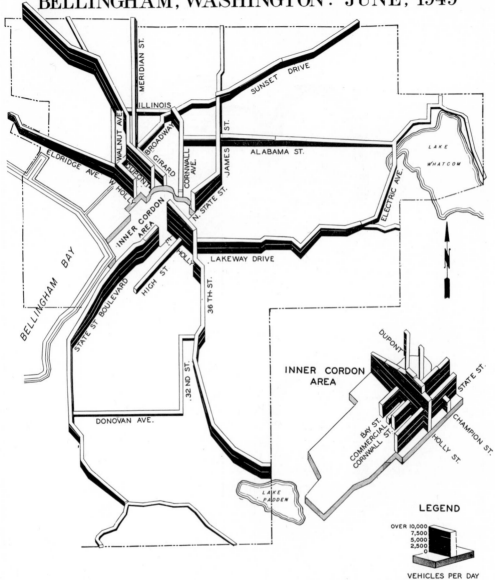

Figure 202. Another Illustration of a Three-Dimensional Flow Chart. It will be observed that the height rather than the width of the bands indicates the volume of movement. (Map prepared by Washington State Department of Highways.)

ORGANIZATIONAL CHART
NATIONAL INSTITUTES OF HEALTH

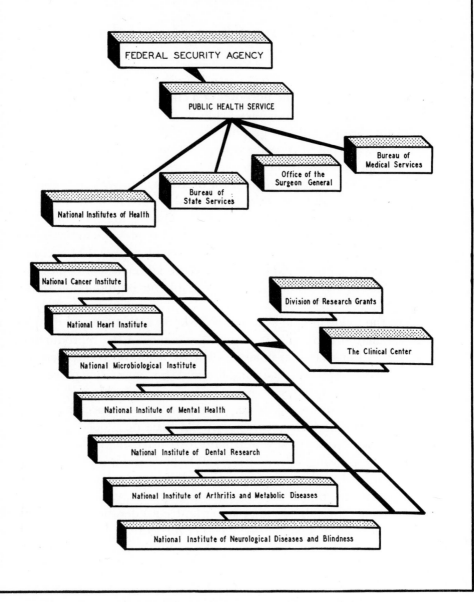

Figure 203. An Organization Chart Drawn in Oblique and Quasi-Perspective Projection. (Redrawn from W. H. Sebrell and C. V. Kidd, "Administration of Research in the National Institutes of Health," *The Scientific Monthly*, Vol. LXXIV, March, 1952, pp. 152-161.)

CHAPTER 11

Reproduction of Graphs and Charts

Whatever may be the purposes of a chart, it is frequently necessary to have duplicate copies made of it. It is especially important for the specialist in graphic presentation to be familiar with the various types of reproduction processes in order to choose the most appropriate type in accordance with each particular need or circumstance. When a process for reproducing charts and graphs is selected, careful consideration should be given to such factors as the following: (1) type, size, and quality of master copy; (2) number of copies required; (3) quality of copies—including clarity, accuracy, and permanency; (4) size of copies; (5) weight, type, and quality of paper or other material on which copies are reproduced; (6) amount of time available for reproduction work; and (7) cost.[1]

In the following pages it will be seen that the type and quality of the master copy greatly restrict the choice of the reproduction process. For example, unless a chart is made on transparent or translucent material, the simpler and for many purposes the cheaper contact types of reproduction, such as blueprints and diazo prints, cannot be made. In recent years a special type of contact printing from opaque copy has been developed, but it is more restricted as to size and more expensive than blueprinting and diazo printing. Bruning's #150 Reflex Film is an example of the film used in this type of contact printing process.

The quality of the copies as judged by clarity, accuracy, and permanency may be another important consideration. If copies are to be used in a committee meeting for more or less ephemeral illustrations, the cheapest form of reproduction may suffice; on the other hand, for permanent, widely circulated reports a more

---

[1] Cf. Irvin A. Herrmann, "Office Reproduction and Imprinting Methods," *The Office* (April, 1951). Revised and expanded; issued as a special reprint.

expensive type of reproduction would be appropriate. Again, as will be pointed out in more detail, the size of the copies—particularly with respect to the size of the original drawing—weight, type, and quality of the material on which the copies are printed, and the amount of time available for reproduction work are other factors of considerable importance. In the over-all problem of reproduction, cost is usually most important; but cost, of course, must be viewed in relation to all the other factors listed. For example, if only a few copies of a chart are required, photostating may be the least expensive as judged by quality and other factors, whereas it may be the most expensive if a relatively large number of copies are run.

Of the many types of reproductive processes, the following will be discussed in the present chapter: hectograph, stencil, contact reproduction, photocopy, and offset printing.

Hectograph Duplicating

The basic idea of the hectograph process came from the inventive mind of James Watt in 1780, when he pressed moistened sheets of paper on an original written in glutinous ink. The modern gelatin process of hectographing was developed in Germany in 1880, but was not widely used until about 1900.

There are three types of hectographic reproduction: (1) gelatin; (2) spirit, direct, liquid or fluid; and (3) spirit-forced fluid.[2] In the gelatin process the master chart is drawn with special ink (aniline dye) and then laid face down on a gelatin roll which receives the ink. When paper is pressed on the gelatin stencil, the chart is transferred to the paper. In the liquid or spirit process the chart is drawn on a sheet of paper to which is attached a reversed sheet of hectograph carbon paper, which transfers the copy of the chart to the back of the face sheet in reverse form. The back of the face sheet is the master copy, which is fastened on the drum of the duplicating machine with inked image up. In the operation of the machine, a small amount of fluid (alcohol) is applied to the master and aniline dye is transferred to the sheets of paper as they are fed into the machine. In the spirit-forced liquid process, the copy is prepared on a porous paper, with the

[2] Herrmann, *op. cit.*, p. 10.

data transferred to the back of the sheet in reverse. Fluid is forced under pressure through the porous master copy, which deposits the dye, mixed with wax, on the paper.

Hectograph inks come in several different colors, but purple and black are the strongest. For the best results it is recommended that in hectographic reproduction only approved paper, fluid, and other materials be used.

In preparing the master copy, the original copy of the chart can be placed on top of a stencil and then traced with a pencil, pen, ball-point pen, or ruling pen in order to transfer the impression to the stencil.

For reproducing a maximum of 300 copies, hectograph is a cheap and quick process and is particularly suitable for committee meeting memoranda and preliminary drafts of reports. The hectograph process lacks the clarity, permanency, and quality that are found in such processes as photo-offset, zinc cuts, and photocopy.

Stencil

The origin of the stencil reproduction process dates back to 1875, when Thomas A. Edison invented the electric pen and press. Edison's pen was an electrically vibrating needle which made a large number of minute holes in the stencil. Without having heard of Edison's invention, A. B. Dick, a midwestern lumberman, in 1884 invented purely for his own use a stencil duplicating process which was later manufactured and marketed under the trade-name "Mimeograph" (imitate + graph).

There are two basic procedures in reproducing charts and graphs by means of stencils: (1) drawing them directly on stencils, or (2) having them reproduced photographically on stencils. If charts are drawn on stencils, it is essential to have proper equipment, including a lighted transparent drawing board (such as the A. B. Dick "mimeoscope"), a T square and other straightedges, styli, and plastic lettering guides. The lettering also may be done with a typewriter or Vari-Typer. The chart is first drawn on paper and then traced with styli and other equipment directly onto the stencil.

If a chart is to be transferred to a stencil by photographic process, it should be done by a company properly equipped for such work. Charts made in this manner are actual facsimiles of the original.

In addition to those already mentioned, there are other accessories and special types of stencils that may be found useful in chart work. For example, ready-to-use outline map stencils of all states, certain regional areas of the United States, and continents are available commercially, and other die-impressed stencils with special guides or other basic designs can be made to order. Plastic lettering guides in more than forty different sizes and styles and plastic screen plates for shading and hatching can be procured from stencil supply companies. In addition to black ink, various colors are manufactured for stencil reproduction.

The main advantages of the stencil reproduction process for charts and graphs may be summarized as follows: (1) it is comparatively cheap, especially for one hundred copies or so; (2) it is simple and fast; and (3) the original equipment is inexpensive and widely available. The disadvantages are that the copies are not so attractive as those made by photostat and photo-offset, and for a large number of copies the unit cost is much more than that for photo-offset.

Contact Reproduction [3]

Blueprinting. The oldest and one of the most frequently used types of contact reproduction is blueprinting. Characteristically, the blueprint has white lines on a blue background. The basic chemical principles on which blueprinting is based were discovered more than a century ago. It was observed that the color of ferroprussiate was changed from pale green to deep blue when exposed to sunlight. Sir John Herschel invented the blueprint process and it was used commercially in 1842. It is interesting to note that blueprinting was not introduced in this country until about 1890.

[3] The author is indebted to Forbes T. Roseth, Manager, Eastern Region Business Copy and Systems Division of Charles Bruning Company, Teterboro, New Jersey, and to Ben Hendley, Educational Sales Division of Frederick Post Company, Chicago, for valuable assistance in the preparation of this section. Certain sentences have been taken from releases prepared by Frederick Post Company.

In the original process, sheets of paper coated with a solution of ferric ammonium citrate and potassium ferricyanide and drawings made on translucent material were placed in a contact frame and exposed to sunlight. The print was fixed by washing in water.

Modern blueprinting techniques, of course, have been greatly improved. The chemicals on the blueprint paper now include a solution of sodium or ammonium ferrioxalate, potassium or ammonium oxalate, and potassium ferricyanide. Instead of coating small sheets of paper with a sponge or brush, huge rolls of paper are mounted on the coating machine and the paper is pulled over a metal roller which revolves in a tray of sensitizing solution. The sunlight exposure frame has been superseded by large, elaborate, blueprinting machines with arc or mercury vapor lights, washing and developer sprays, and automatic driers that can produce in one continuous roll, varying in width from 24 to 54 inches, over 30 feet of blueprints per minute.

The best results from blueprinting are obtained when charts are drawn on tracing cloth with black India ink. Vellum and other translucent paper also can be used. Sometimes heavier paper can be made transparent with a special oil solution manufactured by drafting supply companies.

The vandyke negative, another type of contact print which will be discussed in the following section, can be used as a master for blueprinting. The vandyke negative has white lines on a dark brown background. Copies made on blueprint paper from vandyke negatives have blue lines on a white background and are known as blue-line prints. Photographic negatives or positives and other types of prints, when made on translucent or transparent material, also may be used as master copies with blueprinting paper.

Vandyke Negative. The vandyke negative or brownprint process is in many ways similar to the blueprint process. It requires paper treated with light-sensitive iron salts and silver nitrate. When exposed to light the iron salts are reduced photochemically to ferro-salts, which in turn reduce the silver salt to metallic silver when the print is placed in water, resulting in the dark brown pigment in the negative process. After being washed in water, the print is fixed in a weak solution of photographic hypo (sodium hyposulphite). Vandykes are usually printed on good grade, light-weight stock in order to obtain translucency. To increase translucency vandyke negatives can be treated with a "transparentizing" oil compound or resin. As indicated above, the vandyke negative is used to make blue-line prints or vandyke blackline prints.

Diazo Prints. The diazo process makes use of the light sensitivity of certain types of organic compounds. The diazo process is better known by such popular trade names as "white print," "blackline" and "Ozalid." Modern types of diazo printing were first developed in Germany after World War I and were introduced into this country in the late 1920's.

Light-sensitive diazo compounds are capable of combining with certain other organic chemicals known as "couplers" to produce a very important group of dyestuffs. Almost any shade of color can be produced by the proper selection of diazo salt and coupler. The dyes for these prints are similar to those used in coloring textile fabrics.

There are two major types of diazo prints: (1) ammonia vapor developed process and (2) liquid or semidry developed process. Ozalid (General Aniline and Film Company) and Vapo (Frederick Post) are examples of the first type, and Copyflex (Charles Bruning) is an example of the second type.

In making diazo prints the master copy must be on transparent or translucent material. The diazo type of print is much more flexible than either blueprinting or vandyke negative. Diazo prints may have blue, black, red, or sepia lines. They may be made on several grades, weights, or colors of paper, or on acetate, film, cloth, or plastic-coated paper. Diazo prints on transparent paper, acetate film (matte or clear), cloth, and other materials can be used as intermediates for producing duplicate originals or master copies.

In general, diazo prints are the most satisfactory of contact prints for quickly reproducing charts and graphs. (1) They can be made directly in black lines on a white background without an intermediate negative; (2) in addition to black, the lines on diazo prints may be made in several different colors; (3) the variety of color and type of material available for diazo prints are much greater than for blueprinting or other types of contact printing; and (4) the cost of diazo prints is about the same as that of blueprints.

Photocopying

Photocopying is one of the most frequently used processes for reproducing charts and graphs, especially if only a comparatively few copies are required. Photocopying is better known by the trade-name "photostat."

Photocopying is a form of photography. The subject matter to be copied is photographed through a lens with a prism attached to the front of the lens. The prism provides the means whereby the image, normally reversed by the lens, is again reversed and carried to the sensitized paper in its original position without the need of an intervening negative. Photocopies may be negative or positive. The negative, showing the subject matter white on a black background, is produced by photographing the original. The positive, showing the subject matter black on a white background, is produced by photographing the negative.

The most up-to-date and elaborate photocopying equipment consists of a camera with a magazine for holding a roll of photographically sensitized paper; some models have compartments for developing, fixing, washing, and drying prints.

The main advantages of photocopying for reproducing charts and graphs are (1) copies can be made from originals on either opaque or translucent material; (2) the copies are of relatively good quality; and (3) enlargements and reductions can be made.

Xerography. Another type of photocopy process which has been on the market for a little more than three years is known as xerography (*xeros*, meaning "dry," and *graphos*, meaning "writing"). This process was invented by Chester F. Carlson and developed by the Haloid Company with the assistance of the Battelle Memorial Institute. The trade name for xerographic copying equipment is "Xerox," and it consists of three units: camera, copier, and fuser. Xerography is a dry, direct-positive, electrostatic reproduction process.

Briefly, this process consists of the following steps: (1) the surface of a specially coated plate is positively charged with electricity; (2) the image of the master copy is projected on the plate with a lens, causing positive charges on the plate exposed to light to disappear; (3) a negatively charged powder dusted on the plate adheres to the positively charged image; (4) a sheet of paper is placed on the plate and receives a positive charge which attracts powder from the plate, forming a direct positive image; (5) the print is heated for a few seconds to fuse the powder and form a permanent print.

The advantages of xerography can be summarized as follows: (1) no negative is required; (2) the original may be drawn on any type of material, not necessarily translucent; (3) it is a dry process—without washing and drying equipment; (4) it is relatively faster than other photocopying processes; (5) in contrast to contact types of reproduction, reductions and enlargements can be made with the xerographic process; and (6) the xerographic plate can be used hundreds of times. With this process it is also possible to offset the powdered image onto a positively charged paper master which can be used on office offset duplicating equipment, such as the multilith.

Offset

Photo-offset printing is one of the most accurate, permanent, attractive, and, when a relatively large number of copies are required, cheapest methods of reproducing charts and graphs. The photo-offset process was first developed in the United States in the early 1900's. In addition to the name "photo-offset," it frequently is referred to as planograph printing, photolithography, lithoprinting, offset printing, and by a number of trade or firm names.[4]

Photo-offset is fundamentally a form of lithography which is based on the principle that grease repels water but attracts a greasy ink. The first step in the photo-offset process is the preparation of a photographic negative of the desired size of the

[4] Robert C. Binkley, *Manual on Methods of Reproducing Research Materials*, p. 21.

chart. The second step is to transfer the image by means of the photographic negative to a zinc sheet which first has been "grained," washed, and coated with sensitized emulsion (albumen with ammonium bichromate). Exposure to an arc light hardens the portions of the emulsion under the transparent parts of the negative; when developed, the hardened parts remain on the plate as the image of the copy to be reproduced and have an affinity for greasy ink.[5] In photo-offset printing, the positive image from the prepared zinc plate, which is attached to a cylinder, is transferred to a rubber-covered roller and thence to a positive image on the impression paper that runs between the rubber blanket roller and the impression cylinder. The fact that a reversed image is printed on a rubber blanket from which the wet impression is offset on paper has given the process the name "offset." [6]

When a large number of copies is required, offset reproduction is the most economical form of reproduction. Moreover, the quality of the copies is unexcelled.

Multilith.[7] The multilith process is a simplified adaptation of offset reproduction. There are two general techniques by which charts and graphs can be reproduced with the multilith process: (1) the photographic technique, which is very similar to the methods used in offset printing, and (2) the direct technique, in which charts and graphs are drawn on the master.[8] Graphs prepared by the photographic process are reproduced either from sensitized paper masters or photographic metal masters. Photographic masters will produce from 5,000 to 25,000 copies each. Masters prepared by the direct method will reproduce up to 5,000 copies, depending upon the application. Standard grid duplicating masters are available in several different types of rulings

---

[5] *Ibid.*

[6] There are variations of the process described in the foregoing paragraphs. For example, one process includes a photographically prepared metal printing surface which comes in direct contact with the paper.

[7] The following companies manufacture multilith equipment and/or supplies: Addressograph-Multigraph Corporation, Cleveland, Ohio; Remington Rand, New York; and Keuffel and Esser Company, New York.

[8] Masters also can be prepared by means of the xerographic process. See section above on xerography.

which may be found useful for administrative purposes and committee memoranda.

For reproduction of charts and graphs the multilith process combines high quality and economy for both small and large numbers of copies.

Summary of Comparative Costs

Since cost is such an important consideration in selecting a process for duplicating charts, a brief recapitulation will be made of this factor with respect to the various types of reproduction covered in the foregoing discussion. It will be recalled that for certain types of reproduction, unit cost diminishes very sharply as the number of copies is increased, whereas for others, unit cost may remain relatively constant.

For fewer than 200 or 300 copies of relatively small size (8½ by 11 inches or 8½ by 14 inches) hectographing is probably the least expensive. Similarly, stencil reproduction will be found relatively inexpensive if only a few hundred copies are made. Multilith is an economical process for both small and large numbers of copies. Photo-offset printing is relatively cheap and satisfactory when a large number of copies is required. The unit cost of blueprints and diazo prints is relatively low and constant. At the present time the cost of blueprints per square foot (for orders of less than 100 square feet) is between five and six cents. Diazo prints are slightly higher in price. If more than 15 or 20 copies are made, the unit cost may be reduced slightly, but regardless of the number of copies, it generally does not go below a minimum of three cents per square foot. The same pattern holds for vandyke prints, but the cost is much higher than for blueprints and diazo prints. The first few copies of photocopies are relatively high, but the unit cost curve goes down sharply for 20 or 30 copies and then tends to level out. According to present prices, the unit cost for photocopies, even where 500 or more are made, is seldom less than 20 cents (8½ by 11 inches).

In discussing reproduction costs, the nature of the master copy, particularly the material on which it is made as well as its size, must be taken into consideration. For example, if the original chart is a large-scale drawing on translucent paper, tracing cloth, or acetate, some form of contact printing will be the least expensive form of reproduction. Hectograph and stencil reproduction cannot be used for large-scale copies, and photocopying is relatively expensive and unsatisfactory, especially if the prints have to be pieced together in sections. Photo-offset is highly appropriate for large-sized copies if at least 500 or 600 are required.

Index of Names

Index of Subjects

Abscissas, 43
Age and sex pyramid, 138-41; *see also*
 Simple frequency graphs
Age-specific rates and ratios, charting,
 160-63; *see also* Frequency graphs
 and related charts
Area-bar charts, 85-87
Areal and cubic symbols,
 procedure in drawing, 202
 table illustrating comparative diameters, 204
 three-dimensional, 203
 two-dimensional, 202
 use on spot maps, 198-205
Arith-log charts, 109; *see also* Semilogarithmic charts
Arithmetic charts, 43-67, 110-13; *see
 also* Arithmetic line charts
Arithmetic line charts, 43-67
 differentiating curves, 46, 53, 55-57
 essential components, 46-61
 grid lines, 49-51
 grid proportions, 50
 legends, 47-49
 multiple scales, 60-61
 plotting points, 50
 scale figures, 47-49
 scales, 47-49
 title, 46-47
 trend lines, 57-60
 when to use, 45
 with special features and applications, 61-67
 cumulative curve chart, 66-67
 plotting curves for different periods on same grid, 64, 66
 positive and negative values, 61-
 63
 special referent lines, 63-64
Artype, 40
Axis
 for constructing rectangular coordinate graph, 43-44

of abscissas, 43
of ordinates, 43, 113
Axonometric projection, 259, 261-63,
 268-69, 274-79

Band charts, 68-71
Bar-and-symbol charts, 75-76; *see also*
 Bar charts
Bar charts, 73-94
 standards of design, 78-80
 types of
 area-bar chart, 85-87
 bar-and-symbol chart, 75-76
 bilateral-bar charts, 90
 component-bar chart, 78, 82-85
 deviation-bar chart, 77-78, 92-94
 grouped-bar chart, 77-78, 85, 88-
 89
 one-hundred percent bar chart,
 164-65, 243-44
 paired-bar chart, 77-78, 90-91
 segmented-bar chart, 75-76, 78
 simple bar chart, 73, 75-76, 80-82,
 164-66
 sliding-bar chart, 77-78, 94
 step-bar chart, 84-85
 subdivided-bar chart, 75-76, 78
 subdivided one-hundred percent
 bar chart, 76, 78, 164-66
Barlow's Tables, 204
Base maps, 184-87
 definition of, 184-87
 examples of, 185-87
Bilateral-bar charts, 90
Blueprinting, 301-2

Cabinet projection, 269
Cartesian coordinate graph, 43; *see also*
 Arithmetic line chart
Cavalier projection, 269
Centile graph, 151
Charting techniques, origin and his-
 tory, 4